# ENGLISH AND AMERICAN
# STEAM CARRIAGES AND
# TRACTION ENGINES

CONVERTIBLE TRACTION ENGINE AND ROAD ROLLER WITH CRANE BY MESSRS. CLAYTON AND SHUTTLEWORTH

# ENGLISH AND AMERICAN
# STEAM CARRIAGES
AND
# TRACTION ENGINES

BY

## WILLIAM FLETCHER, M.Inst.Mech.E.

AUTHOR OF "THE ABUSE OF THE STEAM JACKET"
"THE HISTORY AND DEVELOPMENT OF STEAM LOCOMOTION ON COMMON ROADS"
"THE STEAM JACKET PRACTICALLY CONSIDERED"
"A CHAPTER IN THE HISTORY OF TRACTION ENGINES," ETC.

NEW INTRODUCTION BY
### W. J. HUGHES

WITH 250 ILLUSTRATIONS

## DAVID & CHARLES REPRINTS

0 7153 6232 1

D
629·2292'09034

FLE

Printed in Great Britain by
Redwood Press Limited   Trowbridge   Wiltshire
for David and Charles (Holdings) Limited
South Devon House   Newton Abbot   Devon

# INTRODUCTION TO THE 1973 EDITION

As has been described already in my introduction to the 1972 reprint of William Fletcher's *Steam on Common Roads*, that author had a distinguished career not only in the designing of steam road vehicles, but also in chronicling their history. He was a diligent researcher in that field, and brought back to light numerous examples of vehicles of which the memory had not only faded, but in many cases had virtually disappeared.

The present volume, published originally in 1904, is a continuation of Fletcher's first one in many ways, since it too contains the results of further exacting research by him into the earlier uses of 'steam on common roads'. Some of the names of that period—Hancock, Maceroni, Russell—still are familiar enough today, but some of the mechanical details of their vehicles are not so well-known. Besides describing these, however, Fletcher gives also a good account, and in some cases illustrations which are almost unique, of lesser known carriages such as those of Boulton and Dudgeon, and the magnificent Randolph steam coach.

Some steam cars and carriages of the turn of the century period next receive attention, and here again many of the details and illustrations will be new to most readers. The Perkins 'steam motor and van', with its single front wheel drive, is a particularly interesting design, though whether it ever became more than a one-off job is another matter!

But better-known names include Stanley, White, Loco-mobile, Miesse, Serpollet, and De Dion. Of great interest in this section are the tables of performance in the Reliability Trials of 1903.

In the traction engine field, which was more particularly his own sphere, Fletcher deals first with 'undertype' engines—that is, those with the cylinders and motion underneath the boiler, a genus which never became popular—and then with various British makes of the more conventional overtype which of course were produced in large numbers.

Varieties of spring-mounting (with its attendant difficulties) include American designs, and finally the author discusses American traction engines, first in general, and then several makes in detail. Here the great contrasts between American and British practice, largely due to different working conditions, are brought out admirably.

Like *Steam on Common Roads*, the present book is a classic which has been out of print for many decades. This new edition should be a welcome addition to the steadily growing literature about that very fascinating species, the steam road vehicle.

W. J. Hughes
Macclesfield, Cheshire

# PREFACE

THE present work may be divided into two parts: the first part deals with ancient and modern steam carriages, the second treats of road locomotives and traction engines. The book is practically a continuation of the author's work published in 1891.[1] It may be termed a second series, having a much wider scope, and bringing the subject down to date; in the matter of the two volumes there is very little overlapping. In the present work additional examples of steam carriages and road engines are introduced which were not to hand in the earlier volume. The work is divided as follows: Chapters I., II., and III. deal with ancient steam carriages. Chapters IV. and V. are devoted to modern examples of steam carriages; the tables and remarks on Resistances, at the end of Chapter V., were contributed by Mr. R. Edwards, M.I.C.E., Hastings. The remaining chapters are devoted to traction engines. Chapter VI. deals with small road locomotives, employed for the conveyance of parcels and passengers. In Chapter VII. the methods of spring mounting are described. Full particulars of a road train for passenger and goods traffic are given in Chapter VIII. In Chapter IX. undertype road locomotives are dealt

[1] *The History and Development of Steam Locomotion on Common Roads.* By W. Fletcher. London: E. and F. N. Spon, 125, Strand.

# Preface

with. Modern road locomotives and details are touched upon in Chapter XI. The last chapter is devoted to recent types of American traction engines. Tables of dimensions of English and American practice are given.

Respecting the historical examples in this and the former work, it may be remarked that the drawings and descriptions represent the work of many years of research. A series of articles was contributed to *Industries* by the author in 1886, and previous to that date articles on road locomotion were written for other journals. It will be seen that the subject of steam carriages was introduced by the author when no attention was devoted to it from any other quarter. At that date the motor car was not in existence; the steam carriage industry had been strangled in its infancy by short-sighted Acts of Parliament.[1]

The articles contributed to *Industries* were collected, extended, and published in book form in 1891; this is now considered a standard work. At this later date the motor car had not appeared on the scene, and the author believes that his work had some influence, and tended to revive the subject of steam pleasure carriages on common roads. When the previous book was published, twelve years ago, there were no journals devoted to automobiles; there were no steam or petrol cars running. The books dealing partially with the subject of steam carriages were out of print; the only available information was hidden away in corners of old magazines.

[1] Public opinion was against them. The influential people who opposed railways about this time, but in vain, did their utmost to put a stop to steam locomotion on the highway, and in many cases succeeded in their design. The passenger carriages were driven off the roads by the Road Commissioners, who obtained Acts of Parliament allowing them to levy prohibitive tolls upon steam vehicles passing through the toll-gates.

# Preface

At the present date motor carriages are much in evidence, and the manufacture of steam vehicles occupies a place among the world's industries.

It will be noticed that heavy motor vans have not been included in the work, but some small traction engines, intended to work under the Act of Parliament of 1896.[1] Among the old traction engines the celebrated Boydell engine has not found a place, as it and many others have been fully described by the writer in another work. Some readers may regret that some other venerable examples have not appeared. It may be remarked that nearly every form of traction engine has, at one time or other, been described by the author in English or American magazine articles. It was impossible to include all this matter in one volume, and in some instances the copyright has been disposed of by him.

The writer has confined himself to steam vehicles, he being a firm believer in steam as the motive power for carriages from the first, and through all the years when steam motors appeared to be nearly extinguished by the petrol cars; and this belief is more confirmed now than ever before. Every steam carriage which passes along the street justifies the confidence placed in it; and unless the objectionable features of the petrol carriage can be removed, it is bound to be driven from the road, to give place to its less objectionable rival, the steam-driven vehicle of the day.

Some portions of the work have appeared under the writer's name in the columns of *The Engineer*, *The American Engineer and Railway Journal*, *Machinery*, and *The Engineering Times*. For some of the illus-

---

[1] *Liverpool Heavy Motor Trials. Judge's Report*, 1901. P. S. King and Son, Westminster.

# Preface

trations and much information on modern steam carriages the writer is indebted to *The Automotor Journal*.

The author begs to acknowledge the receipt of blocks from *The Engineer*, *Engineering*, *Machinery*, *The Automotor Journal*, *The Engineering Times*, *The Graphic*, and *The Mechanical World*.

For the loan of electros the writer tenders his thanks to Messrs. Toward and Co., Newcastle-on-Tyne; Mr. Brown, Devizes; the Albany Manufacturing Co., Willesden Junction; the Motor Construction Co., Nottingham; the White Steam Car Co., Regent Street, W.; the Speedwell Motor Co., Albert Gate, S.W.; the Locomobile Co., Sussex Place, S.W.; Mr. Crowden, Leamington; Messrs. Foden and Co., Sandbach; Messrs. John Fowler and Co., Leeds; Messrs. Aveling and Porter, Rochester; Messrs. Clayton and Shuttleworth, Lincoln; Messrs. Mc Laren, Leeds; Messrs. Atkinson and Phillipson, Newcastle-on-Tyne; the Clarkson Co., Chelmsford; Messrs. L. Olrick and Co., Bishopsgate, E.C.; the International Steam Car Co., Toledo, Ohio; and others.

128, WEST PARADE,
    LINCOLN

# CONTENTS

# Contents

# LIST OF ILLUSTRATIONS

xiii

# List of Illustrations

# List of Illustrations

# List of Illustrations

# List of Illustrations

# LIST OF TABLES

# ENGLISH AND AMERICAN STEAM CARRIAGES AND TRACTION ENGINES

## CHAPTER I

### SELF-CONTAINED PASSENGER COACHES AND SMALL STEAM PLEASURE CARRIAGES

TO give anything approaching a complete sketch of the origin and development of steam road locomotion from the earliest to the present time would occupy too much space ; neither is such a record needed, for the historical part of this subject was dealt with recently in an exhaustive treatise by the author.[1] It is purposed, however, to give a brief sketch of the work of a few of the early steam carriage promoters, whose achievements have been scantily recognised. The three first chapters will describe some of the missing links in the history of steam locomotion on common roads.

### FOURNESS

Omitting any mention of the early speculations respecting steam locomotion, and passing over the interesting carriages made by Cugnot in France, Murdock and Symington in England, and Evans in America, an

---

[1] *The History and Development of Steam Locomotion on Common Roads,* by William Fletcher. London: E. and F. N. Spon, 125, Strand, 1891.

B

# Steam Carriages

illustration is given of a little steam carriage made by Robert Fourness, of Halifax, in 1788. Figs. 1 and 2 show the carriage, from which it will be seen that a three-cylinder inverted engine communicated motion to the ·crank shaft. The driving power was transmitted from the crank shaft to the axle through spur gearing.

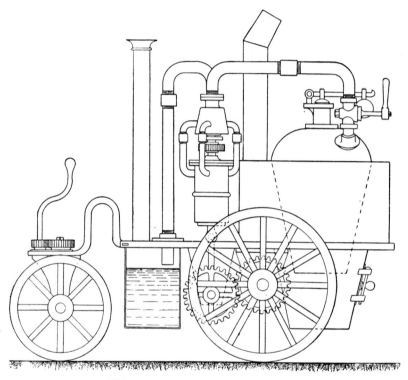

FIG. 1.   STEAM CARRIAGE BY FOURNESS

Hollow plug valves admitted steam into the cylinders, and allowed the exhaust to pass out. The exhaust steam was conducted into a tank for heating the feed-water, from which the boiler was supplied. The feed-pump was driven by a crosshead attached to one of the piston-rods. Only one of the driving-wheels was keyed to the main axle, so as to allow the carriage to turn sharp corners readily. The engine was steered in the usual manner. A safety valve was fitted on the boiler.

A few words respecting the inventor may be of interest here. Robert Fourness was a native of Otley, Yorkshire. His first machine was a hide-splitting appa-

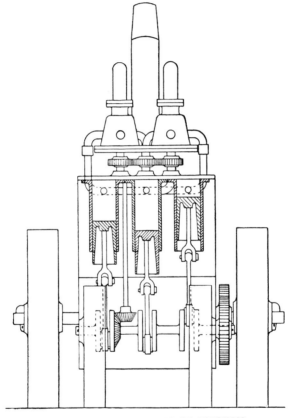

FIG. 2. STEAM CARRIAGE BY FOURNESS

ratus for use in his father's works. The hide-splitting machine was not patented, and, in order to keep its construction a secret, three or four half-witted men from the workhouse were employed to work it by hand-power. Fourness was a practical engineer, and had works of his own in Sheffield, and afterwards at Gains·

borough.   Fourness died at an early age, and we are unable to say what became of the steam carriage.

### READ

It is not our intention to describe the steam carriage made by Nathan Read, of Massachusetts, but his vertical tubular boiler invented as far back as 1788 is worthy of notice.   Fig. 3 shows a section, from which it will be seen that the shell is of cylindrical form, like the now common vertical boiler; A is the furnace door, B a heater and feed reservoir, E the uptake and chimney, F the steam-pipe leading to the engine, and H is the fire-box.   From the fire-box crown is hung a number of tubes closed at their lower ends, and another set of tubes connect the water bottom with the water space above the fire-box.   The boiler was intended for use in steam carriages or steamboats, and was considered by the inventor to be strong, light, compact, and safe.

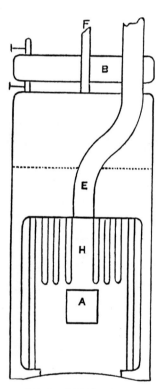

FIG. 3.   READ'S BOILER

### HANCOCK

Walter Hancock was probably the most successful steam carriage maker of the period in which he lived. His first carriage was constructed in 1824, and his last trip took place in July, 1840.   During sixteen years' experience he built ten different carriages, each of which was creditably designed and constructed.   The later carriages were very efficient. It is not necessary to describe any of these vehicles, since Sir F. J. Bramwell, Bart., has made us all familiar with Hancock's inventions.[1] It is very evident that Hancock scaled the mechanical difficulties of steam road locomotion. How was it, therefore, that his steam carriages ceased to run while several of them were in good working order? Mr. Hancock himself said: "Years of practice have now put all doubts of the economy, safety, and superiority of steam travelling on common roads at rest when compared with horse travelling, and I have now in preparation calculations founded upon actual practice, which when published will prove that steam locomotion on common roads is not unworthy the attention of the capitalist, though the reverse has been disseminated rather widely of late by parties who do not desire that this branch of improvement should prosper against the interest of themselves." Later on Mr. Hancock shows by the aid of figures that a profit of 25 per cent. may be made by the employment of steam carriages.[2]

Hancock's boiler is shown by the group of illustrations Figs. 1 to 6, Fig. 4. In the construction of the boiler the following process was adopted, as described by Sir Frederick Bramwell. A flat plate of copper or of soft iron F, Fig. 2, was placed upon a cast-iron slab mould, shown separately in Fig. 3. It was provided

[1] *Report on the Trials of Traction Engines at Wolverhampton,* by Sir F. J. Bramwell, Bart., 1871. Discussion on Mr. Head's paper on *The Rise and Progress of Steam Locomotion on Common Roads,* 1873. Discussion on Mr. McLaren's paper on *Steam on Common Roads,* 1890. And since these remarks Sir F. Bramwell has given some interesting *Reminiscences of Steam Locomotion on Common Roads* in a paper read before Section G of the British Association at Oxford, 1894. It would be interesting if other engineers would give their reminiscences on this and similar subjects.

[2] *Twelve Years' Experiments with Steam Carriages,* by W. Hancock, 1838.

with the indentations H, H, of nearly hemispherical form, and with a larger flat circular indentation H'. Around the margin was formed a raised rim I. Nearly one-half of the plate was laid over this mould, and by hammering was caused to take the forms of the depressions in the mould. Subsequently the other half of the plate was treated in a similar manner, giving the result shown in Fig. 4. The plate was then bent about its

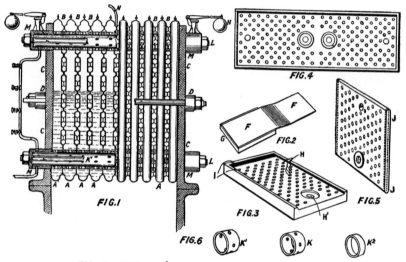

FIG. 4.   HANCOCK'S BOILER FOR STEAM CARRIAGES

middle so that it took the form, when riveted up at the edges, shown in Fig. 1, the riveted edges not being exposed to the fire, the rivets being confined to the top and the two vertical sides. In Fig. 1 of group Fig. 4 the riveted vertical seams are omitted. Each chamber was thus of biscuit-bag form, and an alternate mode of construction consisted in riveting in between the sides of the bent-up plate a piece of channel iron, shown at J in Fig. 5. The circular indentations are from 3 in. to 4 in. in diameter, and were made to receive copper rings or gun metal K, Fig. 6, and a

# Self-contained Passenger Coaches

narrower ring, K 2, was placed between the upper part of the chamber. The internal dimensions of these rings was the same as that of the holes in the chamber plates, and small radial holes were made in each ring. When the chambers were put together these rings formed tubes, as shown in Fig. 1, the lower one for water circulation and the upper for steam. Through them were passed strong tie bolts L, nuts on the end of which bore on hollow sockets M. When these were well screwed up, the whole of the chambers were tightly connected and intercommunicating. The steam to the engine was taken off by a pipe N, and feed-water was pumped into one of the lower sockets M, as shown in section, Fig. 1; and a pipe, connecting the upper and lower sockets M, M, was provided with gauge valves, by which the level of the water in the boiler could be ascertained. For making the joints between the several chambers, copper-wire rings were used, somewhat flattened by the pressure produced by the nuts of the tie bolts.

The literature of the times appears to show that Hancock was a very modest man—a good engineer; but he failed in the commercial part of the business. There were other reasons, however, which influenced the cessation of the steam carriage trials. In 1840 steam locomotion was at a very low ebb; the railway was attracting all the attention of engineers and capitalists. Moreover, as stated in another place, some of the road locomotion promoters had brought an amount of discredit upon their cause by foolishly attempting to rival the railway trains, their extravagances tending to retard progress in road locomotion. The one aim of the carriage proprietors appeared to be to outrun each other, whereas had they been satisfied with a reasonable speed—say of eight or ten miles an hour—instead of boasting of having run twenty miles an hour, and had they regarded their steam road conveyances as feeders to the railway system, good would have resulted from their introduction in many districts. Not only so, but Hancock and his contemporaries had a more formidable obstacle to meet. Public opinion was against them ; the influential men who opposed railways about this time,

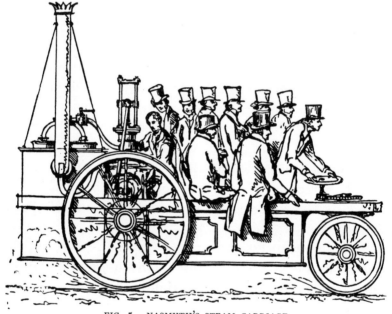

FIG. 5. NASMYTH'S STEAM CARRIAGE

but in vain, did their utmost to put a stop to steam loco-motion on the highways, and in many cases succeeded in their design. The persons who delighted in horses and opposed steam locomotion fifty years ago, showed their objections in hisses and jeers as the carriages passed along the road. Such men are in evidence in our day, but their mode of showing their opposition has assumed a more harmful and injurious form. Instead of hooting groups of people, we have to deal with

# Self-contained Passenger Coaches

individuals who appear to have absolute power on their side. Their crusade against steam on the highway drove the lighter carriages off the road, and thereby crushed an important industry.

## NASMYTH

About the year 1827 Mr. James Nasmyth constructed a small steam carriage, as shown by Fig. 5. Many successful runs were made with it on the Queensferry Road, near Edinburgh, carrying six to eight passengers. The carriage, after running about for some months, was dismantled, and the engine and boiler sold.

## MACERONI

Colonel Maceroni was one of Hancock's most successful contemporaries. In 1833 Maceroni and Squire patented an efficient tubular boiler; the working pressure was no less than 150 lbs. to the square inch. An illustration of this boiler is given in Fig. 6. The boiler is described in Maceroni's book, *Expositions and Illustrations in Steam Power Applied to Common Roads, etc.,* 1835. His steam carriages were thoroughly well made; they ran for months without mishaps.[1]

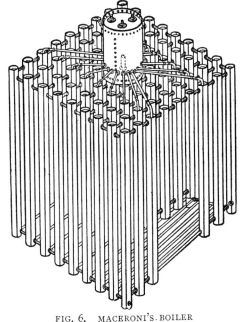

FIG. 6.   MACERONI'S BOILER

[1] *The History and Development of Steam Locomotion on Common Roads,* 1891. See also Sir F. J. Bramwell's *Reminiscences of Steam Locomotion on Common Roads.*

# Steam Carriages

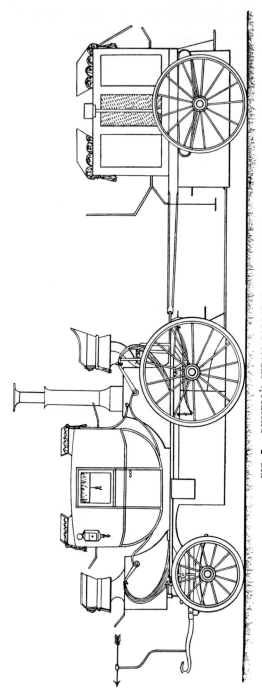

FIG. 7. RUSSELL'S STEAM CARRIAGE AND TENDER

RUSSELL

Among the engineers who have devoted some time to the design and construction of steam carriages, a foremost place is given to Mr. John Scott Russell. As these coaches have thus far received little attention, we purpose to describe them at some length. During Mr. Russell's residence in Edinburgh, he patented a steam locomotive intended for the conveyance of passengers on common roads. Six of these vehicles were built under his patents by the Grove House Engine Works, Edinburgh, for the Steam Carriage Company of Scotland. In April, 1834, this company established a line of steam coaches for the conveyance of passengers between

10

# Self-contained Passenger Coaches

Glasgow and Paisley, which plied hourly for many months with the greatest regularity. The distance between the two places was a little more than seven miles. The trip was run at an average time of thirty-four minutes. The carriages were overloaded, thirty to forty persons repeatedly finding places on a vehicle and its tender, constructed to carry six inside and twenty

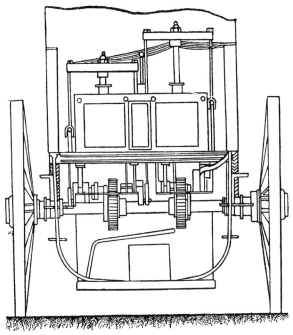

FIG. 8.   RUSSELL'S STEAM CARRIAGE

outside passengers. It was necessary to run slowly in the Glasgow streets, but when in the open country the carriage attained a speed of seventeen miles an hour. Fig. 7 gives a side elevation of one of Mr. Russell's carriages, with tender attached. Fig. 8 shows an end view of the engines. The carriages were superbly fitted up, and very popular with the travelling part of the community. From the drawing it will be seen that

the engine and boiler were placed under the hind part
of the coach. The whole weight of the structure was
supported on springs—the coach on C springs, and the
steam machinery on strong laminated carriage springs ;
and in this respect it was supposed to possess a great
advantage over all other steam carriages. The spring
arrangements will be dealt with presently. Fig. 9 gives

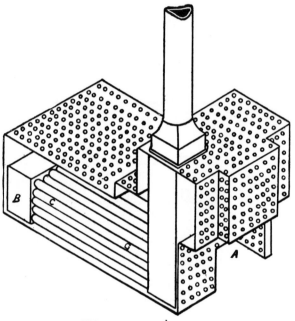

FIG. 9.   RUSSELL'S BOILER

a view of the boiler with the outer casing removed,
in order to show the internal construction. A is the flue
containing the fire bars, giving about four square feet
of grate area. B is the back flue, or combustion
chamber. C C show the return tubes terminating in
the uptake. The steam for the engine was drawn from
the raised part of the shell at the chimney end, and was,
therefore, slightly superheated. A good draught was
produced by means of the exhaust steam which entered

the chimney. We read that some of the critics objected to the noise produced by the exhaust. The failure of many of the early steam carriages was brought about by the imperfections of their boilers. From the following description of Mr. Russell's so-called improvements, it will be seen that he was courting failure in the vital part of his locomotive. The improvements were as follows : First, in constructing the boiler in such a manner that it shall everywhere consist of opposite and parallel surfaces, or as nearly so as circumstances will permit, and connecting these surfaces together by means of wire stays, placed at distances proportioned to their direct cohesive strength, and to the degree of pressure to be resisted ; and secondly, in thus being enabled to employ metal much thinner, and, consequently, more efficient (as regards the transmission of heat) than has been hitherto done. The boiler plates were made of copper one-tenth of an inch thick ; the stays were a quarter of an inch diameter ; there were 1,300 of them used. It is true that the weight of the boiler was reduced, but Mr. Russell remarked that the safety of the boiler was increased, for it was impossible that the whole number of the stays should be of exactly the same strength. The moment that the steam pressure exceeds the calculated maximum the weakest of the stays will give way ; and one rod giving way will instantly let out the whole of the water in the boiler, take off the pressure of the steam, extinguish the fire, and prevent all chance of an explosion. Mr. Russell's ideas respecting the safety of the boiler were unfortunately not realised in practice. The boiler was a rapid steamer. The working pressure has not been recorded, but it is stated that steam was raised in twenty minutes. The stays are not shown in the interior of the boiler, but the number and the direction of the stays may be gathered from the nuts shown on the outer surfaces.

Fig. 8 shows an end elevation of the carriage, with the engine, gearing, main axle, and the boiler front. The engine had two gun-metal cylinders, each 12 in. diameter and 12 in. stroke. The piston-rods passed through the top cylinder covers, and were connected by crossheads and side rods to two separate crank shafts. Each cylinder had four ports, which were opened and closed by slide valves, actuated by excentrics keyed on the crank shafts. Two of the ports were for the admission of steam, and two for the exhaust. The crank shafts communicated motion to the driving-axle by means of spur wheels, the ratio of which was 2 to 1—that is, two revolutions of the engine caused one revolution of the road wheels. Sun-and-planet straps were used to keep the gearing properly in pitch. A clutch was provided on each wheel, so as to throw it out of gear for turning sharp corners. A tender was drawn behind the coach, carrying a supply of coke and water. Two india-rubber tubes conveyed water from the cistern to two brass pumps for feeding the boiler. At different stations on the road there were spare tenders kept in readiness with a supply of coke and water, which were readily connected to the engine when required. The tender was mounted on springs, and seats were provided for passengers as shown.

Three persons were employed to work the locomotive—a steersman on the front seat. The engine-driver had a seat at the back above the engines; the stop valve, the cylinder cocks, and the clutches were within his reach, he could also see the height of the water in the boiler, and keep an eye on the safety valve. The

# Self-contained Passenger Coaches

stoker stood on the foot-plate below, in front of the boiler. Undoubtedly these coaches were well worked out, for it will be remembered that Mr. Russell had written an article or two on the subject of steam carriages in the *Foreign Quarterly Review*. The Glasgow papers spoke of the coaches as a "triumphant success." Of course these coaches were not allowed to run many months before they shared the same fate as Dance's carriages in England. The road trustees at the Glasgow end caused a thick coating of loose stones to be put on the road, in the hope of stopping the carriages, but they successfully ploughed through it, while horse-drawn vehicles had to go a longer route in order to escape this all but impassable piece of road. At last, however, a wheel broke and allowed the whole weight of the coach and the machinery to rest on one portion of the boiler, which was not strong enough to bear any extra strain ; this accident caused the boiler to burst with fatal results. The Court of Session after this accident would not allow any of the carriages to run in Scotland.

Two of the carriages were sent to London, and made a few trips to Greenwich, Windsor, Kew Bridge, and for several days one of them made a journey from Hyde Park Corner to Hammersmith and back. They were eventually offered for sale, by an advertisement in the *Times* for 19th February, 1835, but it is supposed they remained unsold, and it is not known what became of them.

Now that the tubular boiler has come so prominently to the front, it is interesting to note that many of the steam carriages of sixty years ago were fitted with tubular boilers, somewhat resembling the boilers that are being used at this time ; Squire's, Maceroni's, and

Dance's, are examples. We illustrate Dance's boiler in Fig. 10.

## SQUIRE

After Squire had severed his connection with Colonel Maceroni, he patented a tubular boiler in 1843. The

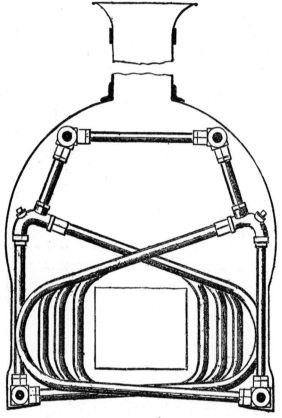

FIG. 10.   DANCE'S BOILER

boiler, he tells us, was the matured result of experiments in which he had for several years been engaged, to introduce steam travelling on common roads. Fig. 11 gives a sectional view of the boiler. It consists of a series of vertical double tubes; the outer tubes are closed at the top and the bottom, and filled with water

to the line W. The inner tubes are opened at the top
and the bottom, to allow the flame and heated gases to
ascend freely through them; and to increase the draught

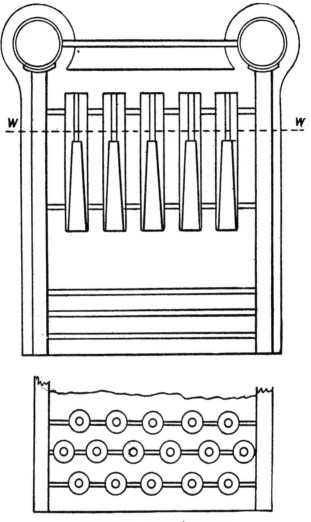

FIGS. 11, 12. SQUIRE'S BOILER

they are made of a conical form, up to nearly the level
of the water line, and then contracted into a smaller
area. There is a pipe connecting the steam chambers

together, and a pipe at the top and bottom of each row of tubes, of which there were six or more rows. The fire-bars were made of piping, the water inside of which communicated with the outer casing on each side. The boiler was suitably enclosed in sheet iron. Fig. 12 shows a portion of the boiler in plan, the tubes were 8 in. in diameter. Instead of the flat chambers at the sides, the boiler could be surrounded with 4-in. diameter vertical tubes.

There are few engineers who have devoted so much time to the construction of steam road engines as Mr. Boulton has. He built his carriage in 1848, and his firm at Ashton-under-Lyne have built six small steam pleasure carriages, all of which were undoubtedly successful.

Most of the carriages varied in size and design. A description is given of two of them. One of Mr. Boulton's small pleasure carriages is shown by Fig. 13, from which it will be seen that the machine is mounted on three wheels; the hind part is hung on two laminated carriage springs; the leading-wheel is also provided with a spring. The chief portion of the weight was placed over the driving-axle. The driving-wheels were made of wood, and being large in diameter, the carriage ran at good speeds as smoothly as an ordinary horse-drawn vehicle. Two cylinders were employed, 3 in. in diameter and 6 in. stroke; they were secured to the side frame, and were supplied with steam through two separate steam-pipes as shown. Motion was communicated from the crank shaft to the driving-axle by means of a pitch chain, the sizes of the chain wheels giving a ratio of five to one for the quick speed. In this instance

FIG. 13. STEAM CARRIAGE BY MR. J. W. BOULTON, ASHTON-UNDER-LYNE

# Self-contained Passenger Coaches

only one wheel was keyed to the axle, the other wheel ran loose on the axle, therefore no clutches or compensating gear were needed. The wrought-iron frame was 9 ft. long, the driving-wheels were 4 ft. in diameter, the leading-wheel was 2 ft. in diameter. No reversing gear was provided, because these small vehicles can be quickly stopped and turned round, so none appeared to be needed; by the omission of this motion a great reduction in the number of the working parts is secured, and the fewer the details to get out of order the better. The boiler was of the vertical tubular type, 20 in. in diameter and 3 ft. high, working at 60 lbs. pressure. Provisions were made for carrying coke and water under the seat behind. This carriage ran well and comfortably at eight to ten miles an hour, and long journeys were frequently made without any accident.

Here are a few particulars of another little steam carriage made by Mr. Boulton. It had a pair of cylinders $2\frac{5}{8}$ in. diameter and 9-in. stroke, placed outside the framing and geared to the driving-wheels, which were 3 ft. in diameter and $2\frac{1}{2}$ in. on face, by means of a pinion and spur wheel. In this case also one wheel was keyed to the axle, and the other was loose. A Field boiler of light and peculiar construction was employed, working at 130 lbs. pressure. Fig. 14 shows a sectional view of the boiler. The top part of the

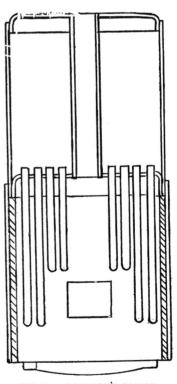

FIG. 14. BOULTON'S BOILER

boiler was 20 in. diameter and 20 in. deep; the uptake was expanded, and beaded in the tube-plate and the crown as shown. The water space round the fire-box was composed of Field tubes $1\frac{3}{8}$ in. diameter, simply screwed into the fire-box crown; outside these tubes there was a fireclay lining all round the fire-box, kept in its place by means of a $\frac{1}{4}$-in. plate. The furnace door is shown; there were no less than sixty-two long tubes and twenty-four short ones, giving a large amount of heating surface; the fire-grate was 15 in. diameter. Mr. Boulton made a number of boilers on this principle, which he used for steam launches as well as steam carriages. They were cheap to make, and worked very well. This small carriage weighed 17 cwt.; the greater part of the weight was over the driving-wheels. One of Mr. Boulton's sons ran this handy carriage about like a tricycle. It was afterwards sent to a customer in Ireland. Such steam carriages as these could be made to run about as safely and pleasantly as bicycles.

### COLEY

In 1853 Messrs. Coley and Co., West London Iron Works, made a steam carriage. The three cylinders were placed beneath the boiler, direct acting. It was mounted on springs and fitted with wood wheels. An engine of the type was made, but was not very successful.

### RICKETT

Mr. Thomas Rickett, of Castle Foundry, Buckingham, made a number of successful pleasure carriages, one of which is illustrated in Mr. McLaren's paper on "Steam on Common Roads."[1] This engine was made for the

[1] Letter from Mr. John Hayes, Excerpt *Minutes of the Institution of Civil Engineers*, vol. ciii., Session 1890-91, pt. i.

# Self-contained Passenger Coaches

Marquis of Stafford in 1858; it was mounted on three wheels. Motion was communicated from the crank shaft to the driving-axle by means of a pitch chain; the relative diameters of the two chain wheels were as one to two and a half. The weight of the carriage when fully loaded was only 30 cwt.

Mr. Rickett built two more steam carriages, substituting spur gearing in place of the pitch driving-chain. One of these carriages was sold to the Earl of Caithness. The cylinders were placed near the passengers' seat, the crank shaft being at the chimney end near to the main axle, to suit the gearing. The bearings of the driving-axle carried the springs, and worked in guides set at an angle from the perpendicular, but at right angles to a line drawn connecting the centres of the two axles, so that the motion of the springs did not materially affect the gearing. There were two sets of gearing giving proportionate speeds of ten and four miles an hour, so that in ascending hills or traversing rough roads, by throwing in the slow gearing, the actual tractive force was multiplied two and a half times. This carriage was intended to carry three passengers. The weight of the carriage fully loaded was two and a half tons. This locomotive did exceedingly well on the steep hills of Scotland.

## HOLT

Figs. 15 and 16 show two views of Mr. H. Percy Holt's steam carriage. It was mounted on three wheels, the driving-wheels were 4 ft. 6 in. diameter; the front wheel was 2 ft. 6 in. diameter. The frame of the carriage was made of 3 in. by 3 in. angle-iron; Fig. 15 shows the frame clearly. A Field boiler—4 ft. high, and 2 ft. diameter at the top—was hung on the frame behind.

# Steam Carriages

The boiler contained 50 ft. of heating surface and 3 sq. ft. of grate area. The working pressure was 250 lbs. per square inch. It will be seen from the plan that there were two distinct double-cylinder engines ; each pair of cylinders drove a separate crank shaft. The cylinders were 3 in. diameter, and 6 in. stroke. On the outer end of

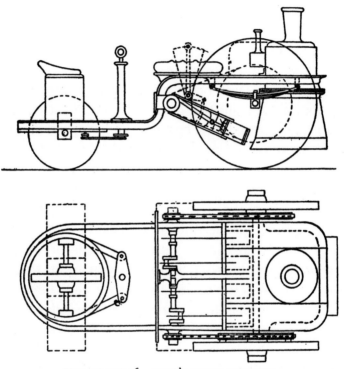

FIGS. 15 AND 16. HOLT'S STEAM CARRIAGE

each crank shaft was keyed a chain pinion 8 in. diameter, which communicated motion to the driving-wheel by a pitch chain on each side. The chain wheel on the axle was 24 in. diameter.

The engines were placed at an angle, and neatly boxed in out of sight. The exhaust from the engines passed into a cast-iron box which formed a baffle plate at the bottom of the uptake above the fire, where the

# Self-contained Passenger Coaches

steam was superheated. The exhaust then issued in five continuous jets up the chimney. Mr. W. Worby Beaumont says: "This arrangement, owing to the large number of beats from four cylinders, made comparatively little noise. Part of the exhaust was used to heat the feed water when required." The carriage complete weighed, in running order, about 30 cwt., and carried from six to eight passengers. It ascended gradients of 1 in 14 at about seven miles an hour easily, and on ordinary roads ran from fifteen to twenty miles an hour; and was thus much more powerful than will be required for the moderate speed vehicles of the future. The bunkers carried sufficient coke for a forty-mile run, and the tanks would hold water for about twenty miles; the coke consumption being about 5 lbs. per mile, under favourable conditions. The method of steering is shown in the illustrations. Each pair of engines, being independent, could be used with the reversing gear as a brake, and the very great advantage of the independence of these engines was the smoothness with which they suited the speed of the wheels in running round corners, and made compensating gear unnecessary. A further advantage was that of being able to use, on good level roads, only one engine, so that little steam was used. The water tanks were arranged on each side of the steering wheel, the top of which formed a seat. The coke bunkers were provided on each side of the boiler. The greater portion of the weight was carried by the driving-wheels, which were made of wood, with 3-in. iron tires. The hind part of the carriage was carried on long, laminated springs.[1]

[1] We are indebted to Mr. Worby Beaumont's Cantor Lectures for particulars of Mr. Holt's steam carriage.

# Steam Carriages

The following interesting particulars of Holt's and Rhodes's carriages of 1866 are extracted from *The Engineer*. Mr. Holt's carriage was sold to Mr. Rhodes, who had previously been making a carriage, which is also illustrated. Mr. Rhodes says of this carriage "it was one he began to build in 1863," and that "when completed it did some very fair running. At first it was direct action on four wheels, and not satisfactory, but when altered to the form as shown in the drawing, it ran splendidly on any road, and over new metal."

He also bought the steam carriage from Mr. Holt. Mr. Rhodes made some alterations in it, including the

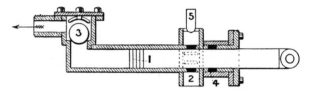

FIG. 17.   FEED-PUMP FOR HOLT'S STEAM CARRIAGE

lap of the valves and the position of the excentrics. Mr. Holt's carriage was also owned by Mr. Edwards, who says that the pump did not work well until another clack had been added. Only two cylinders were used by Mr. Edwards.

Referring to the pump mentioned in our notice of Mr. Holt's carriage, Mr. Rhodes sends a sketch, from which the annexed engraving is made, saying that he had previously used it on his own carriage.[1]

In this engraving 1 is the plunger with rings on the end; 2, a cage round pump barrel over the slots with water inlet pipe 5; 3, ball delivery valve; and 4, packing, which had not any pressure to withstand.

[1] We are indebted to the editor of *The Engineer* for a sketch of the pump and description.

# Self-contained Passenger Coaches

Of this pump he says : "This pump, when running quickly, would lift water in a state of ebullition 3 ft., and force it into the boiler. The plunger bared the slots at the end of the stroke, where it was moving slowly, and coming to a stop."

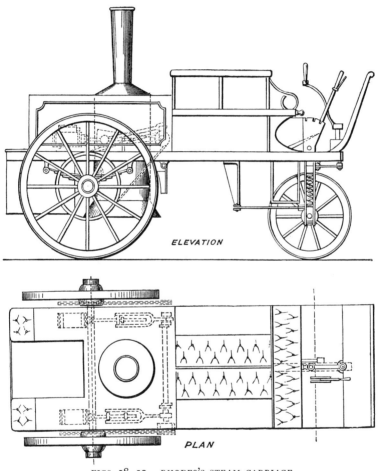

ELEVATION

PLAN

FIGS. 18, 19.   RHODES'S STEAM CARRIAGE

Of his own carriage Mr. Rhodes sends the drawings (Figs. 18 and 19), from which it appears that the two cylinders are connected to one crank shaft with cranks at right angles, and with a chain pinion on each end driving the road wheels, to which chain wheels are attached to the spokes.  Both wheels are equally driven, no arrangement being provided for turning corners. Subsequently the crank shaft was separated into two lengths, and each engine ran independently, thus allowing for corner turning.  The frame was made of 4 in. by $\frac{1}{4}$ in. flat iron, with a $1\frac{1}{2}$ in. angle riveted to the top edge, and was carried on three wheels—two driving-wheels 5 ft. diameter by 3 in. face, and one steering-wheel 3 ft. diameter by 3 in. face, strongly made of oak, and steel-tired ; between the driving axle and frame were long leaf springs, connected with radius rods to the engine crank shaft ; the front wheel was carried by a fork fitted with sliding bearings supported on spiral springs and connected by links to the steering handle.

The boiler was 2 ft. diameter by 3 ft. 6 in. high, and had seventeen Field tubes and thirty-six flue tubes into the smoke-box, and worked at a pressure of 150 lbs. per square inch.  The engines were placed one on each side of the boiler, and had cylinders $3\frac{1}{8}$ in. bore by 9 in. stroke, and geared 5 to 1 to the driving-wheels by means of pitch chains.

The feed-pump, which was worked from one of the engine crossheads, was specially designed, and probably the first of its kind, made to lift and force boiling water, and had only one valve.  A feed-pump made to this design was afterwards fitted to Mr. Holt's steam carriage.

Part of the exhaust steam was turned into the water-tank to heat the feed, the remainder into the chimney, and rendered noiseless by means of a double-cone blast nozzle.  All the machinery was completely enclosed, and the carriage ran successfully for many years without any serious accident or complaint, and would make from twelve to fourteen miles per hour with ease.

# Self-contained Passenger Coaches

In addition to the particulars of Dudgeon's early road carriage,[1] we are enabled to give some details of the later steam waggon, as per the illustration, Fig. 20. Mr. Buck sends the following account. This steam carriage No. 2 was built in 1866. It was steered and driven from the rear. The seats were placed above the

FIG. 20.   DUDGEON'S STEAM CAR

locomotive type of boiler. The cylinders were 4 in. diameter and 14 in. stroke, one placed on each side and coupled direct to the cranked axle. The cylinders were bolted to the boiler barrel, as were also the main axle carriages, the front axle, and the seat brackets.

We stated that the boiler was of the locomotive type, 21 in. diameter, with a firebox 44½ in. long. The boiler was fed by means of a pump and an injector. Before

[1] *Steam Locomotion on Common Roads*, p. 148.

the steam was conducted to the engine it was super-heated. The driving-wheels were $38\frac{1}{2}$ in. diameter, the leading-wheels were 37 in. diameter, the wheel-base was about 7 ft. Plate springs were employed on the carriage. The wheels were made of cedar-wood, built up in sections as shown in the illustration, and hooped with steel tires. In working trim the steam carriage weighed two tons.

### JOCHUMSEN

About this time a steam carriage was made by Mr. Jochumsen in Denmark. The main frame of the vehicle was made of wood. An inverted engine was bolted to a vertical boiler, the reversing lever was placed in such a position as to be under the control of the person who attended to the steering, the levers for operating the clutches for changing the speeds being also placed near the same. A feed-water heater was provided through which the exhaust steam was led before entering the funnel. A front steering wheel was carried by a fork, which supported the fore end of the carriage by means of a spring. The carriage was never tried on the road, the boiler being too small to run the engine at full speed for any time without priming excessively. A number of alterations were made in the boiler without effecting any marked improvement. This Danish carriage was illustrated in *The Autocar* for January 2nd, 1897.

### PATERSON

We must next describe a steam carriage by Mr. A. Paterson as illustrated by Figs. 21 and 22. From a communication we have had from the designer and maker of this machine we quote the following particulars. The carriage is made of sheet iron about 20

# Self-contained Passenger Coaches

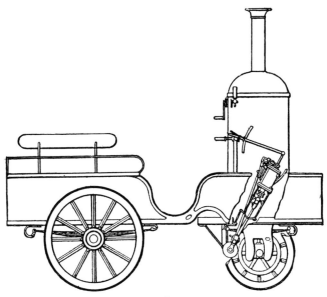

B.W.G. thick carried on a light angle-iron frame.    The length over all is 10 ft. 4 in., and the width 4 ft. 4 in. It will comfortably seat eight persons.   The trailing wheels are 3 ft. 4 in. diameter, and are made of wood ; the driving-wheels are 2 ft. 4 in. diameter.    The gearing mostly used was 3 to 1.    A speed of seven to twelve miles an hour was frequently run over short distances. The police regulations at that date (1860) prevented any fair trial.    A vertical tubular boiler was used.  The carriage was steered very easily and could be turned

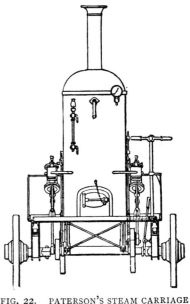

FIG. 22.   PATERSON'S STEAM CARRIAGE

in a narrow road without stopping. A forecarriage supported the boiler and the engines, to which the driving-
wheels were attached as shown; the forepart of the
carriage could turn on the plate in answer to a circular
rack steerage. The cylinders were 3 in. diameter and
6 in. stroke. The working pressure was 100 lbs. per
sq. in., and the weight in working trim about 1 ton. A
clutch was fitted to the 2-in. front axle whereby one
driving-wheel could be thrown out of gear.

### GOODMAN

A neat steam dog-cart was made by Mr. Goodman as
shown by Fig. 23. It was worked by a pair of direct-

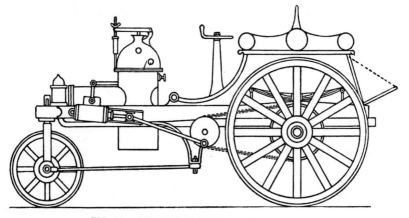

FIG. 23. STEAM DOG-CART BY MR. GOODMAN

acting engines coupled to the crank shaft in the usual
manner. A chain pinion on the crank shaft transmitted
motion to the main axle through an endless pitch chain,
working over a chain wheel on the driving shaft.

### ARMSTRONG

The next carriage illustrated by Fig. 24 was made by
Mr. Armstrong. The following particulars are taken
from *Steam Locomotion on Common Roads*, 1891.

Some time in 1868, Mr. Armstrong, of Rawulpindee,

# Self-contained Passenger Coaches

Punjab, India, made a neat little steam carriage, having two steam cylinders, each 3 in. diameter, and 6 in. stroke. A trunk was used, so as to do away with slide bars. A separate stop valve was fitted to each cylinder.    The

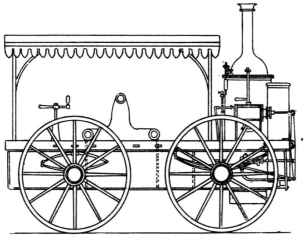

FIG. 24.   STEAM CARRIAGE BY MR. ARMSTRONG.

boiler was 15 in. diameter, 3 ft. high, and was worked at 100 lbs. steam pressure per sq. in.    The carriage travelled at twelve miles an hour on the level road, and up an incline of 1 in 20 at the rate of six miles an hour.    The driving-wheels were 3 ft. diameter.    The engine had been running more than a year when the above particulars were forwarded by Mr. Armstrong to *The Engineer*.

## CATLEY AND AYRES

Catley and Ayres' steam carriage was exhibited at the Yorkshire Agricultural Society's meeting at York in 1871, and has only been briefly referred to in one publication.[1] There are several interesting features embodied in this carriage deserving a full description, which at the present time cannot fail to interest our readers.

The wagonette is illustrated by Fig. 25 on page 34,

[1] *The History and Development of Steam Locomotion on Common Roads*, by W. Fletcher, p. 185.   E. and F. N. Spon.   1891.

from a photograph. Figs. 26 and 27 show a plan of
the machinery, with the carriage body removed, and
a side view of the same. The frame is made of bar
iron $3\frac{1}{2}$ in. deep and $\frac{5}{16}$ in. thick, bent to the shape
required, and the ends welded together. About the
middle of the frame there are two pieces of tee iron,

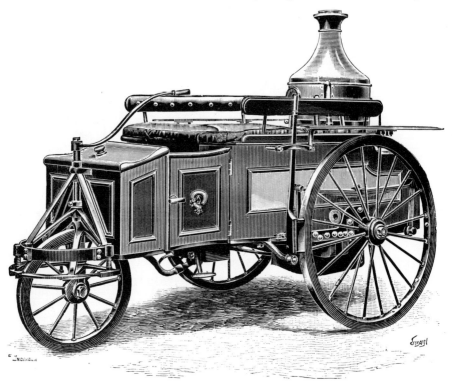

FIG. 25. STEAM WAGONETTE BY MESSRS. CATLEY AND AYRES

and there are transverse bars in other parts for stiffening
the structure. The horn-plates for the axle-boxes and
the deeper plate for the cylinders are welded in the
frame, as shown.

The carriage is propelled by a pair of horizontal
engines, driving a short crank shaft with the two cranks
placed at right angles to each other. The cylinders are
$2\frac{5}{8}$ in. diameter, and $5\frac{3}{4}$ in. stroke; the piston heads are

# Self-contained Passenger Coaches

forged with the rods. The pistons have grooves cut in them for two steel rings; each ring is $\frac{3}{16}$ in. wide and $\frac{1}{8}$ in. thick. Wrought-iron is used for the slide bars and crossheads so as to reduce the weight; the wearing surfaces of these parts are case-hardened. Excentrics are keyed to the crank shaft for actuating the slide valves; the excentrics are shown with the straps and excentric rods removed. No link motion is used, as it was not considered necessary, as the carriage, being

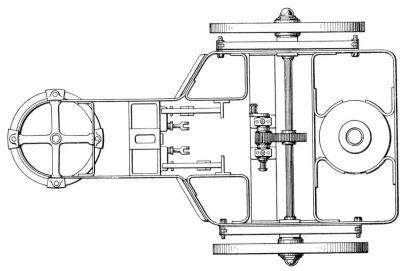

FIG. 26.   DETAILS OF STEAM WAGONETTE

only $8\frac{1}{2}$ ft. long, could be turned round with facility in a small space. The omission of link motion reduces the number of wearing parts, which is an advantage. A wrought-iron flange plate is riveted in between the side plates on which the crank shaft bearings are carried. This plate also acts as a stay to the side plates. A small spur pinion is keyed on the crank shaft, which gears into a wheel on the driving-axle; the ratios of the wheels are 3 to 1. There is only one travelling speed, and the constructor does not consider this a disadvantage, as the speed could be varied by varying the speed of the engines to suit most of the roads to be traversed. The carriage has been run at the rate of twenty miles an hour, and has travelled up gradients of 1 in 20.

The hind axle is 2 in. in diameter; the bearings are made of cast-iron sliding in the iron plates; the weight of the hind part of the carriage is passed to these axle blocks through long plate springs, as shown in the en-

FIG. 27.   DETAILS OF STEAM WAGONETTE

gravings. As the crank shaft and main axle are on the same horizontal centre line, the up-and-down motion of the axle caused by the action of the springs will not affect the spur wheels very much, if the movement is not excessive. An arrangement like this has been used on many traction engines for years without any serious inconvenience.

The driving-wheels are 3 ft. 6 in. diameter; the twenty spokes in each wheel are made of $\frac{1}{2}$ in. round iron, with collars forged on the outer ends faced in the lathe, and chased on the ends beyond the collars, as shown in Fig. 27. The ends of the spokes are screwed into a 2 in. by $\frac{5}{16}$ in. wrought-iron hoop, and into the ash tire also; the felloes are dowelled together with iron pins. At this stage the wheels were sent into the foundry to have the bosses cast on, afterwards they were bored and faced in a lathe; the wood tires were also turned on the sides and on the outer edge. The outer hoop was next shrunk on; it is made of 2 in. by $\frac{1}{2}$ in. iron. It will be seen that the inside hoop, the wood tire, and outside hoop, are riveted together. This makes a light and satisfactory wheel. One of the driving-wheels is keyed to the axle, the other runs loose so as to facilitate turning. The front wheel is 2 ft. in diameter, and is made in the same manner as the hind wheels; the leading-wheel runs in a fork, the spindle of which turns in a double guide of light wrought-iron; the guide is riveted to the fore part of the frame, as shown in the illustrations. Four arms are welded on each side of the steerage fork; these are secured to a ring, or turn-table, which encircles the wheel. This ring turns in four small cast-iron guides; each guide is mounted on a spiral spring, and held in position by the front end of the frame. The weight of the fore end of the wagonette is supported by these springs. The steerage works well; the carriage can be easily guided with one hand on the lever. A feed-pump is fitted, but not shown in the drawing. There are two feed-water tanks, one is placed in the front, the other at the side under the seat; they are connected by a pipe beneath the floor. Under the opposite seat is a locker for canvas buckets and small tools. There are places for coal or coke.

Two of the floor boards are hinged on to the iron cross-stays of the frame; each board is 7 in. wide, and placed directly over the engine. The engine can be readily examined by means of these doors, if needful, but the machinery is of such a simple character that it requires little or no attention beyond the lubrication of the working parts. The driving-wheels are fitted with lever hand-brakes, as shown.

The boiler is of the vertical fire-tube type, constructed of Lowmoor iron plates. It is 3 ft. high, and $17\frac{1}{2}$ in. external diameter. The shell-plates are $\frac{5}{16}$ in. thick, and the tube-plates are $\frac{7}{16}$ in. thick. A spiral tube super-heater is fitted in the smoke box made of $1\frac{1}{4}$ in. piping; the steam passes through this coil on its way to the engine cylinders. The iron smoke-box and chimney are covered with a polished copper casing. To prevent the radiation of heat, the boiler is coated with a thick-ness of non-conducting material, and polished mahogany lagging outside. Mr. Catley tested the boiler with water up to 400 lbs. pressure per square inch. The working pressure is 150 lbs. By using good coal very little smoke was made, but coke could be used if required. The boiler supplied dry steam, and the engines are set to work with an early cut-off. The passage of the exhaust steam into the chimney base causes very little noise, and there-fore was not suppressed. Twenty gallons of water and about 2 cwt. of fuel can be carried.

The engine made many journeys during three years, carrying four passengers for eight or ten miles round York; the speed could be increased up to about twenty miles an hour on good level roads, and slower rates of speed were attained on gradients. Little noise is made by the carriage when travelling; there is no vibration whatever, and Mr. Catley says, " The horses they met during their numerous journeys took no notice of it."

An important feature of this steam wagonette is its

# Self-contained Passenger Coaches

very moderate weight. When the boiler, tanks, and bunkers are full, ready for a run, the total weight is only 19 cwt. Among the objections urged against the steam engine for carriage propulsion the supposed weight is always dwelt upon. But this example appears to show that with careful designing a steam carriage of substantial construction, and well adapted for hard work, need not necessarily be as heavy as many that have been built. The reduction in the weight is secured by the use of light bars of wrought-iron for the frame. No cast-iron is employed except where it is absolutely necessary, and when it is used the parts are made as small as possible. The driving gear is simple. The use of one speed cuts down the number of parts. Although improvements could easily be now made, it will be admitted that Mr. Catley's carriage presents several features of interest.

## TODD

We now illustrate by Figs. 28 and 29 a side elevation and plan of a neat little steam carriage made by Mr. Leonard Todd.

The main frame was made of angle-iron, mounted on three wheels ; the driving-wheels were 4 ft. 6 in. diameter, and the leading-wheel was 2 ft. diameter. The wheels were made of wood in the usual manner, with steel tires. A vertical boiler was used—about 3 ft. 6 in. high and 15 in. diameter—it contained a number of Field tubes ; the heating surface was 16 sq. ft., and the grate area $\frac{3}{4}$ of a sq. ft. The carriage was 8 ft. 6 in. long and 4 ft. 6 in. wide. It was designed to carry two persons ; the top of the seat was hinged to form a locker inside. A tool-box is also shown at the back of the seat, with a sloping hinged lid. The water-tank was fixed below the floor, the filler is shown standing out behind. On the boss of each driving-wheel was fixed a grooved pulley, 14 in. diameter. The main axle was cranked to clear the water-tank, and each driving-wheel ran loose on the axle. The spring arrangement was most efficiently carried out ; the hind part of the carriage was borne by long laminated springs, as well as india-rubber washers. The front part of the vehicle was neatly mounted on a volute spring, as shown, and some rubber washers ;

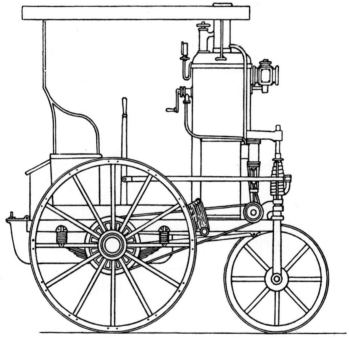

FIG. 28.   STEAM CARRIAGE BY MR. LEONARD TODD

so smoothly did this carriage run, that the maker guaranteed to run one hundred miles in ten hours. Little noise was made by the exhaust steam, as the cylinders were only $2\frac{1}{2}$ in. diameter and 4 in. stroke ; the quantity of steam was almost invisible. A brake was fitted to each driving-wheel, worked by a foot-lever. On the main frame, to the forward side of each coal bunker, were fixed two plummer blocks, which carried

# Self-contained Passenger Coaches

a double-throw crank shaft. The inverted engines are shown bolted to the front of the bunkers, one on each side of the boiler; there was no reversing gear, but a single excentric working forwards, and cutting off at $\frac{5}{8}$ stroke. On each end of the crank shaft is keyed a friction cone, carrying a grooved pulley, 6 in. diameter, and from this pulley motion is communicated to the driving-wheel by a gut cord; by means of these clutches the carriage could be turned with facility. The steering lever and gear are shown clearly. The boiler was fed by a No. 1 brass injector placed through the foot-plate.

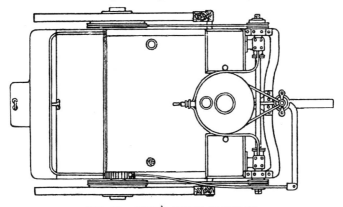

FIG. 29.   TODD'S STEAM CARRIAGE

The engines were covered in from the weather, but the covers are not shown in the illustrations, so as to give views of the engines. An awning was provided, and the whole arrangement reflects the greatest credit on the maker. The weight of this carriage was very moderate. It may be stated that it was the duty of the man on the right to drive and steer, and, if necessary, work the brake; and the one on the left hand acted as stoker. "The carriage was a practical success, and many would have been made but for the Road Locomotive Acts, Mr. Todd having received numerous orders and inquiries for them."

# CHAPTER II

## SELF-CONTAINED PASSENGER COACHES AND SMALL STEAM CARRIAGES

### RANDOLPH

WE now illustrate a steam coach built for Mr. Randolph, one of the partners of the celebrated firm of Randolph and Elder, of Glasgow. The machinery was made by Messrs. Dübs and Co., of the Glasgow Locomotive Works, and the carriage portion

FIG. 30.   STEAM COACH BY MR. RANDOLPH

by Messrs. James Henderson and Co., of North Street, Anderston.   In *The Engineer* for 8th May, 1896, a long extract from the *Glasgow Herald* of November 13th, 1872, gives a full description of the relic.

A few particulars may be inserted here.   The car-

# Self-contained Passenger Coaches

riage is 15 ft. in length. When filled with passengers and provided with water, etc., for a journey, its entire weight was about $4\frac{1}{2}$ tons. The two leading-wheels are 3 ft. 4 in. diameter and $2\frac{1}{2}$ in. breadth, are only 2 ft. apart, while the hind wheels, which are 5 ft. 4 in. apart, are 4 ft. 6 in. diameter and 4 in. breadth. The springs of the carriage were so nicely adjusted, and the weight of the machine itself was so great, that the jerking motion of the wheels was not communicated in any appreciable degree to the body of the vehicle.

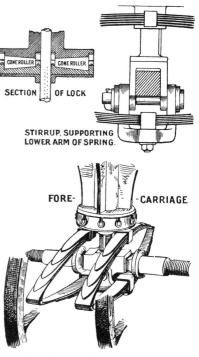

There are two pairs of vertical engines, one on each side of the carriage, with 3 in. diameter of cylinders. A Field tube vertical boiler supplied the steam; the heating surface was about 80 sq. ft., and 2 ft. of grate area. A working pressure of 120 lb. was not to be exceeded. When the engines were running at 300 ft. per minute

FIG. 31. SPRING ARRANGEMENT FOR MR. RANDOLPH'S COACH

the carriage would travel at eight miles an hour. After the coach had made a few trips, there is reason to believe that the authorities prohibited its use in the streets, and nothing was heard of it until 1878, when it was sent to the Paris Exhibition. In addition to the general view of the coach, Fig. 30, a small illustration, Fig. 31, of the spring arrangement of the fore carriage is given.

# Steam Carriages

## MACKENZIE

Mr. Mackenzie's steam brougham must take the next place. Fig. 32 shows a sectional elevation of the machine; Fig. 33 gives a plan; Fig. 34 shows the carriage very clearly.[1]

The engine was a double-cylinder vertical type; the cylinders were each $3\frac{3}{4}$ in. diameter and $4\frac{1}{2}$ in. stroke. The moving parts were carefully balanced to prevent

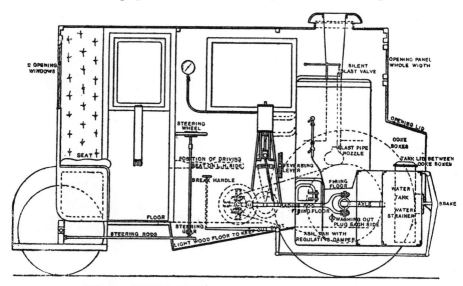

FIG. 32. SECTION OF STEAM BROUGHAM BY MR. MACKENZIE

vibration. In order to economise the steam the engine was run at a high speed, and worked expansively by means of the link motion reversing gear; by altering the cut-off the speed of the engine could be varied to suit the work without touching the regulator. Two spur pinions were fixed on sliding keys on the crank shaft; the large pinion could be geared with the small wheel on the countershaft to give the quick-travelling speed on the road of, say, ten miles an hour; the small

[1] We are indebted to *The Engineer* for this illustration.

pinion, geared with the large wheel, for giving a slower speed for traversing rough roads and for climbing inclines. Both the pinions are shown out of gear on the plan, Fig. 33. When the fast-speed wheels are slid into gear the ratio of engine speed to road-wheel speed is 6 to 1, and when the slower wheels are in gear the ratio is 13 to 1. We may mention here that one writer recommends the use of one speed—one pair of wheels of such a ratio to give a speed of twelve miles an hour when the engine is running at full speed. He proposes to have link-motion notched up like a railway loco-

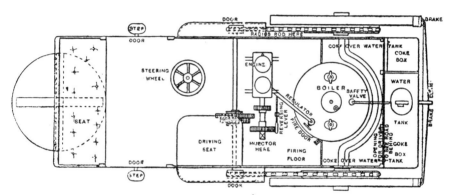

FIG. 33. PLAN OF MACKENZIE'S STEAM BROUGHAM.

motive—full gear for starting and for heavy travelling over bad roads and up steep hills, and then notch up when these difficulties have been scaled and a level piece of good road has to be traversed. This will certainly simplify the amount of gearing, and reduce the weight of the machinery. The fault of many carriages has been the lack of power for emergencies; the extra power proposed would be available at a moment's notice, without stopping, by simply altering the cut-off by means of the reversing lever—the engine at once exerts its full power, and will overcome any difficult work with ease and safety.

# Steam Carriages

We must now describe the driving gear of Mr. Mackenzie's brougham. From the illustrations of the steam carriages given, it will be seen that the compensating gear is placed within the double-speed spur-wheel, on the countershaft. There are several features of interest connected with the compensating gear which are worthy of note. Fig. 35 shows a section of the gear-

FIG. 34. STEAM BROUGHAM BY MR. MACKENZIE

ing, Fig. 36 an elevation ; Figs. 37 and 38 give sections through the pin on which the pinions revolve, and the flat arm at right angles with same ; Fig. 39 shows the mortice teeth and method of holding them in position.

The compensating gear is a device now used on all road locomotives for causing both driving-wheels to do an equal share of the propulsion of the machine, no matter whether the engine is travelling in a straight line, or rounding a curve.

# Self-contained Passenger Coaches

From the illustrations it will be seen that the compensating gear consists of four bevel - wheels, two of which are keyed on the intermediate shaft, and the other two are carried by a wrought-iron cross, which is bolted inside the double spur mortice ring.

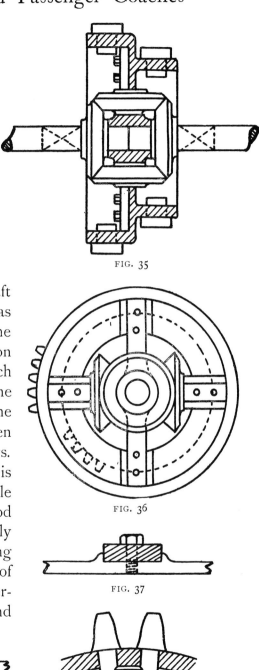

FIG. 35

FIG. 36

The intermediate shaft is made in two pieces, as shown in Fig. 33; the two ends are placed on the centre line. Each bevel-wheel drives one half of the shaft; the gearing is placed between the two middle bearings. The double spur-ring is cast in one piece, suitable for receiving the wood teeth. These were wisely adopted for preventing noise, the importance of which cannot be overestimated; the rattle and

FIG. 37

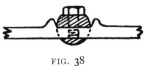

FIG. 38

FIG. 39

47

# Steam Carriages

ring of the gearing was certainly one of the drawbacks of many steam carriages of that period. The wood gearing and chain driving prevent noise.

The action of the compensating gear is as follows. When the carriage travels in a straight line the two bevel-wheels on the wrought-iron cross do not revolve on the spindle, but act as drivers to the two bevel-wheels on the shafts. If the steering-gear is actuated, so as to make the carriage take a circular course, for rounding a corner, or for turning round, both the bevel-wheels on the arms turn on their spindles—slower or faster, as the case may be—to allow one driving-wheel to travel at a greater rate than the other. Compensating gear is now used in all traction engines, and most steam carriages ; in fact, no self-propelling carriage is complete without it, for no other means gives so little trouble and acts so well.

When compensating gear is not used, one of the following more or less unsatisfactory devices must be adopted, for allowing one driving-wheel to travel faster than the other when turning corners.

Many carriages have been made with one driving-wheel only keyed to the axle. This plan answers fairly for small vehicles, and allows easy turning ; but it is of no use for large carriages. In some instances the travelling-wheels are attached to the main axle by clutches. When travelling in a straight line both the clutches are in gear ; for turning a sharp corner, one wheel can be thrown out of gear. The crank shaft is sometimes made in two pieces, and each driven by a separate cylinder or cylinders, each crank driving one travelling-wheel ; by running one engine fast and the other slower, or by running one engine ahead and the other astern, the carriage can be turned perfectly.

# Self-contained Passenger Coaches

Instead of clutches, friction-straps are used. The straps are tightened sufficiently so as to drive when going straight ahead; when any extra strain comes upon one of them it will slip—for instance, when a sharp corner has to be turned. Ratchet wheels have also been used. By placing the driving-wheels nearer each other than usual, and fixing the steering-wheels farther apart, no device is needed; the carriage will turn easily. Of course, if both wheels are keyed to the axle, a carriage will turn a corner; but when so doing one wheel drives, the other wheel skids, or slips. This action throws a severe strain upon the axle, and should not be permitted.

We will now return to the description of Mr. Mackenzie's steam brougham. On the outer ends of the double countershaft a chain pinion is keyed, giving motion to the driving-wheel through a pitch chain. The chain wheel was fitted with teeth, as shown by Fig. 40. The teeth of the form shown were held in the toothed ring by a pair of nuts on a screwed stem, and when it became necessary the diameter of the ring was increased by placing thin strips of iron under each tooth, as indicated by the dotted lines A A.

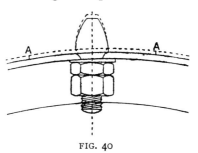

FIG. 40

The driving-wheels were made of wood, with iron tires, in the usual carriage style; the wheels ran loosely on the axle; the axle was bent, as shown in Fig. 33, to escape the boiler. The brougham was efficiently mounted on long laminated springs. The single steering-wheel could be actuated from the inside; the steering-wheel is shown. Two radius-rods were employed for connecting the chain pinion bearings to the axle close to the boss of the driving-wheels. These

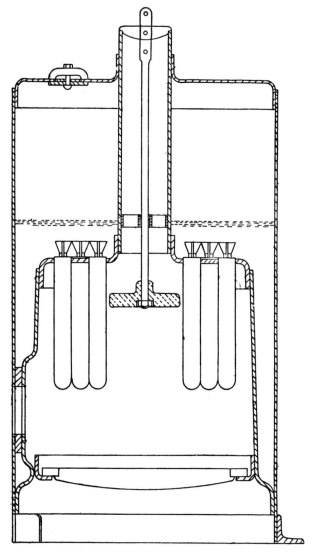

FIG. 41.   SECTION OF FIELD BOILER

rods maintained the proper distance between the chain wheels, and allowed the springs to act without affecting the centres of the chain wheels.   In another chapter mention has been made of the exhaust steam being taken into the cast-iron baffler at the base of the uptake, as shown in Fig. 32. A blast valve was also used, and opened or closed as required. The brake gear is shown. The reversing lever, the starting handle, the injector, and the fire-door are all near together, for convenient manipulation. Fig. 34 shows the carriage very clearly.

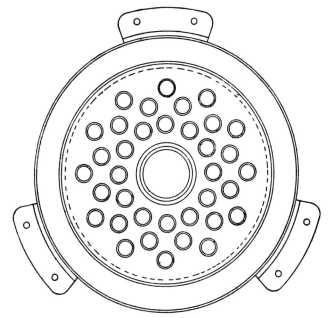

FIG. 42.   PLAN OF THE FIRE-BOX TOP

None of the machinery was in sight, and we are inclined to think that, taking all things into consideration, the vehicle was one of the best made at that early date. The weight of the brougham was 3 tons. The Road Locomotive Act caused it to cease running.

A few notes respecting Mr. Mackenzie's boiler may be of interest here. The illustrations represent the standard type of Field boiler, as used in the steam brougham of 1874. Fig. 41 shows a sectional elevation; Fig. 42 a plan of the fire-box top; and Fig. 43 shows the hand-holes in the top of the shell for cleaning out the boiler. The boiler was 2 ft. diameter and 4 ft. high, worked at 135 lbs. pressure of steam per square inch. The weight of the boiler when filled with water up to the mean water level was about $5\frac{1}{2}$ cwt. It will be seen from the illustrations that there is a water space round the fire-box, which is an essential feature of a boiler intended for using all kinds of water. The im-

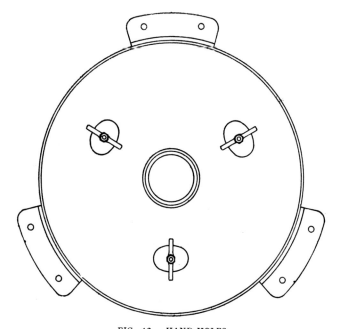

FIG. 43. HAND-HOLES

purities from the water are mostly deposited at the bottom of the water space, and removed from the action of the fire. The mud can be readily cleaned out by means of hand-holes at the bottom of the boiler. " For fuel good foundry coke was best and cheapest in the end. The water I took up was that which ponds and streams afforded, and I was little troubled with the priming tendencies of these hap-hazard waters. My ex-

# Self-contained Passenger Coaches

perience is that a boiler which will not stand and work with almost any kind of water will sooner or later come to grief." A fine strainer was used in the tank to prevent weeds and dirt from reaching the injector. We may remind our readers that Mr. Mackenzie has had practical experience in the working of steam carriages, and we purpose quoting a few passages from letters we have received from him. We believe there is no difficulty in making a simple Field boiler, with a given amount of heating surface that shall not weigh more than some of the tubular boilers of the same heating surface — the tubular boilers being specially recommended on account of their small weight. The advantages of a Field boiler are worth consideration. " For road purposes you must have a certain quantity of water per square foot of heating surface, in order that you may not be blowing off one minute and short of steam the next. A road engine has not such steady work even as a locomotive on the railway, and a boiler that will be manageable enough in a fire-engine or a steam launch may be much too lively for the road ; this is one of the troubles which those who have never worked a steam carriage do not appear to understand."

## PYOTT

This steam vehicle was built in 1876. It was designed by L. T. Pyott, and was owned jointly by Mr. Pyott F. A. Morse, and W. Devine. They were all foremen connected with the Baldwin Locomotive Works, Philadelphia. The carriage was capable of carrying seven persons, at the rate of twenty miles an hour. It was provided with rubber tires on the wheels, in segments, which proved worthless, as they were not suitable for severe work. The driving-wheels were 52 in. diameter ;

the boiler was 24 in. diameter and 48 in. height; the fire-box was 20 in. diameter, it was fitted with eighty-five $1\frac{1}{4}$ in. tubes. The tank capacity was fifty gallons. The two cylinders were 5-in. bore, 8-in. stroke, geared to the driving-wheels in the ratio of 16 to 39.[1]

## INSHAW

The following description of a steam carriage, made by Mr. J. G. Inshaw, appeared in *The Engineer* for November 1st, 1895. Fig. 44 represents the carriage.

FIG. 44.   STEAM CARRIAGE BY MR. INSHAW

"I have much pleasure in handing you a photograph of an experimental steam carriage built by me in 1881; this carriage was well known in Birmingham and district, and its working was most satisfactory. The only

We are indebted to *Motoring Illustrated* for the particulars.

# Self-contained Passenger Coaches

reason I had for discontinuing my experiments was in consequence of the law prohibiting the use of steam-propelled carriages on the common road, although this carriage made no more noise than an ordinary vehicle, and the exhaust steam being entirely condensed, there was nothing against steam, which I am very much in favour of now, and intend making another carriage as soon as the law has been repealed, which I hope will be very soon.

" I have much pleasure in giving you a few particulars of this carriage. The boiler was almost entirely composed of steel tubes, and would generate steam in about twenty minutes to a pressure of 180 lbs. to 200 lbs. per square inch, finding steam for two cylinders, 4-in. bore, 8-in. stroke. There were three different speeds for hill climbing, etc., and the engines could be thrown out of gear for downhill, etc. There was also double driving gear, reversing gear, and, in fact, all the necessary contrivances were to be found in this machine. The steering was very satisfactory and quite easy to manage.

" When loaded with ten passengers, fuel, and water, this carriage weighed 35 cwt., and the speed on a good road averaged from eight to twelve miles per hour. The steerer had entire control over the carriage ; in fact, far more than a coachman has over a pair of horses, and during the whole of my experiments, which lasted for several years, I never had the slightest accident of any kind."

### ATKINSON AND PHILIPSON

Some reliable, powerful, and speedy steam carriages have been made by Messrs. Atkinson and Philipson. Fig. 45 represents one of these made in 1897.

# Steam Carriages

Mr. Philipson has been working in conjunction with Messrs. Toward, a Newcastle firm of engineers, and the outcome is a vehicle which has attracted much attention in the north of England, where it has been put to some very exacting tests.

FIG. 45. STEAM CARRIAGE BY MESSRS. ATKINSON AND PHILIPSON

This carriage has not only developed a speed very much in excess of anything that will be permitted by the Government regulations, but it is unique in its absolute freedom from noise and vibration, and it climbs very easily hills with a gradient of 1 in 9.

It is a wagonette with seats for two in front and four

behind, the latter *vis-à-vis*. The body is mounted by means of three elliptic springs on a double-perch under-carriage of original and protected design. This under-carriage frame carries the boiler and engines, and is, in turn, supported on the hind axles by spiral springs, and on the front axle by side springs, which effectively relieve all vibration. The boiler is of the inexplosible, instanta-neous generating, or "flash" type, and is constructed of spiral coils of very thick solid-drawn steel tubes, arranged inside a vertical cylindrical fire-box with lining and galvanised steel casing. One of the coils acts as a feed-heater, and the others as genera-tors and superheaters. Steam may be generated by a petroleum burner or by a coke fire. Toward's ingenious boiler, as illustrated by Fig. 46, was used in some of the carriages. The coke fire is the method preferred by Messrs. Philipson and Toward, the fuel being fed by an ingenious device

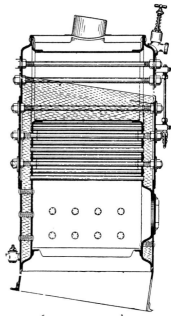

FIG. 46.   MR. TOWARD'S BOILER

from the top by one of those sitting in the carriage. The motor itself consists of a pair of light, high-pressure, horizontal reversing engines, capable of propelling the carriage with six passengers up an incline of 1 in 9, at a working pressure of 175 lbs. per square inch. The engines have long connecting-rods and ample wearing surfaces, and are geared direct from the crank shaft to the hind axle and driving-wheels with pitch chain and sprocket wheels. The driving-axle has a very compact differen-tial gear. The steering-gear is worked by a vertical spindle and lever with chain, and is easily controlled while the reversing-gear, foot and screw brakes are very convenient for the driver. " The wheels have solid rubber tires, which are altogether more suitable for motor cars than pneumatics. The latter are not only liable to puncture, but with fast running and a heavy load, the rubber has sometimes been found to be burned." Sir David Salomons says : "Whether this is due to the successive compressions of the air when meeting obstructions on the road, or whether it is owing to the friction of the air in the tube, due to lag in having to pass through the very restricted opening in that part of the tire in contact with the road, and to friction generally, is difficult to decide."

As a whole, No. 1 looks well and workmanlike on the road, and we may safely conclude that it is a success, as the builders are now engaged on others.

The great point for congratulation is the fact that the difficulty has been overcome by private enterprise, by two old-fashioned firms of coachbuilders and engineers working in harmony, and conclusively proving that more good will be done in this way than by motor companies, promoted by men with no practical knowledge either of engineering or coachmaking.

## BROWN

The accompanying illustration, Fig. 47, represents a neat little steam carriage designed and built by Mr. W. H. Brown, of Devizes. It has ample seating room for four passengers. The machinery is composed of a double-cylinder compound engine of the horizontal type, the cylinders are $2\frac{1}{8}$ and 4 in. diameter by 3 in. stroke, working up to 200 lbs. steam pressure. Link-motion reversing-gear is fitted ; the boiler is of the vertical

FIG. 47. STEAM CARRIAGE BY MR. BROWN.

# Self-contained Passenger Coaches

multitubular type, fired with liquid fuel with a burner designed by the maker, which has proved itself very efficient. The power is transmitted to the rear wheels by pitch chains, the four travelling wheels are fitted with rubber tires of large section. Water can be carried for a run of twenty-five miles on a fairly level road, and oil for seventy to one hundred miles. The machinery is all closed in, and is situated at the after end of the carriage, thus reducing noise and heat to a minimum. It is fitted with two independent brakes, each operating on both the driving-wheels, besides which the reversing-gear forms a powerful emergency brake. With regard to speed, the carriage is capable of doing twelve miles an hour on an average road without effort. It runs in a most satisfactory way and is quite free from vibration, Mr. Brown makes the following remarks : " Steam is more suitable for heavy traffic, and in some cases for light passenger carriages. Where the roads are rough and heavy more power is, of course, required to propel the vehicles, and in such circumstances steam is by far the best power to adopt. A steam engine can be regulated to an infinite number of speeds from the maximum to the minimum simply by adjusting the stop valve. Other advantages of the steam engine are, that when the carriage is standing the engine is at rest also. Again the steam engine is more generally understood by the public at large, and repairs can be more readily accomplished by the ordinary mechanic than would be the case with a spirit or electric motor. The principal disadvantage of the steam carriage are the excessive weight of the boiler and water, and the time spent in raising steam." Since the above was written these weights have been much reduced.

# Steam Carriages

The Serpollet steam carriage has more than once been illustrated in the technical journals, so that a lengthy description is unnecessary, but this chapter would not be complete unless it referred to these very successful road carriages. The most interesting portion of one of these vehicles is shown by Fig. 48. The

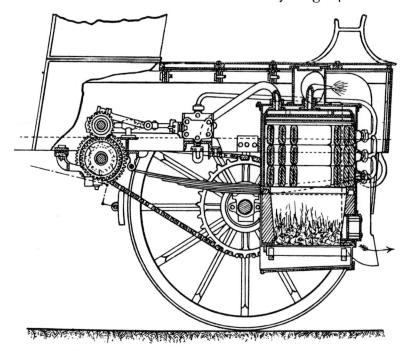

FIG. 48. DETAILS OF STEAM CARRIAGE BY M. SERPOLLET, PARIS

boiler is the chief feature of novelty, and we will give a brief description of this important factor, which is composed of two, three, or more coils, one above the other, of flattened steel tubes. The sides of the flattened tubes nearly meet, only a very small aperture being left, varying from $\frac{1}{16}$ in. to $\frac{1}{32}$ in. The feed-water is forced into the centre of the bottom coil; the small quantity of water which these tubes contain is almost instantly

# Self-contained Passenger Coaches

turned into steam, and this steam is superheated in the higher coils. Some tests carried out in England have proved the boiler to be exceedingly strong. No leakage was detected under pressures of 250 atmospheres. It is nearly impossible for any accident to occur with such a boiler; this favourable characteristic has undoubtedly caused the vehicle to come into extensive use so rapidly. The Serpollet boiler is an economical steamer. Fears were once entertained that the small spaces in the tubes would become choked by deposits from the water; the makers state that the boilers have not suffered in this respect. The engine is shown in the illustration; it works the countershaft through spur-wheels for giving two speeds on the road. A chain pinion is keyed to the countershaft for transmitting motion to the main axle by means of a pitch chain. The exhaust steam is conveyed to the top of the boiler and is superheated in a silencer, and escapes from the chimney in an invisible form. In order to prevent the escape of smoke, which, of course, would be an annoyance on a public road, the fuel employed is coke.

One of the Serpollet motors with a single horizontal cylinder was recently tried, and gave good results. A few figures may be interesting. The cylinder was 5 in. diameter and 5 in. stroke. Steam pressure on admission 45 lbs., cut-off 66 per cent. Revolutions of engine, 284. On a four hours' trial the brake horse-power averaged 4·57. Steam consumption was 29·87 lbs. per brake horse-power. The steam was largely superheated. Heating surface in the boiler, 26·8 sq. ft. Grate area, 2·9 sq. ft. Although the steam pressure was only 58 lbs. per square inch, its temperature on leaving the boiler was 1,009 deg. F. The temperature of saturated steam at the pressure named would be 306 deg.; we have therefore more than 700 deg. of superheating. The output of steam was 5·9 lbs. per square foot of heating surface per hour. The fuel used was briquettes, their value being 8·28 lbs. of steam per lb. of fuel from and at 212 deg.

In M. Serpollet's latest design the capillary tube has been retained, but instead of being arranged in the form

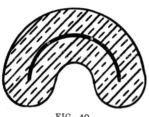

of a coil, it is made in straight lengths, connected in series by suitable bends, running back and forward over the furnace, and arranged in layers or horizontal sections, the number of which may be easily increased or diminished according to the amount

FIG. 49.
THE SERPOLLET BOILER TUBE

of power desired. This type of boiler can be made in larger sizes. The tube itself has also undergone some change in form, its cross section being now like Fig. 49. The working principle, however, remains the same as in the previous model, and all the original advantages of quick steaming, light weight, and practical immunity from explosion dangers have been retained. The Parisian steam carriage trials, which took place in July, 1894, are fully recorded in *The Engineer*.[1]

A more recent type of Serpollet vehicle is shown by Figs. 50 and 51. The engine consists of a pair of horizontal cylinders, $2\frac{1}{2}$ in. diameter and $2\frac{1}{4}$ in. stroke, the crank shaft being connected to the driving-wheels by means of pitch chains. The coke storage is sufficient for a journey, under good conditions, of forty miles, but the water-tank has to be refilled several times in that distance. The pump used for supplying the boiler is of about 1 in. diameter and of $\frac{3}{4}$ in. stroke. In the earlier

[1] We are indebted to *The Engineer* for Figs. 48 and 49.

motor vehicles Serpollet employed one steering-wheel, which was not altogether satisfactory. In the later machines he has adopted a new method of steering,

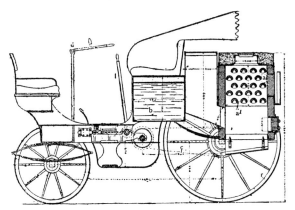

FIG. 50. STEAM CARRIAGE BY M. SERPOLLET

devised by Mr. Jeantaud. In this arrangement the forward axle is not movable, but is fixed parallel to the rear axle, as is shown in Figs. 52 and 53. From these figures it will be seen that the fixed axle terminates in a fork at each end, in which is placed the tee piece made with bearings, and extended to carry the wheel. By this arrangement a free movement is allowed to the wheels in a horizontal plane, around the bearings of the crosshead. The manner of working the system will be understood by reference to the diagram Fig. 54, where it will be seen that the ends of the lever M M are kept at a fixed distance apart by means of a connecting-rod, and any movement transmitted to this rod is transferred to the wheels through the levers, which, however, passed

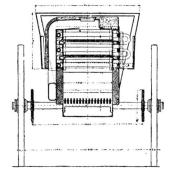

FIG. 51. STEAM CARRIAGE BY M. SERPOLLET

through different angles when shifted, as indicated in the dotted lines in Fig. 54.[1]

From the illustration, Fig. 50, it will be seen that the motor is placed beneath the floor. The engines are shown by Figs. 55 and 56 ; the two cylinders are placed side by side ; the chain wheels on the countershaft drive the axle by two pitch chains on to chain wheels keyed to the driving-axle.

In a later chapter full particulars are given of the Gardner-Serpollet steam vehicles of the day.

[1] We are indebted to *Engineering*, 25th October, 1895, for the above particulars and the illustrations.

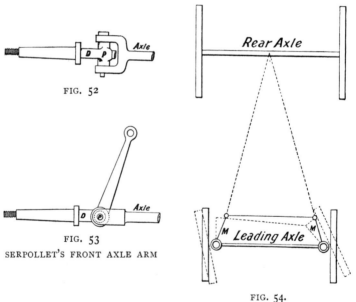

FIG. 52

FIG. 53
SERPOLLET'S FRONT AXLE ARM

FIG. 54.
SERPOLLET'S STEERING GEAR

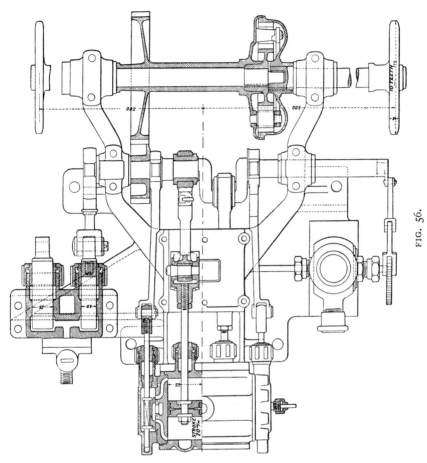

FIG. 56.

STEAM MOTOR BY M. SERPOLLET

*By permission of the Editor of "Engineering"*

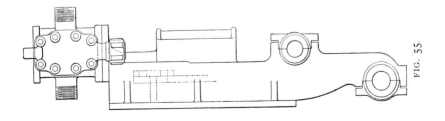

FIG. 55.

# CHAPTER III

## DETAILS OF STEAM CARRIAGES

I N the present chapter some remarks are made on the engine, the boiler, and other details of steam carriages.

### THE STEAM ENGINE

The following are some of the advantages of steam. The steam engine may be stopped and started in an instant; it can be made to give any power from a few foot pounds up to its full power, and is, in fact, what railway men call more flexible than any other form of motor. Another advantage is the great power obtained from a very small motor. When a hill has to be mounted, the four or five horse-power developed on the level road can be raised to twelve horse-power or more. Consequently, with the steam engine steep hills can be scaled at rapid rates, and all difficulties attending bad roads can be overcome without trouble. The steam engine is the simplest type of motor, and simplicity is a cardinal virtue—there are no gimcracks about it. The few parts are understood by everyone. No special knowledge is required to attend or repair a steam engine. No breakages are likely to occur; but should some little derangement take place, any small country engineer could put it right in a little time. The steam engine requires the smallest amount of attention; in fact, there are hundreds of simple steam engines that are

# Details of Steam Carriages

working well, in spite of their receipt of the least possible amount of care and attention. Think for a moment of the badly used portable engine of the farm. These machines, as is well known, work with the regularity of clocks, whether they receive any or no attention at all, and remain at work amid the utmost neglect of the driver. Experience teaches us that a simple steam engine will give the smallest amount of trouble to the user.

The steam engine is a well-tried servant—no experiments are needed, there are no patents to clear, but the best details are perfectly free to all those who choose to harness them.

The steam engine will work smoothly without jerk. It can be well balanced so as to cause no vibration; both vertical and horizontal engines have been used. The moving parts have in each case been carefully designed so that no trace of vibration has been felt. The greatest economy may be secured by the following means. The engine will be run at a fairly high speed—there is, however, a limit to the speed; if we exceed this limit, and run excessively fast, no light engine will live. Very high speeds require heavy bearings and frequent repairs. The speed must be regulated to give the most economical results. The steam will be slightly superheated, so as to prevent cylinder condensation. The working pressure should not be less than 100 lbs. per square inch. Expansive working is essential; the cut-off will be varied to suit the load, and it should be possible to alter the range of expansion while the engine is working, if need be. Another source of waste must be carefully prevented, viz. the enormous clearance spaces that obtain in many small engines. The clearance must be reduced to the utmost—a point that is often overlooked, and serious waste of steam ensues in high-speed engines. The feed-water may be heated by a drainage pipe from the exhaust, but we scarcely like to advocate open heaters, because the tallow carried by the exhaust steam may cause trouble in the boiler. If necessary, the compound engine may be adopted; the valuable features are an economy of thirty per cent. in fuel and feed-water, and a reduction in the noise of the exhaust. We recommend the side-by-side compound type of engine. The strains on the crank-pins are equalised; an auxiliary valve may be used for allowing full-pressure steam to enter both cylinders for over-coming exceptional travelling difficulties. When the auxiliary valve is open both cylinders exhaust into one pipe. If we work the engine as economically as possible, the amount of exhaust steam will be reduced, but in order to further suppress the noise and reduce the pre-sence of visible steam, we must superheat the exhaust. One writer says: "In my engine and boiler the ex-haust steam went down into the baffler, at the mouth of the uptake, which had a proper blast nozzle in the centre, placed at the right distance below the entrance to the chimney. This arrangement gave the exhaust a dose of heat which made it quite invisible in summer, and very nearly so in winter. Some users of Field boilers, with exhaust bafflers, complained that water was carried into them, and caused them to crack; but I had a small drain-pipe at the lowest part of the exhaust pipe, near the cylinder, which effectually saved my baffler, which did not crack or give any trouble." The steam must not only be made invisible, but the noise must be suppressed; this can be well carried out. The gear-ing of the engine must be noiseless, and none of the moving parts must be seen. In order to further

# Details of Steam Carriages

economise steam, we must reduce the weight of the working parts to the utmost limit. It is a simple matter now to make a light and strong steam engine. Wrought-iron can be used for the frame of both horizontal and vertical types ; the cylinders must be thin ; wrought-iron must be used for every available part, and as little cast-iron as possible to be adopted ; but light cast-steel parts can be substituted for cast-iron. Very light engines are now made for launches and torpedo-boats, and we must adopt similar engines for our road carriages. We may suggest that phosphor-bronze slide-valves, pistons, and bearings will tend to reduce weight and prevent wear. The number of parts must be cut down to the lowest limit. In many existing carriages there are too many " bits." The why and the wherefore of every part must be considered ; every detail must pass through the " mill of the mind." The cylinder and valve chests. will be carefully lagged ; this will prevent the radiation of heat, and save fuel also. In some instances, link-motion reversing - gear has been omitted on steam carriages, because they can be readily stopped, and turned round in little space. By abandoning this gear weight and complication are avoided, and a reduction in the number of wearing parts results also. Another advantage of the steam engine is that it can be very readily applied. An inverted cylinder engine possesses some advantages where floor space is limited. The horizontal form lends itself very readily for the purpose. The frame of the carriage can be made to form a suit-able base for the engine. The flooring above can be arranged so as to give access for examination or over-hauling purposes, and can be made dust-proof. It is very essential that the lubricator should be automatic in action, and thoroughly efficient. The working parts would be encased, and work in an oil bath. An injector, as well as a feed-pump, should be provided, in case of any mishap to either.

We must have no experimental details. If the designer has any "fads" or hobbies, they must be carefully excluded, if success is to be certain. If the points we have mentioned be carried out, such a steam engine would meet all requirements, and not fail to be successful. Every condition necessary for rendering the steam engine eminently suitable for the road carriage can be secured if real experience and good mechanical ability set to work. We have had steam carriages in the past which have done fairly well. Let us take up the subject where Messrs. Catley and Ayres, and Messrs. Yarrow and Hilditch, and others left off, and success will be ours.

Mr. W. Worby Beaumont, in his Cantor Lectures, said: "Is it not possible that a steam engine, in the form of a rotary engine—that is to say, a steam turbine —may be used, which would run practically without vibration? The only difficulty—perhaps the one difficulty, in this sense—is the form of gear that shall reduce the very high speed of the steam turbine down to the speed of the road wheels. That overcome, we have, to-day, a steam motor which, for such powers as we require for these purposes, is as economical as the high-speed reciprocating engine."

Sir David Salomons, Bart., after experimenting with a benzoline motor carriage, says: "For motor carriages, I firmly believe in steam, which represents the following advantages :—

(1) The driver need not descend to start the engine.
(2) The power is delivered in direct proportion to the work to be done, and without jerk.

# Details of Steam Carriages

(3) The engine may be stopped at any time in the midst of traffic, without thinking of the trouble of restarting.

(4) The lightness of the motor.

(5) Dispensing with all dangerous liquids.

(6) That repairs can be made by any trained mechanic.

There is the weight of water to carry; but, as you start with the whole and end with none, you only carry on the average *half* the weight the *whole* distance. No one seems to have noticed this; it refers to the weight of fuel also.

If a compound engine is used, a small quantity of water and fuel will be needed. We therefore see no great trouble respecting the water question. Sir David Salomons says: " The advantage of a compound engine is that for a given weight of water and fuel, from twice to three times the distance may be traversed than would be possible with a simple engine. Hence, without increasing the weight of the carriage, a run of fifty or sixty miles could be made, whereas only half that distance is now possible without taking on board more fuel and water."

We have tried to show that an efficient and economical engine must fulfil the requirements we have laid down.

*The Boiler.*—To the designer of the steam carriage the boiler undoubtedly presents the greatest difficulty. The past generation of steam-carriage builders generally encountered trouble with the boiler. Many of the carriages were fairly successful, but when failure overtook them, the cause was traced to the weakness or insufficiency of the boiler. Hancock and Maceroni were more fortunate than their contemporaries, simply because they each had schemed a satisfactory boiler.

# Steam Carriages

The failure of the materials and the lack of good workmanship caused the annoyance in Hancock's time. In this day of tubular safety generators, we have none of the difficulties to contend with arising from faulty materials or bad workmanship. Now that the tubular boiler has come so prominently to the front, it is interesting to note that many of the steam carriages of sixty years ago were fitted with tubular boilers, somewhat resembling the boilers that are being used at the present time. Gurney's, Squire's, Maceroni's, and Dance's, are examples.

The boiler for a steam carriage must fulfil the following conditions : (1) It must be light ; (2) Must take up but little room ; (3) Require a small quantity of water ; (4) Work well with hap-hazard water ; (5) Easily cleaned out ; (6) Not given to priming ; (7) Must raise steam quickly, and readily maintain or reduce the pressure ; (8) Automatic feeding and stoking are essential ; (9) No smoke must be emitted ; (10) No ashes must fall on the ground ; (11) No excessive heat must be given out from its outer surface ; (12) It must be absolutely safe at a high pressure ; (13) Steam must be slightly superheated ; (14) The boiler must be durable ; (15) There must be no smell or other external evidence of machinery.

We would next describe some of the steam boilers that have been made and adopted for steam carriages. The little boiler used by Mr. A. B. Blackburn in his steam dog-cart, is shown by Fig. 57. The copper coil contains the water, which is heated by a benzoline burner. The benzoline is led into a vaporiser heated by warm air, and by the exhaust steam. The coil boiler and burners are enclosed in a cylindrical casing placed horizontally. In the casing there are two or three thin firebrick bafflers, only one of which is shown in the drawing. This tube is calculated to bear 2,000 lbs. pressure per square inch, while the working pressure is only 60 lbs. per square inch, so that there is little fear of the boiler bursting ; and should such an accident occur little damage could be done, as the whole tube only contains one pound of water. A small jet of benzoline is admitted into the burner by the pipe shown ; after the fire is lighted a current of air is produced by turning a small handle for a few minutes until steam is

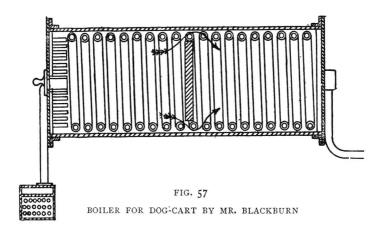

FIG. 57

BOILER FOR DOG-CART BY MR. BLACKBURN

raised. As soon as the engine is started the complete consumption of the benzoline is effected, as mentioned above. The chimney for allowing the fumes to pass out is shown at the end of the boiler. The steam generated in the coil passes at one end into the cylinder of the engine. Mr. Blackburn says : " The steam requires no attention from the driver after filling the boiler and lighting the burner. This entire freedom from the usual trouble of watching and regulating the fire and water is essential to the use of steam in carriages in the hands of ordinary drivers."

# Steam Carriages

Some interesting particulars of another diminutive boiler are given by Mr. Bateman.

The boiler was used on a steam tricycle some years ago. The boiler was constructed out of a hollow casting, somewhat in the shape of the letter A, but having a connecting-bar joining the feet. The two horizontal tubes were pierced at right angles with a series of $\frac{5}{8}$ in. holes, into which were expanded a number of seamless copper tubes bent like the letter M lying sideways, but with rounded angles. The open ends were expanded into the back holes of the above-mentioned casting, and the front ones (necessary for the expanding process) were then closed by screwed plugs. The top part of the A frame formed a steam chest, on which was fixed the stop valve and also the safety valve. The copper tubes were capable of bearing at least 1,500 lbs. pressure per square inch, and were therefore perfectly safe at 200 lbs. pressure. The boiler was heated by benzoline, as under. A small vessel with an air-tight lid, and a pinhole to avoid a vacuum, held one gallon of benzoline, which passed down a diminutive pipe to several clusters of little burners—a sort of cross between a Bunsen gas-burner and a Whitechapel naphtha lamp. These burners could be easily used as a whole or in part, and the regulating valve was actuated by a rod, which automatically turned off the bulk of the burners as the steam pressure rose above 200 lbs. One small cluster, always alight, kept the others hot, and relighted them as fast as the falling boiling pressure restored the supply of fuel. The first start was effected by placing about half a teaspoonful of methylated spirit in a cup under the central burner, which soon became hot enough to volatilise the benzoline and light up, when a handle attached to the blast fan enabled the requisite draught to be obtained to

# Details of Steam Carriages

force the combustion: and the neighbouring burners rapidly joined in until all the twenty-one were in full play. The steam was condensed, and as the water was returned to the boiler, so little additional feed-water would be required to supply the waste.[1]

A few words about the Shipman petroleum-fired boiler may be of interest here. When erected in connection with the engine, they appear to answer very well; they require no skilled attendance, are easily manipulated, entirely automatic in operation, and might be said to take care of themselves after having once been started. The oil burnt under the boiler is introduced into the furnaces in exactly the requisite quantities to maintain a certain steam pressure and supply, and the pressure itself is made to exercise all the functions of a controlling attendant, reducing or cutting off the oil supply when a set limit of pressure is attained, and again turning it on when there is a fall below that limit. The oil, which, by the way, is a good quality of kerosene, gives a clean fire, without dust, ashes, or smoke, and is practically free from danger. The boiler is composed of tubes screwed into a flat oblong chamber at one end, and closed at the outer end, and is fired externally. The two small atomisers, taking steam from the boiler, carry the oil fuel from a chamber below into the furnace in the form of a fine spray. A couple of torches ignite the spray as it passes inward, and the flames produced by its combustion rush round and among the boiler tubes. The amount of steam and oil that is used by the atomisers is regulated by a diaphragm connected to the valve in the steam-pipe that supplies them. The fire is made to vary inversely as the pressure in the boiler, and thus keeps the latter constant. The water in the boiler

[1] *The Steam Tricycle of* 1881, by Arthur H. Bateman, 1895

is kept at a constant level by means of a float connected to a tap in the suction-pipe of the pump. When once steam is up, the fire and the water supply require no further attention ; but, when first starting, a sufficient pressure is required in the boiler to work the atomisers, and for this a hand air-pump is provided. A few strokes of this pump will suffice to start the fires, and it is only necessary to pump slowly for about five minutes to raise steam to keep them going. A few minutes more is required to raise steam to 100 lbs. pressure per square inch. The boilers are made of steel, take up little room, are not heavy, and are tested by hydraulic pressure to 300 lbs. per square inch.

There are some difficulties attending the use of tubular boilers which must be fairly faced. The water must be good. Now for steam carriage work good water cannot always be obtained. The water that traction engines have to take during their travels, would soon fill up the small water spaces of some tubular boilers, and the tubes, filled with deposit, would be ruined very quickly. If it is necessary to boil the water to get rid of the lime before it can be sent into a tubular boiler, this is a fatal defect. No boiler of such a character will be adopted. We believe, however, that it is possible to design a water-tube boiler that can be cleaned out easily, with a proper receptacle for deposit, while the circulation through the tubes will be quick enough to keep them fairly clear of scale. If the exhaust steam is condensed and returned to the boiler (which has been done), then the water trouble is minimised because a small quantity of feed-water will be required to make up for loss ; consequently a greater number of miles could be run so as to secure a good supply in towns, rather than be obliged to take the muddy water from streams by the wayside. The descrip-

# Details of Steam Carriages

tion of other types of boilers which have been used for steam carriages will now be given.

The fire-tube vertical boiler, like the one used on Catley and Ayres' carriage, is not to be despised (Fig. 27). It possesses some good qualities. It will work very well should it not be so tenderly handled as the tubular boilers must of necessity be. The feed-water need not be carefully selected ; this boiler has steamed well with muddy water, such as is found when travelling in country districts. A greater range of water level is permissible ; it need not be so carefully watched by the attendant. It is simple, well tried, and not likely to give trouble should it fall into the hands of a careless driver or an unskilful stoker.

A very simple boiler, like Fig. 14, was used by Mr. Boulton, of Manchester, for one of his steam carriages. There is no water space round the fire-box, but it is lined with thin fire-bricks and cased with sheet-iron. A number of Field tubes of various lengths hang from the fire-box crown as shown. The top vessel contains the water and the steam ; the uptake is expanded into its place and well beaded. This boiler is of the simplest possible description, and we give it a place here because it has answered well in practice. Good provisions were made for effectually cleaning the boiler out when necessary.

Fig. 58 shows another Field boiler that has been used for fire-engines and steam carriages.

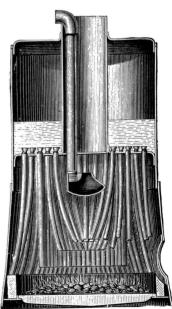

FIG. 58. THE FIELD BOILER

The ring of fire-bricks is sufficiently deep to contain the fire. The Field tubes are bent as shown, the outside row nearly touching the fire-bricks at the bottom; the inner rows are bent towards the centre for preventing the gases escaping too rapidly up the chimney. This type of boiler was used on Holt's steam carriage; it was placed at the back of the hind axle, making the carriage too light in the front and apt to rear. In

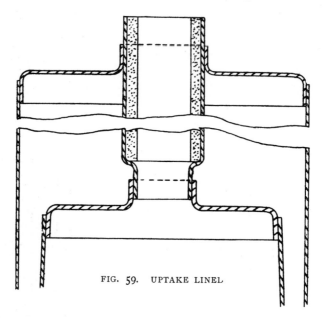

FIG. 59.    UPTAKE LINEL

passing, we may remark that the uptake type of boiler is often condemned. To obviate any danger from this source, the uptake may be lined with fire-clay, as shown by the sketch (Fig. 59).

The chief objection that is lodged against the vertical boiler is the deficiency of heating surface, but this objection does not hold good with regard to the Field boiler. Another disadvantage of the vertical boiler is the lack of horizontal heating surface. There are many vertical boilers with horizontal fire and water tubes that answer

# Details of Steam Carriages

very well, as all the heating surface is below the lowest water line. The small horizontal water tubes as at present used in fire-engine boilers suggest themselves as a remedy for this defect, but the water question must be carefully considered, for these small tubes would soon be ruined if sediment was allowed to remain in them.

The Field boiler is so well known that no lengthy description is needed. We give a sketch (Fig. 60) of the tube, showing its construction and mode of fixing.

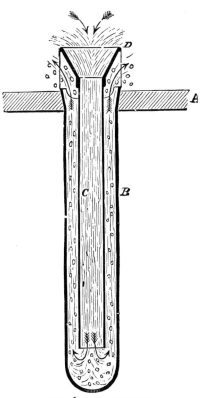

The tube plate is drilled and rymered taper to suit the expanded end of the outer tube. The pressure of the steam tends to keep the tube perfectly tight ; the inner tube is open at both ends and provided with a cone-shaped deflecting top. The effect of this combination is to produce a natural and powerful circulation of the water, due to the fact that a heated column is lighter than a colder column. Glass models show beyond dispute that the two currents are completely separated as shown by the arrows.

FIG. 60.   FIELD TUBE

The Field boiler is a safe generator. In the event of shortness of water, the worst that can happen is the burning of some of the tubes, so that the fire is extinguished without further damage. This was actually proved, in a case of culpable neglect on the part of an attendant, under circumstances which must have resulted in a disastrous explosion had the boiler employed been of another type. The boiler in question was a stationary one, and the fire was lighted and kept burning under it without any water being introduced, beyond the small quantity that had remained in after blowing off, which, as might have been expected, was quickly evaporated into steam of considerable pressure, the result being that several tubes gave way and the fire was immediately extinguished. The boiler received no other injury, and the tubes were quickly replaced and at work again.

Many of the persons who are anxious to use the self-propelled carriage entertain a dread of a steam boiler. This prejudice must be removed, and the only way to gain the confidence of the people is to design a boiler that is practically inexplosive, and prove it by constantly repeated and severe tests. The boiler must be of such a type that it presents the least risk when compared with any other motive power. Boilers have been and are now made that have answered these requirements admirably.

Mr. Hiram Maxim recently said : "With regard to steam boilers, if the tubes were made very hot it was necessary to make them very thick, and if they were very thick they were heavy." He was in favour of using very light boilers, fed and controlled automatically ; and there should be no large quantity of water in any one place. If an explosion occurred it should be harmless, if not noiseless. One writer recently said : "There is no necessity for a boiler to be cumbrous. The boiler of a four-indicated horse-power engine can be brought down to thirty pounds weight. This may seem rather startling, but from practical experience I know it to be a fact." Some of the American boilers correspond with this small weight.

# Details of Steam Carriages

A newspaper some time ago was advocating the benzoline motor for self-propelled carriages, and said: "Petroleum, in our estimation, is the most economical system to adopt"; "With steam you have a furnace and boiler with all their attendant loss in conversion of latent energy into power, cumbrousness, and other troubles." A correspondent replied: "As far as I can find out there are no authentic data concerning trials of motors used on carriages which give the necessary information to warrant this assertion, viz. quantity and calorific value of fuel used, and indicated horse-power. There has always been one of these items missing, which renders record valueless.[1] The loss in boilers need not be so very serious, if it is constructed properly and radiation prevented efficiently, and it must not be forgotten that a great part of latent energy of oil is wasted in the oil-engine in heating the cylinder and the water jacket. There is no necessity for the boiler to be cumbrous, and I know not what the 'other troubles' of a steam engine are."

*The Driving-wheels.*—There is very little choice of

[1] "The petrol engines fitted to motor-cars," says *Engineering*, "are rated by some makers at powers which could only be obtained if the mean pressure during the working stroke was 120 lbs. to 150 lbs. per square inch. We have always had great hesitation in accepting these figures, although assured by the makers that the actual powers stated have been recorded on the brake. Even in the Korting gas-engine, where the compression is 125 lbs. per square inch, and the maximum pressure about 400 lbs. per square inch, the mean effective pressure on the piston is only 90 lbs. per square inch. Further, the motors supplied to the North-Eastern Railway Company for their Hartlepool service, which were rated at 100 horse-power, have, it is reported, proved quite inadequate to the requirements of the traffic. These considerations all point to the conclusion that the engines fitted by some motor-car makers yield in actual fact much below their nominal horse-power. Brake trials by independent experts would, of course, settle the matter; but until authoritative figures of this kind are published we are inclined to the opinion that the actual power of a motor-car or motor-bicycle is often not much more than one-half to two-thirds of its nominal rating."

materials for use in the construction of the driving-wheels. They may be made of wood and iron or of iron entirely; but the method of combining these two materials so as to secure success gives ample scope for any amount of ingenuity. A great deal may be said in favour of a wood wheel. The writer was much pleased with an antiquated self-moving engine some years ago, as it passed along the streets at a fair pace, because some of the objectionable features of modern road loco-motives were entirely avoided in this venerable machine, which was then at least twenty-five years old. This engine was admired because it was a striking contrast to its modern rivals—there was no excessive noise and no excessive weight.

This locomotive was mounted on wood wheels; it is true that the wheels showed numerous signs of repeated repairs. The engine was driven by a pitch chain which ran noiselessly. Moreover, a separate tender was pro-vided, mounted on two wheels, and attached to the engine like Scott Russell's, which was easily discon-nected. The engine only weighed about five tons with-out the tender; there was therefore no danger of such a weight breaking the bridges. No one would credit the difference that wood wheels make to the smooth run-ning of fairly heavy carriages, compared with iron rigid wheels. The engine spoken of passed over a rough road practically noiselessly; the wood wheels acted as a cushion, and suppressed the jarring noise common to ordinary road carriages.

Many of the early steam carriages were mounted on wood wheels. Hancock tells us "that the tires of the driving-wheels gave him the most trouble, owing to their great wear." The wheels were of wood, having very strong spokes, enclosed in a cast-iron nave. A

# Details of Steam Carriages

drawing is given of Hancock's wheel (see Figs. 61, 62). Seaton, in 1822, was probably the first to patent a spring wheel. Neville, in 1827, and Church, in 1835, both used spring wheels on their carriages.

In this day of pneumatic tires for bicycles we should remember that as far back as 1846 Mr. R. W. Thompson had a brougham mounted on pneumatic tires running about in the streets and parks of London. The face of the rubber tire was covered with leather ; it was

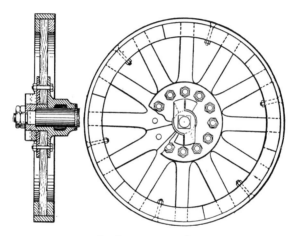

FIGS. 61, 62. HANCOCK'S WHEEL

said that the india-rubber at that time was scarce and gave trouble. Moreover, the railway companies used flat india-rubber tires on the wheels of their handcarts in the stations, and refused to pay Mr. Thompson any royalty. Wood wheels and pneumatic tires are the order of the day. Some modern wheels are referred to later on.

*The Driving-gear and Springs.*—The success of Hancock's steam carriages was in a large measure due to his excellent driving-gear. He used a pitch chain for communicating the motion from the engine crank-shaft to

the main axle. This system of driving admitted of a
good arrangement of springs. By referring to the illustration of Hancock's carriage shown in *Steam Locomotion on Common Roads*, 1891, it will be seen that the up-
and-down motion of the main axle would not seriously
interfere with the driving-chain. For turning sharp
corners Hancock could disconnect one driving-wheel
from the main axle.

Mr. Boulton uses a pitch chain for his steam carriages. He keys one driving-wheel only to the axle,
which answers well for small vehicles. The steering is
easily effected without any clutches being required. The

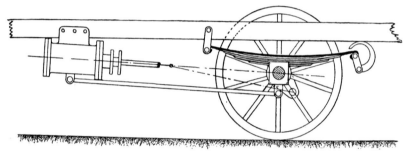

FIG. 63.   DIRECT DRIVING

driving-gear and spring arrangement of the Serpollet
steam carriage is clearly shown by Fig. 48. Some
road locomotives have been made in which spur-gearing
and pitch chains have both been dispensed with, as
shown by Fig. 63, the connecting-rods communicating
motion to the main axle direct, in regular locomotive
fashion. In some instances of this character radius-rods
have been adopted for keeping the axle in its right position in relation to the cylinder, so that the vertical play
of the springs did not interfere with the action of the
cranks or the slide valves. In this system of driving,
the slide valve should be actuated by the connecting-
rod, Joy's or other radial gear being used.

# Details of Steam Carriages

Figs. 64 and 65 show the driving arrangement of a steam road vehicle made by Mr. Leonard J. Todd, intended for and possessing every requisite for running at high speeds. The entire engine is carried on very sensitive springs, the main bearing springs being 6-ft. centres; each leading-wheel is carried on four easy volutes in pairs, according to a plan which rides very easily at extreme speeds. All the steel springs are sup-

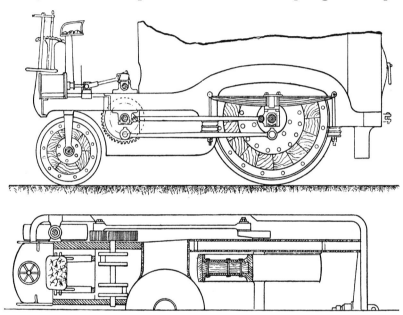

FIGS. 64, 65. DRIVING ARRANGEMENT BY MR. LEONARD TODD

plemented by rubber washers of a total thickness of 5 in., so that no trace of vibration remains. The driving-wheels are kept as close together as possible. The leading wheels are placed as wide apart as possible; the engine is steered with the greatest certainty, and this without any complication of disengaging clutches or differential gear. It will be seen that spur-gearing is employed between the engine crank shaft and the inter-mediate shaft on each side of the vehicle. Motion is

# Steam Carriages

transmitted to the main axle by side rods. By this arrangement the axle can bear any amount of vertical play without the working of the gearing being at all affected. The road wheels are made with solid wood discs and wrought-iron tires.

It is shown by Fig. 48 that when pitch chains are used for driving, the arrangement of superior carriage springs becomes a very simple matter. The use of side coupling-rods like Figs. 64 and 65 also renders the application of springs an easy matter. But when spur driving-gear is adopted, the proper arrangement of springs is a problem that many have tried in vain to solve, but there are a few spring-mounted spur-geared engines that answer very well in practice. Let us see how Mr. John Scott Russell carried this out.

The diagram Fig. 66 is given to explain the peculiar arrangement by which Mr. Russell has contrived that each spring "shall in its flexure describe at a particular point such a point as is also described by the carriage in its motion round the axle of the machinery." The springs K K on which the machinery is suspended are formed ogee, that is, turned up at one end and down at the other. When K is depressed, the centre of suspension S is carried backwards as well as downwards. The small crank axle shown at *e* is fixed, as regards position, to the point of suspension S, and therefore describes a parallel arc of a circle which has for its centre the main axle A. The pinions on the smaller axles thus roll round a part of the circumference of the wheels upon the larger axle without inclining deeper or shallower into the gear of the teeth, whilst the point S is being thrown up or down according to the inequalities of the road. C marks the position of the cylinders, and F that of the framing. The protection which this mode of suspension

88

# Details of Steam Carriages

affords to the working part of the machinery constitutes the best feature of the entire arrangement. The liability of the bolts and pins of the engines to be started by sudden concussions is much diminished, and a uniformity of vibration is imparted to the boiler, which must be greatly in its favour, both as regards efficiency and durability.

It was said by a writer in *Engineering*, when speak-

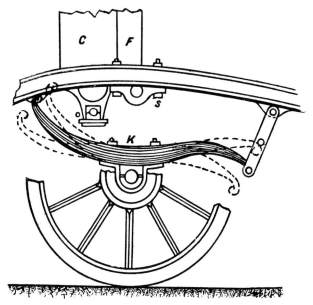

FIG 66. RUSSELL'S SPRING

ing of Russell's carriages : " The springs of his steam carriages, and the manner in which the machinery adapted itself to the irregularities of the road, were triumphs of engineering." To make a successful steam carriage, the spring arrangement must be wisely carried out, and, in addition to an effective method of spring mounting, it will be necessary also to have elastic wheels, so as to reduce the jar for running smoothly and noise-lessly on macadam roads. It is possible to construct wheels with india-rubber tires that answer the purpose admirably, but the price is almost prohibitive. Wood wheels answer fairly well. The disc wheels shown on page 30 of Mr. John Maclaren's paper would, it is thought, prove efficient for carriages of moderate weight. For light carriages, wood or iron wheels could be used, fitted with pneumatic tires.

Wood wheels may be used without india-rubber tires, but the driving-power must not be transmitted through wood spokes. In one of the Parisian steam carriages (see Fig. 128 in Chapter VI.), the following description occurs : " The driving-shaft or axle passes through the hollow axle-boxes of the wheels, and the latter are perfectly loose. Upon each end of the driving-shaft is fixed a boss with four arms of wrought-iron, and these drive against small stops securely fixed to the rim of the wheels." It will thus be seen that no stress is put upon the wood spokes, they merely carry the weight of the vehicle. These driving-arms are further necessary if it is proposed to use a pair of wood brakes on the periphery of the driving-wheels.

In order to reduce the noise, the exhaust can be muffled ; a sleeve like Fig. 67 has been used. Another method of suppressing the noise is as follows. Mr. Inshaw's boiler had tubes or hollow stays extending from the crown of the fire-box to the top of the boiler. They are prolonged so as to form a number of separate flues or chimneys, and in each is discharged a jet through small branch pipes from the exhaust chamber. By these means the exhaust, while increasing the draught, is made almost noiseless and invisible. All pipes used on board the carriage will be made of copper, and arranged so as to avoid leakage. If spur-gearing is used for driving the intermediate shaft, the teeth of the

# Details of Steam Carriages

wheels should be cut by machinery, so as to run quietly. At least two travelling speeds should be given. Pitch chains for these small vehicles will answer admirably. The machinery can then be efficiently mounted on long laminated carriage springs, and, if required, we may use india - rubber washers likewise.

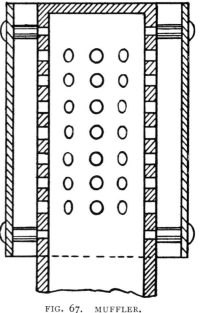

FIG. 67. MUFFLER.

There are several minor points that have been omitted. The steam conveyance must run at eight to twelve miles an hour without noise, without showing any steam or smoke ; it must be steered with facility, stopped instantly on an incline as well as on the level road. The machinery must all be neatly cased in ; the painting and general appearance must resemble horse-drawn vehicles, so as to be no terror to horses. Such a captivating steam carriage will be light in weight, comfortable to ride in, and safer than horse-drawn carriages, and if wisely managed will be no nuisance to man or beast.

Chapters I., II., and III. were written some years before the American light steam carriages made their appearance in England.

# CHAPTER IV

## MODERN STEAM CARRIAGES

IN one of the publications of an eminently satisfactory firm of steam carriage manufacturers, the following comparison is made between the modern petrol car and the latest steam car; it is of interest. The writer has always been a believer in steam as the motive power for the propulsion of carriages.

| THE PETROL ENGINE | THE STEAM ENGINE |
|---|---|
| Derives its motion from a gas explosion, which is momentary, non-elastic—resembling the blow of a hammer. | Derives its motion from the steady and expansive pressure of the steam, which is maintained to the end of the stroke. |
| The strength of the explosion cannot be increased. | The pressure can be doubled at will. |
| Is noisy, causes violent vibration, and exhausts offensive fumes. | Is practically silent and free from vibration. |
| Has to be started by hand, frequently resulting in injury to the starter from back-firing, and always necessitating considerable exertion and caution. | After lighting the burner, can be started immediately. |
| Is always difficult to reverse. | Is instantly self-reversing. |
| Requires knowledge and experience in manipulating the numerous admissions of gas, air, mixture, etc. | Only requires the steam turned on or off. |

# Modern Steam Carriages

| THE PETROL ENGINE | THE STEAM ENGINE |
|---|---|
| Requires a battery, coil, and a complicated system of electrical sparking to ignite the gas. | Requires no ignition. |
| Necessitates the use of a highly inflammable and dangerous spirit, a spark only being sufficient to cause explosion. | American paraffin is used as fuel. |
| Petrol can only be obtained at places where it is specially kept. | Paraffin can be obtained anywhere. |
| Petrol costs from 1s. to 1s. 6d. a gallon. | Paraffin costs from 5d. to 8d. a gallon. |
| Requires circulating water to prevent it from becoming red hot. | Does not heat beyond the temperature of the steam. |
| Is liable to refuse to work from an infinitude of causes, requiring expert knowledge to locate. | Should troubles occur, are easily located. |

LIGHT STEAM VANS

The steam car is very suitable for farmers, tradesmen, and carrying purposes between the villages and the market town. The number of carriers' carts and vans which ply between the villages and any large town may be counted by scores. In one town of 60,000 inhabitants, in the course of a week 200 carriers' carts and vans enter from the villages and smaller towns around. These vans bring passengers with market produce, and return the same day with the same passengers and their purchases. The carrier also brings orders for goods from village customers, and delivers the articles on the doorstep of the shopkeeper, at the farmstead, or anywhere the customers may require. In most cases these cars run between villages out of the reach of the

# Steam Carriages

main line of railway. But in other cases the carrier takes passengers and their produce to many towns through which the railway actually passes. How do the carriers' vans, drawn by horses, manage to compete with the powerful railway company? For these reasons, possibly: The passengers are carried at the same fare, but at a slower rate; the carrier brings the people close to the market-house, where his customers dispose of their eggs, poultry, butter, etc.; the railway station in many towns is two miles or more from the centre of the place where all the business is done. Instead of walking the distance and paying one penny a mile on the railway, the country people prefer the carriers' cart, because it starts at a suitable time for the passengers' convenience, and starts near the place where the business is transacted, and delivers them on their doorstep in the evening. If these horse-drawn vehicles can compete with the railway there is every reason to suppose that a good steam van worked on the same lines would be a great boon to the villager and shopkeeper. The country carrier touches spots out of the reach of the railways, that is why he succeeds. The carrier's waggon is a lumbersome affair, and the keep of two horses is a serious item of expense. A steam van would reduce the working expenses; the passengers and goods could be taken at a quicker rate, and, possibly, at a lower cost. The carrier himself would have more time on his hands; there would be no horses requiring his constant attention; no harness to keep in repair; no room required for chaff, straw, and fodder; no chaff-cutting machinery; and no time occupied by taking the horses to grass. It has often been noticed, when a man has one or two horses to keep, how much of his and the horse's time is taken up by leading hay, straw, and

FIG. 68. THE CHELMSFORD STEAM CARRIAGE

# Modern Steam Carriages

oats, solely for the horse's requirements. When horses are not at work they continue to eat. The mechanical car would only require fuel and water when at work. The Chelmsford, Gardner-Serpollet, or similar steam car

FIG. 69. CHELMSFORD COVERED TONNEAU

would replace the carrier's cart with advantage, and prove a good investment, and the day is not far distant when the steam car will be running between the large market town and the sparsely populated hamlets and rural districts.

# Steam Carriages

The three illustrations, Figs. 68, 69, and 70, represent the new Chelmsford steam car. The body is constructed largely of aluminium. The car is fitted with artillery wheels shod with 3-inch solid rubber tires. Figs. 71 and 72 give two views of the boiler; it is of the vertical fire-tube class, solid drawn steel tubes being used. It is tested to a pressure of 750 lbs. to the square inch, and its normal working pressure is 250 lbs. The

FIG. 70. CHELMSFORD STEAM CAR

boiler is heated by one of the Clarkson burners, using ordinary paraffin oil, and it is automatically regulated by the boiler pressure. " The oil-tank holds twenty-four gallons, and is fixed at the rear, beneath the frame, a gauge enabling the level of the oil to be seen at a glance. The oil is pumped from this tank to a pressure receiver in the front of the car; this receiver contains a certain amount of air, which acts as a cushion and as a reserve of energy for forcing the oil to the burner."

A relief valve on the oil delivery pipe is set to come into operation at the desired pressure and to thus return any surplus oil back to the suction side of the pump.

# Modern Steam Carriages

The automatic device which regulates the burner is not of the diaphragm pattern, but contains a small plunger, which is operated upon by the steam pressure, against the action of a spring. It closes down the fire to a minimum when the pressure reaches 250 lbs. per square inch, and it opens it up full at about 180 lbs. per square inch. A very neat burner is fitted beneath the front footboard for initially heating the vaporising coil of the main burner. It enables the same fuel to be used for this purpose, and avoids the use of alcohol or petrol entirely.

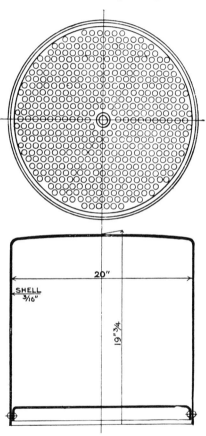

The water is carried in two long tanks, which are placed beneath the seats in the main portion of the body, and which project forward beneath the front seat. They have a combined capacity of thirty-four gallons, which has been found sufficient for a run of 120 miles, the oil supply also lasting for a similar period. A large gauge-glass on the left of the dial-board shows the level of the water in the tanks.

FIGS. 71, 72. CHELMSFORD BOILER.

The water is pumped by a mechanically operated pump into the boiler, and the driver regulates the quantity delivered to it by a by-pass.

The engine, as illustrated in Fig. 73, consists of two double-acting cylinders, having a bore and a stroke of

# Steam Carriages

4 inches. It develops 12 horse-power, and is of the horizontal pattern. It is fixed centrally beneath the floor, with its cylinders projecting to the rear. The crank chamber is entirely enclosed, and the differential gear on a transverse countershaft is also arranged inside it. The slide valves are placed beneath the cylinders and are operated by Joy valve gear. The power is transmitted from a steel spur-wheel between the two cranks to a phosphor-bronze wheel surrounding the differential gear. The transverse countershaft is mounted in four double ball-bearings, in which half-inch balls are used. Four separate pumps are driven by the counter-shaft ; one of these is a feed-water pump for the boiler, another circulates the oil which lubricates the moving parts of the engine and its gear, another pumps the condensed water back from the condenser to the main tanks, and the fourth pumps the paraffin from the main tank to the feeding pressure tank. The countershaft carries sprocket wheels at each end, from which side-chains pass to the rear wheels in the usual way. There are separate exhaust pipes from each cylinder. The exhaust is made to enter a feed-water heater, but the bulk of the steam passes to a large condenser shown on the front of the car. The condensed steam is pumped through filters into the water-tank. The whole of the driving machinery is carried upon the main frame of the car, this being supported in the usual manner by semi-elliptic side springs, front and rear. Two in-dependent pairs of brakes are fitted, both operating direct upon the rear wheels, and each being worked by a foot-pedal in front of the driver. The average travelling speed is sixteen miles an hour, and the full con-sumption has been found to work out at less than a penny per mile. The weight of the car is 28 cwt.

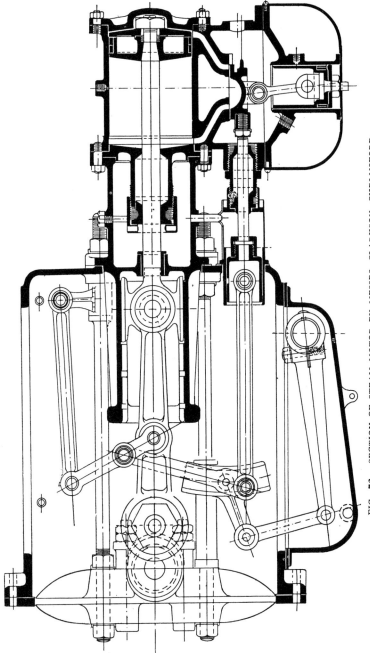

FIG. 73. SECTION OF STEAM MOTOR BY MESSRS. CLARKSON, CHELMSFORD

# Steam Carriages

We are indebted to a reprint of articles which appeared in *The Automotor Journal* for the above particulars of the Chelmsford car.

### THE ALBANY MANUFACTURING COMPANY

The Lamplough - Albany steam car is an English-made carriage possessing some original features. An automatic expansion motor is used, the action being as follows. A pair of engines are coupled together with the cranks set at right angles; each engine is arranged to operate its own lap and lead, and its opposite engine's cut-off; consequently the parts are few; excentrics, links, and the attendant parts are dispensed with. The advantage of using this style of gear is great economy in the consumption of steam, owing to the full boiler pressure being admitted to the engines. The speed of the car is regulated by the cut-off, while the operations of stopping, starting, reversing, and controlling the speed are effected by means of one lever. When steam engines are fitted with a fixed cut-off the speed is regulated by strangling the steam through a throttle-valve, causing a loss of economy. When the car is running on the level road at a moderate speed, the cut-off may be set at one-eighth of the stroke, so that under these conditions an economy is effected greater even than that of the best-designed petrol engine.

The valves are preferably of the mushroom type ; the engine is also fitted with trunk pistons, entirely dispensing with the necessity of stuffing-boxes and glands, the whole running in a bath of oil. The wear and tear of these engines is so small that, after running several thousand miles, they appear to be none the worse for their experience.

The Lamplough-Albany car is illustrated by Fig. 74.

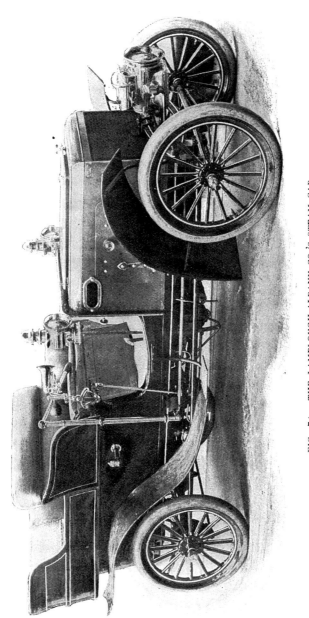

FIG. 74. THE LAMPLOUGH-ALBANY CO.'S STEAM CAR

# Modern Steam Carriages

An entirely new method of steam generation is employed which is the result of considerable experiment ; it might be termed the generation of steam within steam, first

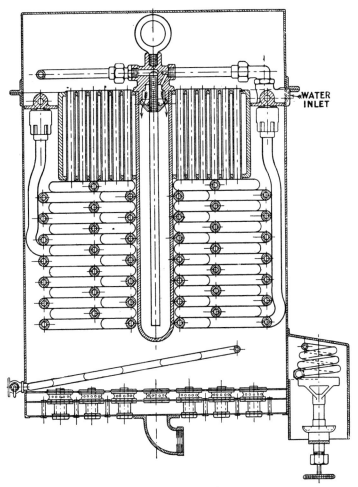

FIG. 75.   GENERATOR FOR LAMPLOUGH-ALBANY CAR

advocated by Lamplough in 1884.   The present type of generator is a considerable advance upon the Lamplough method of 1884 and 1897.

With the generator shown by Figs. 75 and 76, fitted with a petroleum burner, the makers have succeeded in evaporating 14 lbs. of water with 1 lb. of oil while standing. The principle of the latest boiler, as shown, possesses a steam receiver placed above the generator coils. To start the generator, this is heated up in the usual way, and water by a stroke of the hand-pump is admitted into the central chamber. Half of the central chamber forming the primary generator, it will

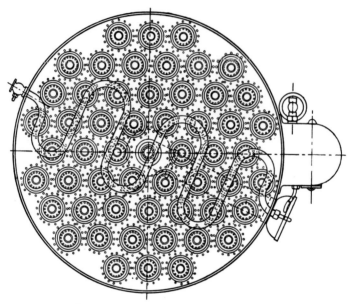

FIG. 76. GENERATOR FOR LAMPLOUGH-ALBANY CAR

be noticed, is in the fire, the other half in the steam space of receiver, so that at starting, the lower part being excessively heated, the first flow of water forms steam, and the after-flow from the pump is sprayed through it ; the aqueous vapour rises up the central tube to the steam coils, where, having passed through these, it finally emerges from the bottom coil, and on entering the receiver is in an excessively superheated condition, so much so, that the pipe connecting that particular coil with the receiver is usually at a dull red heat when the generator is working properly. The entrance and exit to receiver are arranged so that this highly superheated steam must pass right across and friction the walls of the central chamber, which has the feed-water spraying upon the inside, so that the steam in passing to the engines loses a considerable amount of its excessive superheat, and becomes a more tractable quantity, the temperatures being on entering the superheater 1,000 to 1,100 deg. F., and on leaving to the engines 700 to 800 deg. F. The advantage of this method of generation of steam is that in dry steam or flash generator practice it has been found impossible to properly flash water into steam in direct contact with metals on account of the tubes being so excessively heated that the water entering forms spheroids and bullets completely through the generator, whereas if it is heated to about 250 or 300 deg. before entering the coils, it readily atomises, and steam is generated without any of the before-named troubles. Of course on a larger-size generator the economy would be much greater.

The burner is the outcome of several years' experiment. It is automatic, or can be regulated by hand, and will burn both light and heavy hydrocarbons such as paraffin, petrol, alcohol, methylated spirit, etc., the method being to divide up the air for combustion with the flame, and prevent any possibility of a quantity of air passing through the furnace as happens where an ordinary single burner with an open space all round it is used, in other words, the idea has been to imitate a fuel-covered grate similar to ordinary boiler practice as near as possible, so that no air can pass up through the boiler that is not excessively superheated or burnt. To attain this you will note that the burner is divided into two chambers; the lower chamber, being in connection

with the induction tube, receives the mixture of vaporised oil and air. This passes up through the central
ring of holes in each burner and is burnt. To assist
combustion a further supply of air enters by the central
tube to the flame, and from the upper chamber which
communicates by means of the small stay tubes in the
lower chamber with the outer air, the air from the upper
chamber being fed through the circle of holes in the
sides of burner ring, and also out through the outer
circle of holes surrounding the outer top ring of each
burner. The starter shown to the right of boiler is
simply an ordinary petroleum burner starter with a coil
above it, and has no special features. This can be cut
out when the main burner is alight, the advantage of
this system being that the burner can be started into
full flame with paraffin, with a tablespoonful of methylated spirit, in a little over a minute.

The plunger is connected by means of levers to an
oscillating lever in the suction chamber of pump, which
is fulcrumed to the rod held back by a spring which
presses the piston against the diaphragm. When the
fulcrum is in a certain position, the pump will be de-
livering its full stroke of water, but as the pressure increases on the back of the spring-controlled diaphragm,
which is in connection with the steam receiver, the
fulcrum of the lever in suction chamber alters its position, causing the foot-valve to be held up for a more
or less proportion of the stroke, consequently as the
pressure rises, the fulcrum travels nearer the valve, until
the maximum pressure the spring is set for is reached,
when the pump will be doing no work whatever. As
soon as a slight fall in pressure takes place, the pump
will commence to deliver even to one-hundredth part of
its stroke, consequently an absolute and even pressure is

# Modern Steam Carriages

maintained in the boiler. This pump is simply connected to any reciprocating part of the engine, but not illustrated.

The driving is done by means of a flexible shaft connecting the engine to the gear-box, dispensing with chains and sprocket wheels, the whole running in oil. By means of the maker's system all the exhaust steam is perfectly condensed and the water is returned to the tank, enabling the car to be run for 200 miles at one filling, the oil being separated by gravity, which, in practice, has been found the only method capable of achievement. The wheels are of the artillery pattern, fitted with steel hubs and roller-bearings to the main axle, and ball or roller-bearings to the front axle. The whole of the work is of English manufacture, and the materials and the workmanship are of the best.

Fig. 77 is a longitudinal section of the motor showing the valve gear. Fig. 78 is a half-plan, while Fig. 79 is a transverse section. Figs. 80 and 81 give views of the motor valve gear as applied to a railway locomotive engine.

A description of the mechanism, with reference to the engravings, follows.

The lever A is attached by the lower end by means of short link L to the crosshead of the left engine, the oscillation of this lever transmits the motion through the shaft to quadrant B. Lever C is attached to crosshead of right engine in a similar manner and communicates motion through shaft to quadrant D. Two small levers E E are fulcrumed at their lower ends to the levers A and C, as shown. The upper part of these levers are connected by radius-rods E F to blocks G G, sliding on quadrants B, D. When the reversing lever is placed at point 2, the reversing arms E, by means of vibrating

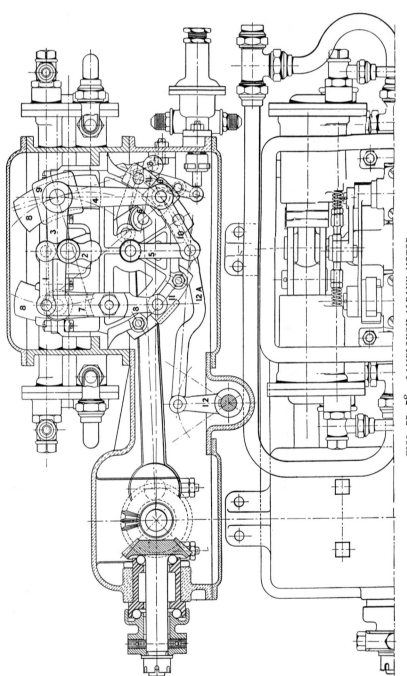

FIGS. 77, 78. LAMPLOUGH-ALBANY MOTOR

# Modern Steam Carriages

levers H H, will keep the blocks in mid-position on centre of the quadrant ; in this position the levers A E and C E move as one piece, simply communicating lap and lead to the valves, and according as the distance blocks G G are radiated from the centre of the quadrants, so is the amount of port opening determined, and, of course, cut-off in proportion to port opening, enabling any degree

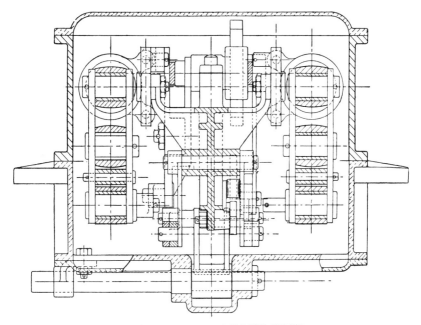

FIG. 79.   LAMPLOUGH-ALBANY MOTOR

of cut-off from one inch to full stroke, the latter being a great desideratum when starting against a heavy load.

The inventor makes for this gear the following claims :—

Saving of initial cost of construction, being a fewer number of parts and much simpler.

Compactness, saving of space, and allowing an extension of the fire-box 8 inches, thereby giving extra grate-area, enabling a cheaper fuel to be used.

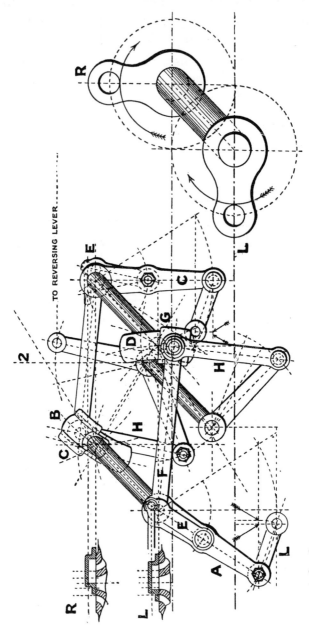

TO REVERSING LEVER

FIGS. 80, 81. LAMPLOUGH-ALBANY VALVE GEAR AS APPLIED TO AN AMERICAN RAILWAY LOCOMOTIVE ENGINE

# Modern Steam Carriages

Perfect arrangement of mechanism, allowing of light construction, dispensing with balance weights, and giving great rigidity with considerable less weight.

Saving of fuel, as this gear can be cut up without altering the lead, thereby allowing the steam to be used expansively, and ensuring perfect distribution.

Saving in cost of maintenance, and in oil.

Reduced chances of breakdown, as the gear is under the eye of the engineer while in motion, and is so placed as to permit of inspection at all times.

Extreme regularity in running and easier handling on account of the perfect balance of reversing motion.

Increased pulling capacity of engine, 10 per cent.

Lessens the chances of the gear running hot, on account of very little motion of the moving parts.

Doing away with the excentrics and straps.

Will allow the main rod to be attached to third pair of drivers on consolidation engines now fitted with short rods attached to second pair.

The lead is constant under all circumstances. The valve opens rapidly for admission of steam, dwells in a marked manner when full open, and closes very rapidly at cut-off. The opening and closing of exhaust are likewise rapid.[1] Some of the claims refer to railway engines only, but all the advantages have been inserted.

MR. CHARLES T. CROWDEN

This maker's No. 8 pleasure steam brake is illustrated by Fig. 82. The frame is composed of steel, well stayed, and mounted on laminated springs; the wheels are fitted with phosphor-bronze axle boxes, oak spokes and felloes, steel rims, and solid rubber tires. Akerman's system of steering is adopted for actuating the leading-wheels. A compound engine drives the car; it is fitted with link

[1] *Railway Gazette.*

motion, chain gear, and an intercepting valve by means of which high-pressure steam can be used in the low-pressure cylinder for starting, and for climbing steep

FIG. 82.    PLEASURE BRAKE BY MR. CROWDEN

hills. The whole of the motion work of the engine is composed of steel ; the bearings are of phosphor-bronze ; the cranks and excentrics are solid with the crank shaft.

# Modern Steam Carriages

Motion from the engine is transmitted by means of a pair of wrought-iron spur-wheels properly proportioned for giving the speeds required; the smaller wheel is attached to the crank-shaft, and the larger one to the compensating gear shaft; the motion from the counter-shaft is transmitted to the driving wheels by means of two chains and sprocket wheels, for which a simple chain adjustment is provided. The water tank is fitted with a coil in order to pass a portion of the exhaust steam through to heat the feed-water. All the pipes are made of copper, with gun-metal flange connections. The exhaust-pipe is connected to a superheating coil in the smoke-box to render the exhaust invisible.

A vertical multitubular boiler, fitted with cross tubes in a somewhat novel manner, is employed; the fire-door opens inwards; the fire-bars are capable of being rocked. Both the water and smoke tubes are $1\frac{1}{4}$ in. diameter; the boiler has large water spaces, and is capable of using nearly any kind of water to be found in the country.

THE SPEEDWELL MOTOR AND ENGINEERING CO.

The Gardner-Serpollet steam carriage is a very efficient machine. It is much nearer perfection than some other automobiles. The makers have repeatedly convinced the most prejudiced supporters of the petrol system that by their noiselessness in running, simplicity in structure, and freedom from vibration and smell they are immeasurably superior to even the best of the petrol cars. In fact, these superb carriages have all the good points of vehicles driven by electricity, without the disadvantage of a short-running radius, the inconvenience of perpetual recharging, and the expense of battery maintenance. The Gardner-Serpollet has no boiler to burst, but is fitted with a steam generator on an entirely new and simple method, by which superheated steam, of greatly enhanced power, is injected into the motor, of 6 horse-power nominal, but developing considerably more when necessary ; climbing hills of 1 in 6 with a full load, and being equal to forty miles an hour on the level road.

Fig. 83 is a diagram showing the general system, which can be easily understood. The system is al-

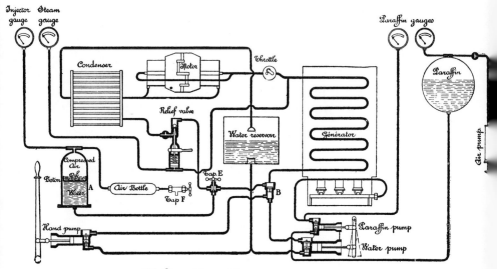

FIG. 83. THE GARDNER-SERPOLLET SYSTEM

together different from anything that has preceded it. The generator consists of coils of steel tube. One of the coils is shown by Fig. 84. A section of the boiler is illustrated by Fig. 85. The coils of steel tube are heated by paraffin burners of a new type ; water is forced into these hot tubes in small quantities. This water is instantly converted into steam of a highly super-heated character, probably hotter, drier, and more powerful than that which is produced by any other form of generator.

In fact, it is claimed that M. Serpollet has in this

# Modern Steam Carriages

system brought the use of steam up to date for road vehicles. By means of the superheated steam the size of the generator can be reduced, and at the same time treble its power. Only those who are conversant with the old and new system can rightly appreciate the advantages of the Serpollet type of generator. When the steam is produced it is conveyed to the motor, which is

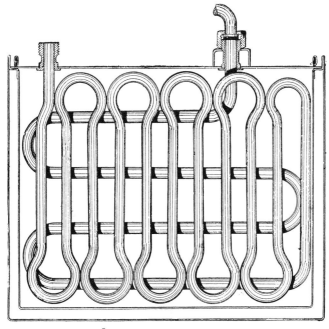

FIG. 84.   GARDNER-SERPOLLET COIL.

illustrated by Fig. 86. The valves of the engine are of the mushroom pattern, and are mechanically operated, never requiring attention. An automatic device ensures that the supply of water to the boiler and paraffin to the burner shall be in the same ratio to each other. This is effected by an ingenious arrangement of sliding step cams, which are controlled by a lever beneath the steering-wheel; this apparatus is illustrated on page 27 of

# Steam Carriages

Mr. Olliver's book on *The Management of the Gardner-Serpollet Steam Motor Car.* The safety-valve is arranged to pass water back to the reservoir, instead of blowing off steam. In the motor there are no packing glands to renew. The lubrication is automatic, and is governed by a revolving pump. It is said the motor gives no trouble, and the less it is interfered with the better it will go. Very much the same may be said of the boiler, which never requires cleaning out; and the pressure gauges need cause no anxiety, for when the details of the car are once properly mastered it is unnecessary to look at them, their use being to locate the difficulty when the car ceases to travel well.

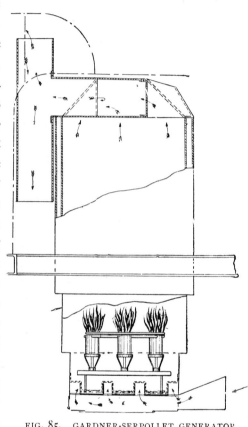

FIG. 85.　GARDNER-SERPOLLET GENERATOR

The following are offered as some of the reasons why the Gardner-Serpollet is becoming popular with automobilists : Absence of vibration, which secures a maximum speed with a minimum wear and tear to the working parts. Economy in cost of running ; the commonest paraffin being the most suitable fuel, it can be easily and cheaply obtained anywhere. This is a very important advantage. No change speed-gears ; being driven by a

# Modern Steam Carriages

single chain, direct from motor to back axle, there is no complicated machinery to cause trouble, no expensive gears to replace, and no loss in transmission. Every working part is interchangeable. The steam carriages advance and reverse with equal facility, and, although capable of travelling at high speed, they can be driven with the greatest comfort in the slowest London traffic,

FIG. 86.  GARDNER-SERPOLLET MOTOR

without the attendant noise, vibration, and odour invariably associated with petrol cars. Fig. 87 shows the under carriage without the coach work. Fig. 88 represents the carriage complete, and the next, Fig. 89, illustrates a neat bus or delivery van.

Many other advantages could be urged in favour of the Gardner-Serpollet vehicles, but the following must suffice : " Mr. Alfred C. Harmsworth, a gentleman of great experience with automobiles of every class, stated

# Steam Carriages

to a Press representative that he inclined to the Gardner-Serpollet as an ideal touring car, describing it as a delightfully comfortable carriage, gliding along with ease, and in absolute silence." Some very good performances have been made in France and England with the above cars in hill climbing, non-stop runs, and reliability trials.

INTERNATIONAL STEAM CAR CO.

The Toledo steam carriage is an American vehicle which possesses some very interesting features. Fig. 90 shows an illustration of the model A carriage. The success of a steam carriage depends on the design and manufacture of the leading elements that enter into its construction, and the important features, as the engine, the boiler, burner, and the method of control, should receive attention by intending purchasers. Most of the steam carriages are fitted with fire-tube boilers, but the Toledo car is fitted with a water-tube generator. Fig. 91 shows the boiler partly in section to reveal its construction. The boiler possesses all the advantages of the flash type in its ability to generate steam rapidly, combined with the advantage of the shell type, in having great capacity to draw upon. There are two unique features which enter into the make-up of the boiler. First, that of a centrifugal separator within the shells; secondly, the addition of a superheating coil, the upper end of which is shown in the illustration. The centrifugal action causes the entire body of the water contained between the walls formed by the inner and outer shells to horizontally circulate. This rotary movement throws the water against scoops placed at the mouth of each tube, which direct the water into the lower ends of the tubes, thus producing the rapid steam-making ability of this

FIG. 87. GARDNER-SERPOLLET CAR

FIG. 88. GARDNER-SERPOLLET CAR

FIG. 89. THE GARDNER-SERPOLLET BUS

FIG. 90. TOLEDO STEAM CAR

type of boiler. A mud-settling drum is placed below the line of the fire. The water and mud can be blown

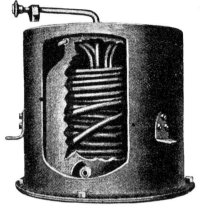

out. Every boiler is tested to a cold-water pressure of 600 lbs. per square inch, but they will stand double this pressure without undue stress. The Toledo burner is cast solid of bronze; it is not subject to rapid deterioration. It is provided with a pilot light, which, after once being lighted, maintains a steady small flame,

FIG. 91. TOLEDO BOILER

irrespective of the regulator. The regulator acts on the main burner, and either cuts out or admits gas to it automatically. The automatic regulator action is such that steam being raised to within a few pounds of the pressure required, the flow of gasoline is cut off. Should the carriage be started and the steam pressure reduced, the regulator will again admit gasoline to the burner, and the steam pressure is once more raised to the cutting-off point of the regulator. Steam has been raised to 150 lbs. from cold water in five minutes. Fig. 92 shows the auxiliary water pump. " In addition to the water pump attached to the crosshead of the engine, an auxiliary feedwater pump of their own patented design has been adopted. It is located at the base of the steering lever and in combination with it. Thus it is easily operated from the seat, which is a very

FIG. 92.

COMBINED HAND-PUMP AND STEERING TILLER

important advantage; for in case of failure of the regular automatic pump to operate, which is sometimes occasioned by carelessness in allowing dirt to accumulate, the water may be pumped by hand without effort."

The engine is illustrated by Fig. 93, it is of the ordinary two-cylinder high-pressure type, each cylinder being three inches in diameter and of four inches stroke; the piston valves are clearly shown. The crossheads are made of phosphor-bronze, and their wearing surfaces are of ample proportions. Most of the details are drop forgings and carefully hardened. The main bearings are ring oiled, a perfect system of lubrication much used in fast-running machinery. It will be seen that the crank chambers are fitted with dust-proof

FIG. 93.   THE TOLEDO ENGINE.

covers, thus forming oil wells into which the cranks dip at every revolution. In carefully carried out tests the engine develops considerable power and only requires 24 lbs. of water per horse-power per hour, a good result for small engines. An efficient feed-water heater is provided, which economises the fuel. Eighty-five miles can be run on nine gallons of gasoline, and thirty-five miles on thirty gallons of water. An ordinary feed-water pump is provided and a water

# Modern Steam Carriages

lifter for filling the tank from a wayside stream. The gasoline and air tanks are tested to 200 lbs. pressure. The differential gearing is completely encased and protected from dust and dirt. Before a Toledo carriage is delivered to a customer it is tested on the road for a fifty-mile run. The travelling wheels are 28 in. diameter.

# Steam Carriages

## TABLE I.—STEAM CARS, 1903 RELIABILITY TRIALS.

### Size, Speed, and Type of Engines, Heating Surface and Type of Boilers, Approximate Steam Consumption, and Weight of Cars.

| Official Number. | General Description. | No. of cylinders. | Bore. | Stroke. | Double-acting=D, single-acting=S, compound=C. | Total area pistons, sq. inches. | Approx. amount of steam used per revolution in cubic inches.* | Ditto used per min. when car is travelling at 20 miles per hour. Throttle wide open. Cub. ft.* | Gear ratio between crank-shaft and road wheels. | Engine speed when car travels at 20 miles per hour. Rev. per min. | Piston speed, at car speed of 20 miles per hour. | Type of boiler (fire-tube or flash generator). | Fitted with superheater=S, fitted with condenser=C. | Approx. heating surface in sq. feet (boiler only). | Heating surface in sq. feet per cwt. of running weight of car.† | Approx. mean boiler pressure, lbs. per square inch. | Kind of fuel, paraffin=K (kerosene); petroleum spirit=P. | Fuel and water tanks empty. | Fuel and water tanks full. | Running weight with passengers at 160 lbs. each, Tanks half-full. |
|---|---|---|---|---|---|---|---|---|---|---|---|---|---|---|---|---|---|---|---|---|
| 11 | 5½ h.-p. Stanley | 2 | 2½ | 3½ | D | 9·81 | 34·3 | 11·49 | 2½:1 | 579 | 337 | Fire | S | 37·9 | 3·50 | 350 | P | 6·93 | 9·0 | 10·81 |
| 84 | 10 h.-p. White | 2 | 3 & 5 | 3½ | DC | 26·71 | 24·7 | 9·63 | 3:1 | 674 | 396 | Flash | C | 40 | 1·89 | 300 | P | 14·66 | 16·23 | 21·15 |
| 116 | 10 h.-p. White | 2 | 3 & 5 | 3½ | DC | 26·71 | 24·7 | 9·63 | 3:1 | 674 | 396 | Flash | C | 40 | 1·74 | 300 | P | 15·84 | 18·5 | 22·88 |
| 95 | 12 h.-p. Chelmsford | 2 | 4 | 4 | S | 25·13 | 100·5 | 35·53 | 3·1:1 | 611 | 407 | Fire | SC | 96·6 | 2·61 | 250 | K | 26·13 | 30·63 | 36·93 |
| 105 | 10 h.-p. Gardner-Serpollet | 4 | 75** | 70** | S | 27·36 | 37·6 | 14·68 | 25:8 | 675 | 310 | Flash | C | 56·5 | 1·83 | 300 | K | 23·53 | 26·75 | 30·85 |

\* The steam is assumed to be " cut off " at one half-stroke.   \*\* The Gardner-Serpollet cylinder sizes are given in millimetres.

† Weight of car is taken with full complement of passengers at 160 lbs. each, and with fuel and water-tanks half full ; water at 10 lbs., paraffin at 8 lbs., and petroleum spirit at 7 lbs. per gallon.

Possibly the most interesting points of a general character brought forward by the steam vehicles in the Trials are that superheaters in connection with fire-tube boilers have proved their undoubted advantages, that in the Clarkson car it has been very clearly shown that a system of condensing in which the water is used over and over again, is practicable, even although an ordinary fire-tube boiler be used, and that (as with the long-distance White steam car) it is possible to run a very much longer distance than has been hitherto supposed, without refilling the tanks, and without requiring their capacity to be abnormally great.

*(These interesting Tables are inserted by the kind permission of the Editor of " The Automotor Journal.")*

# Modern Steam Carriages

## TABLE II.—STEAM CARS, 1903 RELIABILITY TRIALS.

*Horse-power as shown by performance during Hill Climbs and Speed Trials, also Relative Power, Size, and Speed of Engines, Heating Surface of Boilers, and Weight of Cars.*

| Official Number. | General Description. | Running weight of car, cwts.† | Bexhill Speed Trial: Speed of car, miles per hour. | Bexhill Speed Trial: Average speed of engine, revolutions per minute. | Bexhill Speed Trial: H.-P. as shown by performance.* | Hill Climbs — Bury: Time. | Hill Climbs — Bury: H.-P. performance.* | Hill Climbs — Westerham: Time. | Hill Climbs — Westerham: H.-P. performance.* | Hill Climbs — Hindhead: Time. | Hill Climbs — Hindhead: H.-P. performance.* | Hill Climbs — Handcross: Time. | Hill Climbs — Handcross: H.-P. performance.* | Best h.-p. performance. | Average speed of engine during best performance. Revolutions per min. | Best performance h.-p. per cwt. of running weight of car. | Corresponding consumption of live steam in cubic feet per minute, assuming half cut off. | Average mean pressure per sq. inch on pistons during best performance (calculated from h.-p. shown, and engine speed).‡ | Best performance h.-p. per sq. feet of heating surface of boiler. |
|---|---|---|---|---|---|---|---|---|---|---|---|---|---|---|---|---|---|---|---|
| 11 | Stanley | 10·81 | 32·14 | 931 | 2·594 | 8·17 | 1·962 | 38·24 | 3·82 | 7·81 | 3·27 | 2·106 | 3·831 | 3·831 | 413 | ·354 | 8·20 | 53·47 | ·101 |
| 84 | 10 h.-p. White | 21·15 | 33·58 | 1131 | 5·300 | 3·3 | 9·50 | 4·31 | 6·63 | 7·89 | 6·33 | 2·88 | 5·482 | 9·50 | 460 | ·449 | 6·58 | 43·75 | ·237 |
| 116 | 10 h.-p. White | 22·88 | 29·12 | 981 | 4·970 | 4·43 | 7·66 | 3·87 | 7·808 | 5·26 | 10·275 | 2·15 | 7·944 | 10·275 | 769 | ·449 | 11·01 | 28·31 | ·256 |
| 95 | 12 h.-p. Chelmsford | 36·93 | 31·91 | 975 | 8·86 | 6·60 | 8·30 | 7·97 | 8·26 | 8·27 | 10·54 | 1·81 | 15·09 | 15·09 | 507 | ·408 | 29·48 | 46·56 | ·156 |
| 105 | 10 h.-p. Gardner-Serpollet. | 30·85 | 42·85 | 1451 | 9·87 | 2·65 | 17·26 | 1·65 | 25·27 | 3·54 | 20·58 | 1·12 | 20·56 | 25·27 | 750 | ·819 | 16·35 | 177·02 | ·446 |

† Weight of car with fuel and water-tanks half full, and with passengers taken at 160 lbs. each.

* Assuming draw-bar-pull on level = 56 lbs. per ton.

‡ No allowance has been made for mechanical efficiency of engine.

# CHAPTER V

## MODERN STEAM CARRIAGES (*continued*)

### THE LOCOMOBILE COMPANY

THE Locomobile steam car, of American manufacture, is pretty well known in England. The steam is generated in a vertical boiler consisting of copper tubes, the heat being produced in a burner by means of ordinary petrol, which can be obtained nearly everywhere now. Steam can be raised in about eight minutes to a pressure sufficient to set the car in motion, The boiler feed-pump is driven off the crosshead of the engine ; the pump works all the time the car is in motion ; the feed is automatically regulated. A small hand-pump affords another means of filling the boiler with water in case of emergency. The steam pressure required for driving is 180 lbs. Fig. 94 shows a general plan of the locomobile, which is simple and straight-forward. The following remarks respecting the boiler are of interest. " We have before now referred to the fact that, if regularly blown out, the small multitubular boilers fitted to the American light steam carriages do not ' fur up,' though almost every practical man who sees them for the first time will suggest that one of the first troubles will be due to scale deposits. Mr. Owen H. Bayldon made an examination of a locomobile boiler which was at least three years old. The boiler was taken out and examined. There was no trace of scale in the boiler, but both the water leads from the bottom of the boiler were nearly choked up. This proves that these little boilers do not fur up if blown out occasionally.

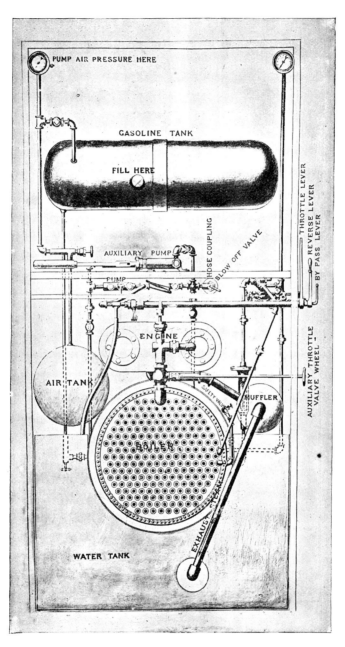

FIG. 94.   PLAN OF A LOCOMOBILE CAR

Showing position of boiler, engine, tanks, etc.

# Modern Steam Carriages

The choking of the water pipes was due to bad treatment. For those not acquainted with steam cars it may be stated that blowing down is a simple process. When the car is brought in and the burner turned off, the boiler pressure is allowed to fall to 50 lbs. to the square inch. The blowing-out cock is then opened, the water is all blown out of the boiler, and with it any sediment or deposit which may be inside the generator, and which, if left for any length of time, would cause a scale or fur to form on the tube-plate and tubes of the boiler, not only corroding them, but also greatly reducing the steaming powers of the boiler, as the efficiency of the heating surface is greatly reduced by scale. Some careful users blow down their boilers after every day's work." If these boilers are properly used they will give no trouble. Fig. 95 illustrates the engine, which has two double-action cylinders with cranks set at 90 deg. An ordinary Stephenson link-motion is used; the lubricator on the cylinders contains sufficient oil for a run of about fifty miles. Two steel frames support the machinery. The four road wheels are fitted

FIG. 95. THE LOCOMOBILE ENGINE

with pneumatic tires. A simple and efficient steering-gear is provided. The handle of the lever is firm, and precludes any jolting of the hand when the carriage is running over a rough road. The hind axle is composed of two parts, connected by a differential gear, which enables the driving-wheels to revolve each at their various speeds, in order to turn corners without sliding. The spur differential gear runs in oil; it is shown by Fig. 96. The feed-water, after leaving the pump, passes through a coil of pipes in the muffler, and is thus heated by the exhaust steam. The use of this device is most economical, resulting in a saving of petrol and water. Spring coil piping is introduced at the necessary places in order to prevent any straining of pipes and leaky joints. Fig. 97 shows a locomo-

FIG. 96. LOCOMOBILE COMPENSATING GEAR

bile with the Victoria top lowered, an excellent carriage, fitted with mud-guards. It is claimed that the power used possesses advantages over motor vehicles otherwise driven in the way of freedom from vibration, noise, odour, etc. It is the opinion of the makers that steam will be the future power for motor carriages of all kinds.

Since the above was written, the Locomobile Company have introduced a very neat brougham, and a 10 horse-power Surrey. The fire-tube boilers are 14 inches in diameter and have 290 tubes, are made with copper shells, copper tubes, and steel tube-plates, the shell being wound round with steel wire. It is stated that this company has sold over 1,000 steam carriages in this country. The 10 horse-power engine has two cylinders,

FIG. 97. THE LOCOMOBILE STEAM VICTORIA

# Modern Steam Carriages

each of 3-inch bore and 4-inch stroke. Most of the small parts are steel drop forgings. The crank chamber is made in four pieces, and is dust-proof, and allows the moving parts of the engine to run in oil. Full particulars of these later types are given in *The Automotor Journal* for 28th February, 1903.

This is an English company, and in order to compete in price with the American cars, they have adopted the course of quoting two prices for their automobiles. The lower-priced cars are fitted with American engines, while the higher-priced ones are fitted with engines of their own make. With the exception of these engines, all the cars are, as before, of British manufacture. Fig. 98 illustrates the engine and boiler; the former is of the double high-pressure type with link-motion, and is so designed that the frame, which is made of aluminium, forms an oil-tight crank case enclosing the cranks and connecting-rods. The engines are fitted with piston-valves and circular crosshead slides. The boiler illustrated is of the usual fire-tube type, which for simplicity is hard to beat. But the makers are in a position to supply a water-tube or semi-flash boiler. With this latter boiler it is possible to use the feed-water over and over again in a way which is not practicable in a fire-tube boiler, as the trace of oil (after filtration) is always present in the water, which is returned by the condenser; this causes trouble in the fire-tube boiler, which is absent in the water-tube type. The makers recommend a fire-tube boiler where a running distance of 20 to 25 miles with one tank of water is sufficient; but where it is required to run 50 or 100 miles with one filling of the water-tank, they prefer to supply a semi-flash boiler, in conjunction with their patent condenser; the latter

# Steam Carriages

returns a large percentage of the exhaust steam as water. By the adoption of the feed-water level regulator, the use of a gauge-glass becomes unnecessary, and

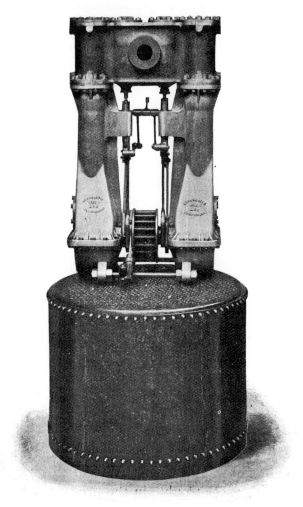

FIG. 98.   STEAM ENGINE AND BOILER

the "taking on and off" of the pump is done away with. The apparatus maintains the level of the water in the boiler at a practically uniform height; it is quite automatic in action; it is also simple, and certain in construction. Part of the apparatus consists of an

FIG. 99. STEAM MOTOR CAR

THE MOTOR CONSTRUCTION CO., NOTTINGHAM

# Modern Steam Carriages

"alarm" which, should the engine-pump fail from any cause, gives immediate warning to the driver. The burners are made to burn paraffin or petrol as required. But the burners that are made suitable for the former

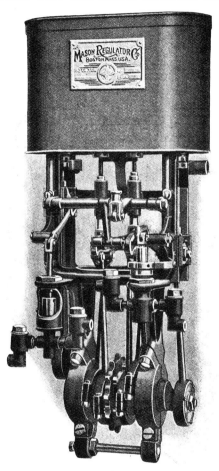

FIG. 100.  MASON'S STEAM MOTOR

will burn the latter. The underframes are made of English solid-drawn steel tubes of heavy gauge and large diameter. A large amount of cooling surface is provided by the condenser; no back pressure is produced, while a certain amount of forced draught is obtained.

Fig. 99 represents the Motor Construction Company's

No. 4 double phaeton. It contains four seats ; it is driven by an 8 horse-power engine ; the boiler is 19 inches in diameter. The wheels are of the artillery pattern. Sufficient water can be carried for a run of 25 to 30 miles, and oil for 50 miles. In their cheaper cars the well-known Mason engine is used, as illustrated by Fig. 100. This engine, it is stated, has acquired a high reputation in America.

## THE MIESSE STEAM MOTOR SYNDICATE

This is a neat and efficient steam carriage, made at Wolverhampton. In appearance it resembles some of the petrol cars, but the faults of the petrol cars are eliminated. It is powerfully built, and made of the very best materials. The Miesse generator is constructed of solid cold-drawn steel. It is heated by a special burner, and as the boiler at no time contains more than half a pint of water, no water-gauge is needed. The burner having been started, no further attention whatever to the generator is required, all that is necessary being to set the water-valve according to the speed required, The admission of too much water to the boiler will cause the car to run at an excessive speed, and if no water is injected the engines stop ; in either case no damage to the generator can result. In ordinary steam boilers the process of incrustation commences from the moment that the boiler comes into use, which not only greatly reduces its efficiency, but becomes a source of danger. Especially is this so in small boilers, where the water-space of which cannot be cleaned. With the Miesse steam boiler no incrustation occurs, the interior remaining for an indefinite period in the same condition as when new, consequently the efficiency does not deteriorate in the least. The explosion of such a steam gene-

# Modern Steam Carriages

rator is an impossibility—a point of the greatest importance to inexperienced persons who buy a car. The
boiler requires neither cleaning nor attention. It is so
very compact that it can be placed in the front of the
car, thus improving the appearance, distributing the
weight, and greatly reducing the probabilities of "side
slip." Steam can be raised in six minutes. The value
of the Miesse burner lies in its high efficiency, which
obtains from a minimum quantity of paraffin the greatest
possible number of units of heat. Unlike most vaporising burners which use the dangerous petrol spirit, this
burner requires only the ordinary paraffin, and, apart
from the security so obtained from fire or explosion, the
cost of running is greatly reduced. In this burner the
paraffin is vaporised in a coiled tube, and allowed to
take up as much atmospheric air as can be consumed
with it, and then, instead of igniting at some twelve
nozzles, the vapour issues from 1,200 holes with a pale
blue flame, forming a mat covering the entire area of the
under part of the boiler, and free from any trace of smoke
or smell. So perfect is the combustion that after months
of constant use no soot or unconsumed carbon can be
found upon any part of the generator. The Miesse
burner is silent in action (a valuable feature), and entirely automatic, not requiring any attention while the
car is running; when the car is at rest the burner can be
turned down. For town travelling, the burner can be
used at half-strength, with a corresponding economy
in the fuel, under which conditions the supply will last
for fifteen hours' continuous running. The illustration
Fig. 101 represents the class B 10 horse-power *Tonneau*
style Miesse steam car, seating four persons. It is
fitted with 10 horse-power engines, developing 17 horse-
power on the brake ; can be speeded up to forty miles

an hour on the level. The wheels are of artillery type, all the same diameter. It is capable of running 100 miles without replenishing the paraffin. The engines are fitted with three single-acting cylinders of the trunk type, and are capable of running at a very high speed; the steel cranks are set at an angle of 120 deg., consequently there is no dead centre, and the engines are always ready to start either forward or backwards. They can be linked up for slow running or steam econo-

FIG. 101. MIESSE STEAM CAR

mising, and can be reversed instantly. The engines run in an oil-bath, the cranks, connecting-rods, and pistons being thoroughly lubricated. This arrangement excludes all dust, secures silent and smooth running, and ensures a long life for the wearing parts.

In the engine-casting is also fitted the differential apparatus, which is geared down to half the speed of the engine-shaft, and receives its lubrication from the crank chamber.

This arrangement results in the rigidity of the whole, and secures true running. The steam inlet and exhaust valves are actuated by sliding cam rods, and the valves

# Modern Steam Carriages

are of the poppet or petrol engine type, thus avoiding the loss of power resulting from the use of excentrics and slide valves. The whole is easily accessible for inspection, and there is nothing to get out of order. All the cars are fitted with thoroughly efficient condensers, which return the exhaust steam from the engine to the water-tank; this enables the cars to run long distances without requiring additional water. These so fully answer their purpose, that unless the cars are run for a long distance and driven at a great speed, no trace of steam is ever visible.

The feed-pump for the boiler is driven direct from the engine, and is so placed that it can be readily reached and examined in case of need. After studying the construction of the Miesse steam carriages, there can be no doubt in the minds of engineers and experts that steam under suitable conditions possesses possibilities for the propulsion of road vehicles with which no other power could compare. The chief difficulty, however, has been to devise means of generating and utilising it in such a way that a carriage so equipped might be placed in the hands of a person of ordinary intelligence without danger to himself or others. Full particulars and drawings of the latest Miesse steam car have appeared in *The Auto-motor Journal* for 21st and 28th March, 1903.

## THE PRESCOTT AUTOMOBILE MANUFACTURING COMPANY

The Prescott carriage is an American production of great interest, and possessing some good features which are worthy of attention. It is said of this steam car " that the general construction is heavier than usual, that means are provided by which the steam is super-heated while passing from the throttle-valve to the engine; that the burner is of entirely different construc-

# Steam Carriages

tion from that of most other cars ; that roller-bearings are employed on the rear axle ; that the cylinders are automatically and positively lubricated, and that the box-

FIG. 102.  THE PRESCOTT STEAM CAR (CLOSED)

dash is arranged in such a manner as to form a comfortable seat when required."[1]

The illustration Fig. 102 shows style 10 of the Prescott carriage closed, and the next illustration, Fig. 103, repre-

FIG. 103.  THE PRESCOTT STEAM CAR (OPEN)

sents the same carriage open, with a seating capacity for two or four persons as may be required.  The wheels are 28 in. in diameter, with heavy steel spokes, and $2\frac{1}{2}$-in. tires, single-tube pneumatic.  Capacity of fuel-

[1] *The Automotor Journal*, August 23rd, 1902.

tanks is 10 gallons, and the capacity of the water-tank is 32 gallons. The wheel base is 68 in., and the tread 54 in. Fig. 104 represents the underframe and running gear; the frame is made of seamless steel tubing of

FIG. 104.   UNDERFRAME

heavy gauge, and drop forged connections. As shown in the illustration Fig. 105, the American roller-bearings are used in the hind axle, giving a reliable bearing, eliminating ball-bearings which have heretofore occasioned some annoyance, as they were unable to stand the severe strain in this connection. The boiler is 16 in.

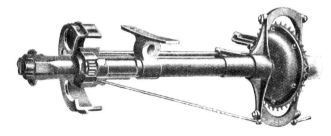

FIG. 105.   HIND AXLE

in diameter, made with a seamless drawn-steel shell with a dry plate fitted inside. The boiler contains 367 tubes, $\frac{1}{2}$ in. diameter, of 20 gauge seamless drawn copper. The special features of the construction of the generator provide for the superheating of the steam after passing through the throttle-valve, at the same time obviating the possibility of overheating, which would result in injurious action in the cylinders of the engine. All the advantages of the fire- and water-tube boiler are thus combined without the faults of either, giving reserve power under all conditions, and nearly twice the usual efficiency to a given amount of water and fuel. With this boiler high speed can be maintained over any road, as ample steam is supplied under all conditions. The boiler is covered with asbestos, which is held in place by steel sheeting.

The Prescott burner is shown in Fig. 106, where it will be seen there are fourteen parallel tubes, having air-

FIG. 106. BURNER

spaces between them, and fixed so that the ends are closed by a circular casing. It is constructed in such a manner that it cannot warp or burn out, and is practically indestructible. It secures perfect combustion, and there is no back-firing or troubles usual to some burners.

The Prescott diaphragm valve is shown by Fig. 107. "It will be noticed that an upper and smaller air-cone is also provided, and that a separate jet feeds petrol vapour into it. The latter passage leads nearly half-way through one of the tubes forming the burner, this particular tube being stopped off internally at this point, and forming the pilot light. Two rows of holes are pierced through the upper side of each tube forming the burner as seen

# Modern Steam Carriages

in the illustration, the combustible mixture issuing from these to feed the furnace. The main fuel-feed leads to

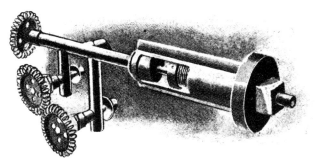

FIG. 107. DIAPHRAGM VALVE

the diaphragm fitting, seen in Fig. 107, the petrol passing through a coil placed above the boiler and leading through two of the boiler tubes before being led across,

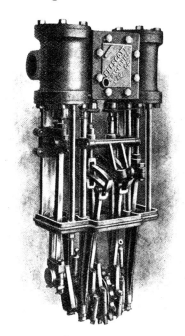

FIG. 108. PRESCOTT ENGINE

above the burner, to this fitting. The main feed to the burner is automatically controlled by the steam pressure in the diaphragm valve in much the usual manner, and an adjusting needle valve regulates the maximum flow of fuel. The auxiliary feed to the pilot light is not controlled by the diaphragm."[1] Full steam-pressure can be raised in six minutes, without smoke or soot. The engine, as shown by Fig. 108, is of a vertical, two-cylinder type; the cylinders are $2\frac{1}{2}$ in. diameter and $3\frac{1}{2}$ in. stroke. The engine is enclosed, fully

[1] *The Automotor Journal*, August 23rd, 1902.

protected by a detachable case which is easily removed and replaced when desired, thus protecting all the working parts from mud and dust. A foot-lever, conveniently arranged, is used to reverse the engine. The automatic lubrication of the cylinders is accomplished by a pump, which feeds the required amount of oil per mile regardless of the speed at which the carriage is running. The brake fitted to the hind axle-hub is illustrated in Fig. 109. There are two such brakes which are operated simultaneously by the usual foot-lever; these will hold the carriage satisfactorily when running forward or

FIG. 109. PRESCOTT BRAKE

backward. Three pumps are used for feeding the boiler —one actuated by the engine, the second is a separate steam-pump, the third is a hand-pump. The capacity of the water-tank is 32 gallons. A water-lifter is fitted which is very useful for filling the tank from a wayside stream. The petrol tank holds $7\frac{1}{2}$ gallons; it is made of heavy seamless drawn copper; the shell is tested to 350 lbs. pressure. An auxiliary tank carries $2\frac{1}{2}$ gallons. The feed-water is heated by being passed through a coil in the muffler. The exhaust steam is scarcely visible, owing to the fact that it is superheated to such a degree as to be very dry, and under ordinary conditions no vapour whatever is visible.

# Modern Steam Carriages

We are indebted to the makers for the above particulars and the illustrations.

The steam carriage introduced by Mr. Sardy, of Snow Hill, E.C., is shown in the accompanying illustration (Fig. 110). The makers state, after an extensive experience in handling various steam cars, they have gained a knowledge of the weak points of such cars, and have

FIG. 110.   SARACEN STEAMER

now produced a reliable steam carriage. They have given the utmost attention to the details of construction, resulting in a carriage which may be said to conform to English ideas respecting solid construction coupled with a good appearance.

A fire-tube type of boiler is employed, 16 in. in diameter and 14 in. high, supplying steam to a $5\frac{1}{2}$ horse-power double-cylinder engine. Three double-acting brakes are fitted to the carriage, two on the hind-wheel hubs controlled by the Bowden wire system, and quite independently of the usual differential brake. There are four feed-pumps, two on the engine driven from the crossheads, one hand-pump, and an auxiliary steam-pump, thus accomplishing that most important feature— the certainty of supplying water to the boiler under all conditions. Link-motion reversing-gear is fitted to the engine. A water-lifter is included in the outfit. The petrol pipes are of large diameter, and are not likely to clog; a petroleum fire can be fitted if required. An independent steam air-pump is fitted for maintaining the air-pressure in the fuel-tanks; it has also an attachment for pumping up the tires. The carriage is mounted on heavy artillery wheels, with either solid or pneumatic tires. The carriage-body is a strong flexible tubular frame; the back axle is well braced, supporting the body on two transverse semi-elliptic springs. The steering-gear is particularly strong, and the whole steamer neatly arranged.

## THE STANLEY STEAM CAR

These steam vehicles are built by Messrs. Stanley Bros., the original designers and inventors of this type of American steam car. The engine is geared directly on to the hind axle; there is no chain or flexible shaft. The boiler is of an improved form; it is 14 in. diameter; it is of copper, lapped with extra strong copper-plated steel wire, therefore there is no rusting-up of wire. An engine having a $2\frac{1}{2}$ in. diameter cylinder and 4 in. stroke is employed; it is enclosed in a copper case. The engine is guaranteed for twelve months, if properly handled. It is impossible to burn the boiler out; a reliable fusible plug prevents accident; the burner is of a new pattern, and the makers assert that it will not light back. No water-gauge in the boiler

# Modern Steam Carriages

is necessary, and the steam is superheated. A fairly long wheel-base gives easy riding; the wheels are 28 in. diameter; the tires of 2½ or 3 in. double tube. There is never more than one pint of petrol under pressure; the petrol tank carries sufficient for a run of 200 miles. The car will run 15 miles on one gallon of petrol: as much as 20 miles has been obtained. A ratio of 2½ to 1 is employed; this gives a travelling speed up to 25 miles an hour on good level roads. The water-tank holds 19 gallons; the water consumed is about one gallon for every·two miles run. A water-lifter is included in the outfit. The lubrication to the engine cylinders is automatic, and enough oil is carried for a 200-mile run. The carriage will seat two or four persons at will. Trial runs up to 50 miles from Manchester will be given to genuine purchasers.

THE WESTON MOTOR SYNDICATE

The touring steam carriage is illustrated by Fig. 111. It possesses some special features. By means of a patent by-pass the carriage can be started almost instanta-

FIG. 111.   THE WESTON TOURING STEAM CARRIAGE

neously. The steam superheater greatly enhances the steaming qualities, enabling the car to attain very high speeds. It also improves the hill-climbing capabilities. The superheater reduces the fuel-consumption by about 20 per cent., making the Weston car an economical steam-raiser. The running capacity of the water-tank is about forty miles.

Superheated steam being used renders the exhaust practically invisible. No condenser is used, and very little trouble is experienced by water in the engine-cylinders. A positive automatic lubricator is employed ; it is worked by the engine ; the flow of oil is therefore proportional to the speed ; the supply ceases the moment the engine stops. The lubricating reservoir is not under pressure, and the flow can be graduated to a nicety. Copious lubrication prevents the danger of scored piston-rings, and the hitherto unexplained temporary unsatisfactory steaming.

The capacity of the reservoir is sufficient for a run of forty miles. An automatic steam air-pump is fitted below the footboard, out of sight ; the driver can obtain the required air-pressure by merely turning on a tap ; no hand-pumping is required. Special stress is laid by the manufacturers upon the fact that the burner can be started with a match. The burner is shown by Fig. 112. There are two separate pipes leading to it from the supply tank ; one feeds the pilot-light, and the other leads through the vaporiser to the main burner. A portion of the boiler is shown in Fig. 113. We are indebted to the *Automotor Journal* for these three illustrations, where a full account is given of the Weston carriage in the issue of August 9th, 1902.

FIG. 112. THE WESTON BURNER

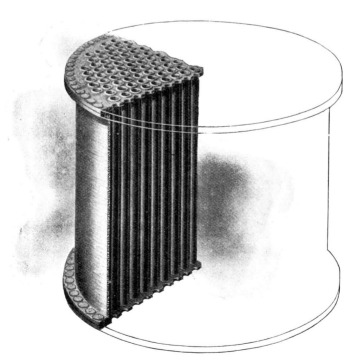

FIG. 113. THE WESTON BOILER

# Modern Steam Carriages

For touring and pleasure purposes this car holds a very high place. It is of the *châssis* construction, fitted with a removable aluminium body of *tonneau* design, providing a simple and readily accessible arrangement of the working parts. Fig. 114 represents the steam *tonneau*, with canopy over it. Fig. 115 gives another view of the car. Fig. 116 represents a side view of the *châssis*, while Fig. 117 shows a plan of the *châssis* from above. From these views it will be noticed that the carriage is, extremely simple in construction. Accessibility has been secured in the arrangement of the details. The engine is in the front, and the drive is direct through a simple shaft and universal joints to the revolving rear driving-axle, without the intervention of clutches or change-speed gears. The generator is carried midway in the car, and all the connections from the boiler to the engine, or from the water-tank to the pumps and generator, are simple, direct, and easily followed. This is the system upon which the White steam car is run :—

The water is pumped by the engine from the water-tank into the generator, where it is changed to steam. The steam passes from the generator to the engine, where, after doing its work, it is exhausted into the condenser and changed back into water. From the condenser the water is pumped back into the tank from whence it came, to be used over again.

The supply of water is automatically regulated in such manner that the amount admitted to the generator, no matter at what speed the car is running, is always sufficient to furnish enough steam for the engine. At the same time, the amount of water admitted to the generator so acts upon the automatic fire-regulator as to furnish sufficient heat to thoroughly vaporise all the water that passes through the generator. The control is such, on the other hand, that a certain temperature of the steam shuts down the fire and prevents any excessive heat.

The White steam car is equipped with a steam generator which is not a boiler, and has none of the disadvantages peculiar to the latter. Fig. 118 shows the generator with the casing removed. It consists of helical coils of seamless tubing, placed one above the other, and surrounded by a casing of insulating material, and at the bottom the heat is applied by means of a burner. The coils of tubing are so connected that the water, entering the top, cannot pass through the successive coils below by gravity, but is held in place entirely subject to the action of the pump. The water comes in, and is at all times in the top of the coils, while the steam is in the lower coils and goes out of the lowest coils next to the fire. There is no boiling water to generate steam. The upper coils act practically as water-heaters, and the water is converted instantly into steam at some variable point in the lower coils, depending upon the amount of steam which the engine is using. There is no water-level to maintain, consequently no water-gauge glass is needed. The generator is non-explosible, impossible to burn out, and no fusible plug is required. The formation of any deposits or incrustation in the generator is rendered impossible by the rapidity of the circulation. Hence the generator never needs cleaning. The water supply is automatically controlled by the steam pressure, thus dispensing with any hand regulation of the pump. The steam as it comes from the lowest coil is superheated, ensuring perfectly dry steam,

FIG. 114. THE WHITE STEAM CAR

FIG. 115. THE WHITE STEAM CAR

FIG. 116. THE WHITE STEAM CAR

Side view of the *châssis*

FIG. 117. THE WHITE STEAM CAR

Plan of the *chássis* from above

# Modern Steam Carriages

which gives the utmost efficiency, and practically invisible when being exhausted into the open air. A special device regulates the flame so as to meet all requirements. The above operations take place automatically without entailing any care on the part of the

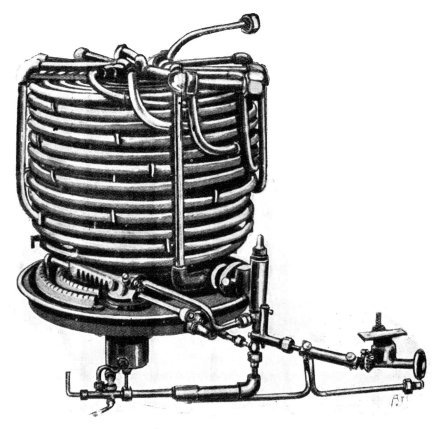

FIG. 118.   THE WHITE GENERATOR

driver. The car can be run until the water-supply is exhausted, and it only comes to a stop by reason of lack of water in the generating coils, without the slightest danger of explosion or damage to the coils.

The engine is on the compound principle, and so arranged that it can be instantly changed, by pressure on a foot - pedal, to a simple engine, in which both cylinders are acting under high pressure. The simple engine is only used for starting, and on occasions when a slow, strong pull is required. For ordinary running the engine is worked on the compound style, and its economy in water and fuel consumption is remarkable. The cylinders are insulated and covered with an aluminium jacket or sheet lagging, the crank-case is of aluminium and thoroughly enclosed.

It gains the advantage of splash lubrication, and makes the engine impervious to dust and dirt, and at the same time allows easy access to the parts. The engine is fitted with link-motion reversing-gear. The engine is well balanced and perfectly free from all motor vibrations, and the exhaust steam is muffled so as to be absolutely noiseless. Hence the White steam car is really noiseless and vibrationless, a combination of virtues frequently claimed and only obtained on steam conveyances. The lubrication is automatic. The lubricator is fastened to the dashboard; it is driven by a belt from the engine, and supplies oil both to the cylinders and to the crank chamber. The engine shaft runs in oil, and the system of splash lubrication has proved in every way efficient. The hind axle is encased, and the driving and compensating gears all run in oil. Two independent sets of double-acting brakes are fitted to the car, One is operated by a foot-pedal and acts on the engine-shaft. The other set is worked by a hand lever, and acts internally on the brake drums attached to each rear wheel; the hand-brake may be fixed by a ratchet, absolutely locking the car on the steepest incline. The *châssis*, looking from the left, is shown in Fig. 119.

The White steam car is a touring carriage and not

FIG. 119. THE WHITE STEAM CAR

By permission of the "Automotor Journal"

# Modern Steam Carriages

a racing machine. That fact does not prevent the car from averaging 20 to 25 miles an hour, carrying four persons, on a fairly good road. A much greater speed than this can be maintained if required. But reliability is the chief consideration nowadays. A reliable car is one which will do the work expected of it consistently and regularly, without requiring constant repair and adjustment. A reliable car, with intelligent driving and care, will run 365 days in the year if required. The White car has established its reliability beyond dispute, both in Great Britain and America. The following points may be named in conclusion :—

The driver starts the car without leaving his seat ; the car is free from all vibration when running slowly or fast, or when standing ; *the engine does not run when the car is not in motion.*[1] The car can be run a long distance at a speed of two miles an hour as easily as a higher speed, and can stop and start at frequent intervals subject to the simple action of the throttle-valve. It is said that these are tests which should be applied to all motors if one is seeking to discover imperfections. The motion is smooth, noiseless ; the car raises extremely little dust, and has no exhaust to aid the tires in stirring up the dust. A brief specification is given : Rated horse-power of the car, 10 ; wheel-base, 6 ft. 8 in. ; tread, 4 ft. 8 in. ; diameter of wheels, 30 in. ; weight, 15 cwt. ; extreme length, 10 ft. ; extreme width, 5 ft.; extreme height over all, 5 ft. 2 in.; fuel-tank holds two gallons ; water-tank 10 gallons; 100 miles on one filling of fuel ; 100 miles on one filling of water. We are indebted to the makers for the particulars, and to the *Automotor Journal* for the illustrations.

To the writer this appears to be an irritating defect of the petrol motor and one that should be obviated.

# Steam Carriages

Before leaving this part of the subject it may not be amiss to offer a few remarks respecting the little engines used on the steam carriages. They range from 6 to 10 horse-power, they are of the double-cylinder type, with cylinders $2\frac{1}{2}$ to $3\frac{1}{2}$ in. diameter by $3\frac{1}{2}$ or 4 in. stroke. Link-motion is usually applied; Messrs. Clarkson, Limited, use Joy's valve gear. One or two makers use piston slide-valves, but the ordinary slide-valves are in favour. Messrs. White are adopting a compound engine. It has been stated that the compound engine gives very little better results than the simple cylinder type, but the former engine is in great favour for nearly all classes of work, and there must be some economy of fuel and water by the adoption of the compound system for steam carriages. The simple type of engines run up to 380 or 400 revolutions per minute, and at this speed the cars travel at 12 to 15 miles an hour. The working steam pressure is from 180 to 250 lbs. per square inch, the steam is very dry and usually super-heated. On account of the dry steam used, profuse lubrication of the cylinders and the slide-valves is essential. The engines are very economical because of the high speed at which they are worked; the small clearance spaces, the superheated steam, and the high pressure all tend in the direction of economy.

Ball-bearings and roller-bearings are sometimes adopted for reducing the friction of the working parts. Most of the engines are of the inverted type, several engines are illustrated in the foregoing two chapters. In some instances the cranks, gearing, and excentrics work in an oil-bath. In the Locomobile and the Prescott steam engines the cranks are overhung, the

# Modern Steam Carriages

sprocket wheel for the chain-drive is between the crank bearings; the same plan is adopted by some of the other makers.

THE SPEED OF STEAM CARRIAGES

In the table given (page 174) the ordinary travelling speeds have been stated. The question of speed is just now a very delicate question. Opinions differ on the subject, and since the fatal accidents attending the badly managed Paris-Madrid race happened, many wild statements have been expressed by the people who are opposed to all machinery on the road. There is a class of persons who would curtail the speed to a crawling rate, so that their spirited horses should not be made afraid. At the same time, it appears to be unwise to attempt to remove the restrictions respecting the speed on public roads. No further races are now necessary, the only tests required are endurance trials and reliability; freedom from breakages and efficiency must be sought for also. Moreover, the carriage should always be ready for work when wanted. Steam carriages should be used for touring and business purposes. There can be no need to rush about the country at a rate of fifty miles an hour, endangering the lives of cyclists, pedestrians, and residents of villages. For real pleasure purposes much lower speeds are sufficient. A safe speed for motor carriages would be eight to ten miles an hour in villages and towns, and twenty-five miles an hour in the open country.[1] As the cars increase in number the risks increase. The speed-limit must not be removed but modified. Unless this question is dealt with in a give-and-take spirit, the

Since this was written an Act of Parliament has fixed the limit at twenty miles an hour.

## TABLE III.—SOME PARTICULARS OF STEAM CARRIAGES.

| Name. | Cylinders. | Pressure. | Gearing Ratio. | Passengers. | Speed. | Weight. | Date. | Type of Engine. | No. of Speeds. |
|---|---|---|---|---|---|---|---|---|---|
| Boulton | $2\frac{5}{8}'' \times 9''$ | 130 | — | 2 | 10 miles. | 17 cwt. | 1850 | single cylinder. | — |
| Rickett | $3'' \times 9''$ | 100 | $2\frac{1}{2}$ to 1 | 3 | 12 ,, | 30 ,, | 1858 | double cylinder. | 2 |
| Paterson | $3'' \times 6''$ | 100 | 3 to 1 | 8 | 12 ,, | 20 ,, | 1860 | double cylinder. | — |
| Holt | $3'' \times 6''$ | 250 | 3 to 1 | — | 15 ,, | 30 ,, | 1860 | 4 cylinders. | — |
| Rhodes | $3\frac{1}{8}'' \times 9''$ | 150 | 5 to 1 | 6 | 14 ,, | — | 1863 | double cylinder. | — |
| Dudgeon | $3'' \times 16''$ | — | — | 6 | 10 ,, | 40 cwt. | 1866 | — | — |
| Armstrong | $3'' \times 6''$ | 100 | — | — | 12 ,, | — | 1868 | double cylinder. | — |
| Catley and Ayres | $2\frac{5}{8}'' \times 5\frac{3}{4}''$ | 150 | 3 to 1 | 4 | 20 ,, | 19 cwt. | 1871 | — | 2 |
| Mackenzie | $3\frac{3}{4}'' \times 4\frac{1}{2}''$ | 135 | 6 to 1 | 3 | 12 ,, | 60 ,, | 1874 | — | 2 |
| Inshaw | $4'' \times 8''$ | 200 | — | 10 | 12 ,, | 35 ,, | 1881 | — | 3 |
| Brown | $2\frac{1}{8}'' \& 4'' \times 3''$ | 200 | — | 4 | 12 ,, | — | — | compound | — |
| Clarkson | $4'' \times 4''$ | 250 | — | — | 16 ,, | — | 1902 | double cylinder. | — |
| Toledo | $3'' \times 4''$ | 150 | — | 2 | — | — | 1903 | — | — |
| Locomobile | $3'' \times 4''$ | 180 | — | 2 | — | 8 cwt. | 1903 | — | — |
| Miesse | — | — | — | 4 | 40 miles | — | 1903 | 3 cylinders. | — |
| Prescott | $2\frac{1}{2}'' \times 3\frac{1}{2}''$ | 180 | — | 2 | — | — | 1903 | double cylinder. | — |
| Stanley | $2\frac{1}{2}'' \times 4''$ | 180 | $2\frac{1}{2}$ to 1 | 2 | 25 miles. | — | 1903 | single cylinder. | — |
| White | $3\frac{1}{2}'' \times 4''$ | 250 | — | 4 | 25 ,, | 15 cwt. | 1903 | compound. | — |

# Modern Steam Carriages

industry may be ruined. A few more accidents such as we have had to deplore, may soon damage the cause we are anxious to foster. When the cars are running at excessive speeds steering is rendered more difficult, while the brake power is far from sufficient for preventing accidents. The carriages are somewhat unpopular just now, their character may be redeemed by the drivers of cars showing more consideration for other vehicles on the road. To sportsmen the above statements may be unpalatable.

## RESISTANCES

The following remarks and some of the tables beneath have been contributed by Mr. R. Edwards, M.I.C.E, Hastings.

Self-propelled vehicles have several resistances to overcome, both internal and external, which, for convenience, may be divided as under :—

1. The internal friction of the engine gearing and axles.
2. The external resistance of the road.
3. The resistance due to a rising gradient.
4. That due to moving through the air.

1. The internal friction of the engine itself will vary with the construction of the moving parts, and the means of lubrication; but in a well-constructed engine it should not exceed $\frac{1}{5}$ of the indicated power, though in some engines probably not more than $\frac{1}{6}$ is absorbed. The friction due to the gearing used to transmit the power of the engine to the driving-wheels should be reduced as much as possible, by the adoption of the simplest means, and using as little gearing as possible. Taking the engine friction and that of the gearing and axles together, it will be found that from $\frac{1}{3}$ to $\frac{2}{5}$ of the

175

total indicated horse-power of the engine will be absorbed, leaving $\frac{2}{3}$ to $\frac{3}{5}$ available for the propulsion of the vehicle.

Some light steam carriages for passengers have been made without gearing, the engines being coupled direct to the main driving-axle.[1]

With the faster speeds now obtainable with these vehicles and the use of small driving-wheels, it is possible that direct driving may become more common; by using driving-wheels 28 in. diameter, running at 120 revolutions a minute, a travelling speed of 10 miles an hour would be obtained. If the stroke of the engines were 10 in. it would give 200 ft. piston speed per minute. By the use of such engines the friction due to gearing would be saved, resulting in a greater freedom from breakages, and the cardinal virtue of simplicity obtained.[2]

2. The resistance due to the road varies very considerably according to the materials used in its construction, and its state of repair; thus, well-laid asphalt gives the least resistance of any of the present form of roads, other materials increasing the resistance till we come to loose sand of considerable depth, when propulsion by a steam vehicle becomes practically impossible. If the sand is of less depth, with a hard bottom beneath it, steam carriages can travel over it without much inconvenience.

[1] In *Steam Locomotion on Common Roads*, 1891. A carriage made by Yarrow, in 1862, the cylinders were coupled direct to the cranks, p. 161. About the same date Messrs. Tangyes constructed a steam carriage on the same lines, p. 167.

[2] Turning to *Steam Locomotion on Common Roads*, 1891, again. In 1853 Mr. Fisher used direct engines, the two cylinders were 4 in. diameter and 10 in. stroke. Mr. Yarrow's two cylinders were 5 in. diameter and 9 in. stroke. Tangyes' cylinders were $5\frac{1}{2}$ in. diameter and 11 in. stroke. All these carriages were intended for four to eight passengers.

# Modern Steam Carriages

Several experiments have been made from time to time in order to test the variable resistances of different forms of roads. The tractive power in pounds necessary to overcome the same for each ton weight of the vehicle is given in the table (No. 4) below :—

| | |
|---|---|
| Asphalt . . . . | 20 to 26 lbs. |
| Wood . . . . | 24 „ 30 „ |
| Good stone pavement . . . | 36 „ 40 „ |
| Inferior stone pavement . . | 50 „ 60 „ |
| Macadam, good . . . | 50 lbs. |
| Macadam, bad . . . | 60 to 70 lbs. |
| Macadam, soft . . . | 80 „ 100 „ |
| Gravel . . . . | 150 „ 200 „ |
| Arable land . . . . | 200 „ 300 „ |
| Soft grass land . . . | 300 lbs. |

## GRADIENTS

3. The resistance encountered by rising gradients varies directly as to the steepness of the hill, and is readily calculated by dividing the weight of the carriage by the rise of the gradient ; the result being the resistance in pounds. Thus, a vehicle weighing, say, $1\frac{1}{2}$ tons (3,360 lbs.) would require a traction power of 168 lbs. to overcome the resistance of a hill with a rise of 1 in 20. This does not, of course, take into consideration the resistance due to the road, but only of the gradient itself.

On a falling gradient, the tractive power to overcome the road and other resistances is helped by the gradient in a similar proportion ; thus, on a falling gradient of 1 in 20 with a 30 cwt. vehicle, the 168 lbs. would go to assist the power required to overcome the road resistance, and also the engine and gearing friction.

# Steam Carriages

4. The resistance due to the air in slow-moving vehicles need hardly be considered as it is so small. At 10 miles an hour it only amounts to $\frac{1}{80}$ of a horse-power for each square foot of frontage in cross section of the car. When, however, the car attains a speed of 50 miles an hour (a speed recently achieved by a steam car), the resistance rises to $1\frac{1}{2}$ horse-power for each square foot of frontage. The following table (No. 5) gives the approximate resistances due for other speeds :—

| 10 | . | 15 | . | 20 | . | 30 | . | 50 | . | 75 | miles per hour. |
|----|---|----|---|----|---|----|---|----|---|----|----|
| $\frac{1}{80}$ | . | $\frac{1}{20}$ | . | $\frac{1}{10}$ | . | $\frac{1}{3}$ | . | $1\frac{1}{2}$ | . | $5\frac{1}{2}$ | resistance in h.-p. for each square foot. |

The resistance due to the air can, however, be very much reduced, even to one-half of the above or less, if a suitably tapered or pointed hood or front is arranged with a continuous covering to the whole vehicle.

### ADHESION

In considering the power required to propel a vehicle on the road, it is also necessary at the same time to know what kinds of roads are likely to be encountered as no propulsion can take place if the adhesion or grip of the wheels on the road surface is not sufficient. As before mentioned, it is almost impossible to negotiate loose sand.

In heavy haulage or traction engines adhesion has more particularly to be considered, and for fairly good roads it is found in practice · that the diagonal cross-plates universally riveted to the road wheels is sufficient. These are supplemented occasionally by short spikes

# Modern Steam Carriages

fastened in the tires of the wheels,[1] for traversing frozen roads, while on soft ground paddles or spuds are used. When a soft patch of road occurs, a long chain is sometimes employed; the engine passes over the patch on to the hard road without its load; the chain is then attached to the waggons or other load, and they are drawn over the soft ground. Most of the traction engines are now fitted with a winding drum and wire rope; if necessary, the load may be divided and some left behind, the engine hauling part of its load over a bad piece of road, or up a steep bank, as the engine travels forward. The rope is fixed to the waggon left behind, and paid out; when the engine arrives at the summit of the hill, or on solid ground, the engine wheels are chocked and the brake applied. The engine hauls the remaining part of its load by means of the wire rope.

With motor waggons or lorries in this country smooth tires are generally used. The adhesion has mostly been found sufficient, as the load carried is placed over the driving-wheels, and is available for adhesion, so that the greater the load the greater the adhesion. The same remarks apply to passenger omnibuses or private carriages. These, as a rule, are fitted with solid india-rubber or pneumatic tires, which give ample adhesion. The following may be taken as the adhesion of different types of wheel tires on a good macadam road.

| | | |
|---|---|---|
| India-rubber tires . . . 1,000 | } | Maximum adhesion |
| Iron-shod, with diagonal plates . 840 | } | in pounds per ton |
| Iron plain tires . . . . 500 | } | of weight. |

[1] The use of spikes is now illegal, and they must not be applied on public roads.

# Steam Carriages

In considering the tractive power required in self-propelled vehicles, as it varies considerably, it may be conveniently placed under three heads, viz. :—

1. Tractive power required by traction engines drawing heavy loads at slow speeds.
2. Motor lorries carrying their own load.
3. Carriages conveying a few passengers.

In a traction engine, the load hauled behind it, of course, varies with the road and its gradients. Taking a modern road locomotive, it will be found that the tractive power provided in the slow speed will be about 1,100 lbs. per nominal horse-power, so that an 8 nominal horse-power traction engine, weighing in working trim 11 tons, will have a maximum tractive power at its wheels of 8,800 lbs., and presuming it was hauling on a gradient of 1 in 10 on a fairly good macadam road, with a resistance of 76 lbs. per ton, it would draw, in addition to its weight, a gross load of 18 tons. This would, however, not allow any margin, so that a gross load of 14 tons drawn behind would be a fair everyday work.

In considering the tractive power, the adhesion of the wheels (previously referred to) must not be lost sight of. With reference to the case just considered, with an engine weighing 11 tons, the maximum adhesion at 840 lbs. per ton, we have 9,240 lbs. adhesion on a good hard macadam road ; and if a gross load of 14 tons is hauled, the adhesion required would be 7,500 lbs., a fair margin on an ordinary road.

In the motor waggon or steam lorry class, the tractive power, owing to the present restrictions of weight, is

# Modern Steam Carriages

none too great, and may be taken at about 290 lbs. per gross tonnage of the motor and the gross load carried. When compound engines are employed, the tractive power can be considerably increased at times, by giving boiler steam to the low-pressure cylinder. In simple engines the maximum tractive power allowed is greater. Here, again, the adhesion must be considered ; but as the whole load is carried and not hauled, the margin is much greater and will generally be found sufficient.

When we come to steam carriages, made to carry two or more persons, it is found that the tractive power (per ton weight of the car loaded with water, fuel, and passengers) allowed varies from about 350 lbs. per ton to 400 lbs., and this will carry a vehicle anywhere.

Experience has shown that a less power gives trouble if bad roads and hills are met with. Thus, at 350 lbs., if we take a hill rising 1 in 8, 280 lbs. would be required to overcome the gradient, leaving 90 lbs. for the road resistance, which, of course, would be none too much for a bad road. If we had 400 lbs., there would be another 50 lbs. per ton to spare. It is not necessary to design all carriages with so much power where the requirements are known. Again, a racing car for travelling at 50 miles an hour, a special power would have to be arranged for it.

In the following table (page 182) an ordinary traction engine has been taken, drawing an average load behind it. The motor lorries all carry their load on their own self-contained waggon, whilst the passenger carriages only have their passengers to carry, except Rickett's,[1] which drew an omnibus weighing four tons loaded behind it. The tractive power provided runs, as a rule, fairly regular;

[1] Rickett's carriages are illustrated in *The History and Development of Steam Locomotion on Common Roads*, 1891.

## TABLE VI.

## TABLE SHOWING THE TRACTIVE POWER PROVIDED IN LBS. PER TON OF TOTAL LOAD IN VARIOUS TYPES OF STEAM-PROPELLED ENGINES OR VEHICLES.

| Type of Engine or Vehicle. | Date. | Nominal H.P. | Brake H.P. | Type of Engine. | Steam Pressure. | Weight without load in tons. | | | Weight drawn or carried in tons. | No. of Passengers carried. | Slow speed in miles per hour. | Tractive power at slow speeds in lbs. per ton of total weight of engine and load carried. |
|---|---|---|---|---|---|---|---|---|---|---|---|---|
| | | | | | | T. | C. | Q. | | | | |
| Ordinary Traction Engine | 1903 | 8 | 40 | single | 120 | 11 | 0 | 0 | — | — | — | 800 |
| „ „ „ | 1903 | 8 | 40 | single | 120 | 11 | 0 | 0 | 14 | — | — | 352 |
| Thorneycroft's Steam Waggon | 1901 | — | 30 | compound | 225 | 6 | 8 | 0 | 7 | — | 2·4 | 280 |
| „ „ „ | 1901 | — | 20 | compound | 200 | 3 | 16 | 0 | 4 | — | 2·2 | 345 |
| Coulthard's „ „ | 1901 | — | 25 | compound | 225 | 3 | 14 | 0 | 5 | — | 2·75 | 313 |
| Musker's „ „ | 1901 | — | 25 | single | 250 | 3 | 16 | 2 | 5 | — | 2·3 | 380 |
| Mann's „ „ | 1901 | — | 16 | compound | 160 | 4 | 0 | 0 | 5 | — | 2·1 | 250 |
| Lancashire Co.'s „ „ | 1901 | — | 25 | compound | 225 | 2 | 19 | 2 | 5 | — | 2·45 | 360 |
| Lough and Messenger's Carriage | 1858 | — | — | single | 120 | 0 | 8 | 3 | — | 2 | — | 285 |
| Caithness Steam Carriage | 1860 | — | — | single | 160 | 2 | 7 | 0 | — | 3 | — | 360 |
| Carrett and Marshall's Carriage | 1861 | — | — | single | 175 | 6 | 10 | 0 | — | 6 | — | 341 |
| Rickett's Carriage | 1865 | — | — | single | 200 | 6 | 0 | 0 | 4 | — | — | 348 |
| Mackenzie's Steam Brougham | 1874 | — | — | single | 135 | 3 | 0 | 0 | — | 3 | — | 408 |
| American Light Cars | 1902 | — | — | single | 180 | 0 | 8 | 0 | — | 2 | — | 375 |

# Modern Steam Carriages

350 lbs. per ton appears to be a fair average, and one that should under most circumstances give satisfactory results. In fact, with a steam-propelled carriage, it is not easy to obtain a much greater power per ton.

Before taking leave of this part of the work it is interesting to note that new types of steam carriages are from time to time being introduced, such as the Chaboche, an efficient vehicle for touring or for town work. The Clincoe Automobile Syndicate have also brought a new car to the front. Cremorne carriages, with the novel motors, have recently been described in the *Automotor Journal*. There may be other additions ; we welcome them all, feeling certain that the efficient steam carriage is bound to be a favourite wherever automobiles are used.

# CHAPTER VI

## ROAD LOCOMOTIVES FOR PASSENGER SERVICE

I N this chapter separate locomotive engines intended for drawing an omnibus for passengers, and one or more light vans for goods, will be described. There is a great future for this system of road locomotion, to act as feeders to the railways in our Colonies and foreign countries, where no laws are in force such as we have to contend with in England. As soon as these laws are modified, the same means of communication between the village and town, and between the farmyard and the nearest railway station, will be used in England also. In this place all reference to purely historical examples will be omitted, but a few road engines and trains that have been put to actual work in comparatively recent times will be described.

### MESSRS. PERKINS AND SON

A brief description is given of a small road steamer made by Messrs. Perkins and Son, Regent Square, London. This road engine is of very novel design, and possesses several features of interest. From the engraving, Fig. 120, it will be seen that the engine, boiler, and driving-gear are mounted on a circular frame, above the single driving-wheel; this machinery turns with the wheel in the act of steering. It is claimed for this arrangement that the machine pulls in the

# Road Locomotives for Passenger Service

direction that it is steered. The engine is coupled to a carriage upon which an atmospheric condenser is placed. The condenser is composed of a number of small pipes, through which the exhaust steam is passed as it leaves the engine, the lower part of the waggon being used as a tank for catching the condensed steam. The following are some of the dimensions of the engine and boiler. Engines are of the double-cylinder com-

FIG. 120. STEAM MOTOR AND VAN. MESSRS. PERKINS AND SON

pound type; two high-pressure cylinders, $1\frac{13}{16}$ in. diameter; two low-pressure cylinders, $3\frac{1}{8}$ in. diameter; stroke of each cylinder, $4\frac{1}{2}$ in. Diameter of the driving-wheel is 25 in., and 12 in. on face. Section of india-rubber tire, 10 in. by 5 in. thick. The vertical boiler is constructed entirely of thick wrought-iron tubes, with welded ends, and is perfectly free from any liability to explosion. The boiler is 26 in. high, $15\frac{5}{8}$ in. wide, and $20\frac{3}{8}$ in. long. Fire-grate area $\frac{3}{4}$ of square foot. The working pressure is 450 lbs. per square inch. These

# Traction Engines

engines have been run at a speed of considerably over 1,000 revolutions per minute. The engine only weighs 32 cwt.; the condenser, waggon, and passengers, 52 cwt. It runs on the road at eight miles an hour, without emitting any smoke or steam into the atmosphere, and is practically noiseless. The consumption of coal is only 2 lbs. per ton per mile. This high-pressure high-speed miniature engine developed 20 horse-power when running full speed under a load.

Mr. Thompson's road steamers must not detain us, as these were referred to in Mr. Head's paper.[1] Many particulars of Thompson's road steamers will be found in *Steam Locomotion on Common Roads.* The inventions of Mr. Thompson undoubtedly promoted steam locomotion on common roads. A considerable number of road steamers were made by Messrs. Burrell and Sons, Messrs. Ransomes, Sims, and Head, Messrs. Robey and Co., and others. Many of these were shipped to foreign countries for passenger service. Some particulars of four road steamers made by Messrs. Ransomes are given in a paper read in 1879, by Mr. Crompton, on "The Working of Traction Engines in India," before the Institution of Mechanical Engineers.[2]

## MESSRS. CHARLES BURRELL AND SONS

Soon after Messrs. Burrell took up the manufacture of Mr. Thompson's road steamer, they very wisely discarded the "pot" boiler, because of the trouble it gave; and substituted in its place the more reliable locomotive type of boiler. The engines were entirely rearranged to suit the altered conditions, and numbers of engines

[1] "On the Rise and Progress of Steam Locomotion on Common Roads," Mr. by John Head, *Minutes of Proceedings* of Inst. C.E., vol. xxxvi. p. 63.
[2] See *Steam Locomotion on Common Roads*, E. and F. N. Spon, 1891.

# Road Locomotives for Passenger Service

of this type were sent to various parts of the world, mostly for running passengers and light goods at fairly high speeds. An engine of this design was made for the Turkish Government.

Fig. 121 shows an outline drawing of a large passenger engine of this class connected to a well-constructed omnibus intended for forty passengers. This engine was fully tested in England, and sent to Greece. It will be seen that the engine is mounted on the top of a locomotive multitubular boiler; the cylinders are placed at the fire-box end of the boiler. The coal bunkers, steering column, and boiler are mounted upon a wrought-iron frame as shown. This end of the engine leads, the two leading-wheels are placed inside the wrought-iron frame, and are, like the driving-wheels, provided with india-rubber tires properly protected. The driving-axle is situated about the middle of the

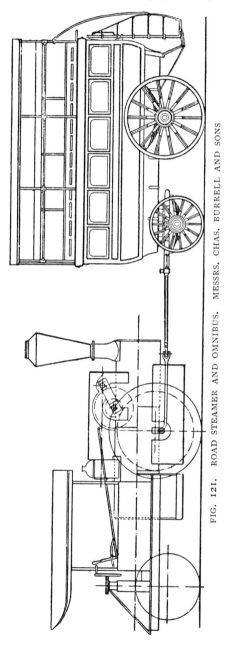

FIG. 121. ROAD STEAMER AND OMNIBUS. MESSRS. CHAS. BURRELL AND SONS

# Traction Engines

boiler, the chief weight of the engine, boiler, and water-tank resting on the driving-wheels. Spur driving-gearing is employed for transmitting the motion from the counter-shaft to the wheels. The main axle is fixed, the driving-wheels revolve on it, so that no power is transmitted through it. It will be seen that a pinion on each end of the intermediate shaft gears into a spur ring bolted near the periphery of the drivers, by which means the weight of the driving-wheels may be reduced. The following are some of the dimensions of this engine. The two steam cylinders are $7\frac{1}{4}$ in. diameter and 10 in. stroke ; the two driving-wheels are each 6 ft. diameter, and the leading-wheels are 4 ft. diameter. Two speeds are provided, the ratios arranged for running at four miles or eight miles an hour, according to the nature of the roads. A cab is erected for protecting the driver and steersman from the heat of the sun, or from rain. The engine work is all neatly closed in, so that the working parts are not seen and are also kept free from dust. The working pressure was 130 lbs. per square inch. Several engines of this type were made for quick running ; in some instances smaller engines were used, and slight modifications in the arrangement of the parts took place, but in the main the engines were all similarly equipped, and were, we believe, successful.

An outline drawing is given of a special road loco-motive, made by Messrs. Charles Burrell and Sons. From the illustration, Fig. 122, it will be seen that the countershaft is placed in a line with the main axle, to admit of chain driving, and an efficient method of mounting the heavier part of the engine on laminated springs. The countershaft under the boiler barrel is provided with compensating gear ; a chain pinion is attached to each end of this shaft ; therefore two driving-

# Road Locomotives for Passenger Service

chains are employed, and the engine answers to the steering-wheel, both driving-wheels doing an equal share of work when passing along a straight road or when turning sharp corners. This engine was not built for particularly quick travelling, but the silent-running driving - chains and excellent arrangement of springs render it worthy of note. If a pair of elastic wheels were added, this type of engine would run smoothly on common roads at six miles an hour or more.

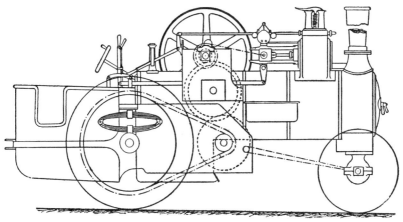

FIG. 122.   A SPECIAL ROAD LOCOMOTIVE

The showman finds it to his advantage to adopt a road locomotive for working his steam circus, lighting up the show by electricity, and also as a means of drawing the entire paraphernalia from town to town, the same engine performing the three duties efficiently. Some fine compound spring-mounted engines have been constructed by several firms for this work, with a dynamo erected over the smoke-box. It is well known that the showman has often to cover a good many miles of road during the night and early morning, in order to fulfil his printed engagements. The road locomotives travel well at high rates, irrespective of Acts of Parlia-

ment, and do more work than horses could possibly
achieve.

Messrs. Aveling and Porter have manufactured a
large number of road locomotives for all manner of
purposes. They have been favoured with orders from
several European Governments for a number of quick-
speed road locomotives for military purposes—the transport of troops and materials. As these road engines
and trains are suitable for passenger service, and have
been employed in a similar capacity, a few particulars
of results achieved may not be without interest. It is
twenty-five years since Messrs. Aveling and Porter
built the steam sapper No. 1, when a committee of the
Royal Engineers made a thorough trial of it. From
that time to the present no adverse report has ever
been made by the authorities in charge. . Experiments
were made during the end of 1893 with some of these
steam sappers in Paris, when a speed of twelve miles an
hour was reached on ordinary roads.

Lieutenant-Colonel Templer says : "At present a
train of waggons can, on the best roads, only traverse
fifteen to twenty miles a day, while a traction engine
would in the same time reel off sixty to seventy-five
miles a day."[1] Road locomotives are used in the
Italian Army, and by the Swiss Government. In an
official report on the employment of road engines in
the Russian Army it is stated : "The road engines,
although only a part of them were employed, did not
only completely reimburse their purchase money and
the cost of maintenance, but brought an actual profit.
The road locomotives have received in the military de-

[1] *Steam Transport on Roads*, by Lieutenant-Colonel Templer.

# Road Locomotives for Passenger Service

partment the right of citizenship, and will, there is no doubt, render great services to that department in future."

"During the Berkshire manœuvres of 1893, eight steam sappers were employed in taking stores and material to Uffington, Idstone, Liddington, and the different rest camps *en route*, being a total tonnage of 356 tons, a distance of 150 miles, and although the engines were of different patterns and age, this service was accomplished without accident and at small cost, which I venture to say fully proves that steam transport by road locomotives for the army and reserve forces would render most valuable service, both in peace and war, and effect an enormous saving to the country." Lieut.-Colonel Templer goes on to say : "The steam horse consumes only cheap coal or wood, while animal muscles must be renewed with expensive hay and oats. At the halt the engine

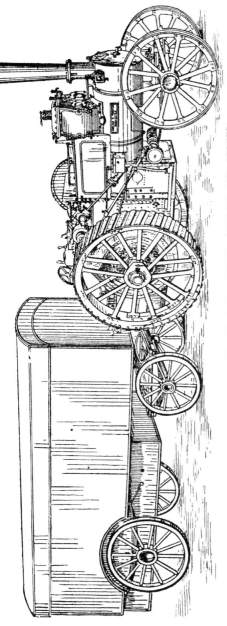

FIG. 123. ROAD LOCOMOTIVE AND VAN. MESSRS. AVELING AND PORTER

ceases to require fuel and water, whereas horses require forage and water in the same quantity as when on the march. When the engine does not work it does not eat, and is costing nothing. Again, the horses would be very much harassed with a continuous march, whereas the capabilities of the steam locomotives are, at least, an average of fifty miles per day, for month after month. The steam sapper 'Queen' came from Chatham to Aldershot, viz. seventy-two miles, in twenty-six hours, and went to its regular work the next morning." It is interesting to note that the modern road locomotive is being advantageously used for many purposes, and is equally successful when applied to the requirements of the army. Some of these road trains are illustrated in Lieutenant-Colonel Templer's pamphlet.[1] A compound traction engine drawing a food van is reproduced by Fig. 123. Messrs. Aveling and Porter's spring arrangement will be illustrated in due course.

### MESSRS. ROBEY AND CO.

Messrs. Robey and Co. have made a considerable number of road steamers for passenger service in foreign countries. Fig. 124 shows one of these road locomotives, and a two-wheel omnibus. The engine is of the vertical type, as introduced by Mr. Thompson, but Messrs. Robey have carried out many improvements in the details of the engines, suggested by a twenty-years' experience. There is certainly something to be said in favour of this type of engine for running light loads at brisk speeds. The chief drawback of the original Thompson road steamer was the "pot" boiler, which was a constant source of annoyance ; this has been replaced by Messrs. Robey's patent tubular boiler with

---

[1] *Steam Transport on Roads.*

# Road Locomotives for Passenger Service

satisfactory results. The engine is mounted on three wheels with india-rubber tires five inches thick, protected by bands of steel plates. Most of the weight is placed

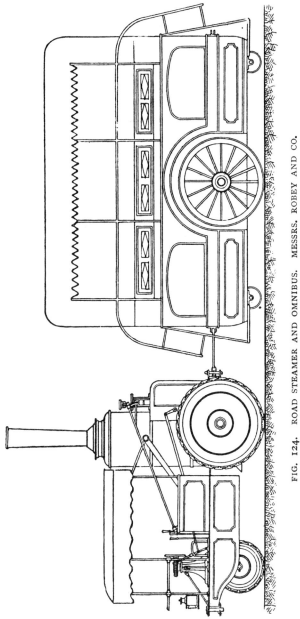

FIG. 124. ROAD STEAMER AND OMNIBUS. MESSRS. ROBEY AND CO.

# Traction Engines

over the driving-wheels; the single leading-wheel is lightly loaded; the engine is steered with ease. An experienced driver can manœuvre these engines with the utmost facility. The engine carries a large water-tank. All the working parts are neatly boxed in. A canopy is provided for the driver and steersman. The engines run silently, and very little trouble is experienced in meeting horses on the road when running at eight miles an hour. Messrs. Robey and Co. have supplied some of these engines recently to customers who have had engines of their make in use for nearly twenty years. The india-rubber tires act as an excellent spring, and are placed where the spring should be situated; that is, in the nearest point to the road, thus saving the machinery from a great amount of wear and tear. The enormous cost of the tires is a great drawback; we may, however, be able to scheme a good wheel possessing the advantages of the rubber tires at much less expense.

Messrs. Clayton and Shuttleworth, and Messrs. John Fowler and Co., have made a large number of road locomotives that are available for a variety of purposes, and a not inconsiderable number of engines have been sent to the Colonies, suitably equipped for making long journeys at high travelling speeds.[1]

MESSRS. J. AND H. McLAREN

Messrs. McLaren have supplied road locomotives and coaches for passenger and light goods service in India, France, etc. A side elevation of the engine and train for running a parcel service in France is illustrated by

[1] Some interesting particulars of road locomotive performances by the two firms named are recorded in a later chapter.

# Road Locomotives for Passenger Service

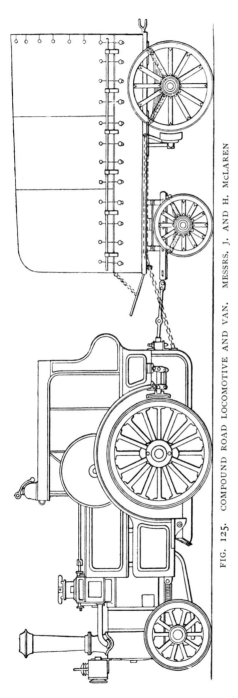

FIG. 125. COMPOUND ROAD LOCOMOTIVE AND VAN. MESSRS. J. AND H. McLAREN

Fig. 125. Three of these trains ran regularly between Lyons and Grenoble, which are about seventy miles apart. The parcels were collected and packed into the van during the day; one engine started out of each town in the evening, and delivered its load at the other end the next morning. As the journey was made in the night, over a very rough and dangerous road, it was important that the engines should be fitted with ample brake - power, a reliable steering - gear, and an efficient system of lighting. They were, therefore, fitted with a steam - brake, as well as the ordinary hand-brake. The steering-gear was of the worm-and-rack type. The engines were fitted with an arrangement for burning ordinary gas. One charging of gas was sufficient to give a brilliant head-light, and supplied the signal-lights for the round trip of 140 miles. These are favourable examples of quick-speed road trains.

The spring mounting arrangement fitted on the above engines is illustrated in Chapter VII.

## MESSRS. DE-DION AND BOUTON.

The De-Dion and Bouton steam generators and road motors should have a place in this chapter. An early tractor by these makers was shown, coupled to a light wagonette; the fore wheels and front axle of the vehicle

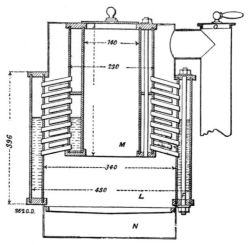

FIG. 126.  STEAM GENERATOR.  DE-DION AND BOUTON

were removed; the locking-plate rested on the steam bogie, and was secured in its place. Any kind of vehicle can be coupled to the steam tractor in a similar manner. The first of these motors was placed on the streets of Paris in 1884; a few years later the machine had been much improved. The boiler claims the first attention. Fig. 126 gives a sectional elevation of the generator. It is intended to be fed with coke from the top; the two annular vessels are connected together by 816 copper tubes. The boiler can be readily taken to pieces

# Road Locomotives for Passenger Service

for cleaning; the bottoms of the two rings are held in their places by bolts, as shown. The grate is 13·4 in. diameter; the heating surface is 24 square feet. A compound engine drives the tractor; the cylinders are 4·72 and 7·08 in. diameter and 5·11 in. stroke. No reversing-gear is employed, which vastly reduces the number of the working parts. The engine is rated as being of 20 horse-power; it must run at 330 revolutions per minute to give a travelling speed to the carriage of 12½ miles an hour. The weight in working order is 2 tons; it is claimed that the engine can haul 2½ tons at 20 miles an hour on a level road. A later tractor is illustrated by Fig. 127, coupled up to a 40-seat omnibus of the Paris Company, which is usually drawn by three horses. This type of vehicle is furnished with a compound engine, which can be worked up to 30 horse-power, and which is to be capable of hauling a load of 5 tons at a speed of 12·5 miles; the principal points of difference between this machine and the other, which we have already described, lie in the great care which has been bestowed on the details, the precautions taken to secure the moving parts from dust, and the oil-bath in which the engine works. The water-supply carried is sufficient for a run of 25 miles over an average road, with a load of 3 tons; the manufacturers state that the cost of hauling this load amounts to 1*d.* per kilometre.

Great care has been taken as to the quality of the steel employed in the frame and other parts of the machine. By reference to Fig. 127 it will be seen that the boiler (2) is surrounded by the fuel-tank, while the water reservoir forms a seat; the motor (1) is placed beneath the platform as usual. The driver has all the controlling levers conveniently at hand; the starting-lever is shown at 9, whilst at 5 is a small wheel con-

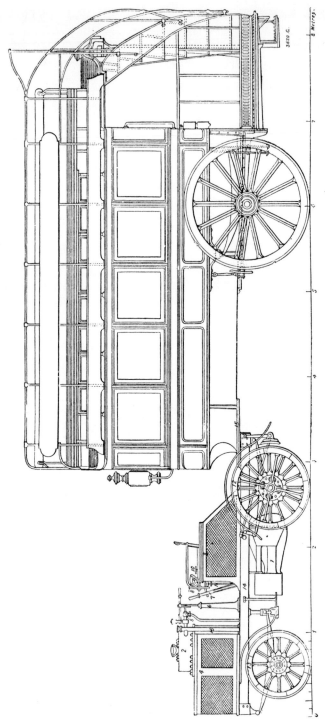

FIG. 127. MOTOR AND OMNIBUS. MESSRS. DE-DION AND BOUTON

# Road Locomotives for Passenger Service

trolling the steam-admission ; the reversing-gear is actuated by the lever 7.[1] The vehicle is steered by means of a turning-bar, similar to those of hand-brakes

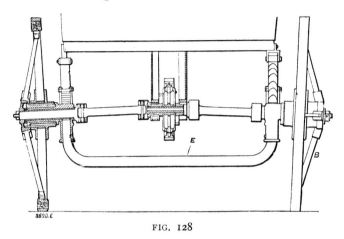

FIG. 128

on some waggons ; the feed-pump is started and stopped by a small wheel marked 10, whilst 8 and 11 are the hand and steam brakes respectively.

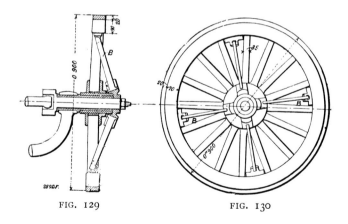

FIG. 129        FIG. 130

In this tractor the pitch chains and sprocket wheels attached to the wood spokes of the driving-wheels were discarded, and the method of driving as shown in

[1] In the earlier tractor no reversing-gear was used.

Fig. 128 adopted. Power is transmitted to a short rigid shaft carried in two bearings; this shaft communicates motion to the driving-wheels through universal joints, which allow the outer ends of the axle to ride on the springs, and adapt itself to the inequalities of the road without affecting the driving gearing. Figs. 129 and 130 show the driving-wheels; these are provided with four arms which form a spring-drive and transmit the power from the nave to the tire of the wheel, a very commendable plan which tends to deaden the shocks, and causes the bogie to run very smoothly and satisfactorily.[1]

[1] We are indebted to *Engineering*, August 14th and 21st, 1896, for these particulars, and we have to thank the editor for permission to use the blocks.

# CHAPTER VII

## SPRING-MOUNTED TRACTION ENGINES

ONE of the most difficult problems connected with spur-geared road locomotives, is the effective mounting of the engine on springs. Many of the plans introduced for this purpose have been much too complicated to be of any real service. Provision must be made in the arrangement of the details, so that the up-and-down movement of the main axle when passing along a rough road at a fair speed, shall not affect the pitch circles of any of the spur driving-gear, or interfere with the proper action of the compensating gear. It is equally important that the springs should be free to act without being influenced by the transmission of the power through the gearing. In addition to these essential requirements, some traction-engine makers insist on the axle being suspended in such a manner that one end of the axle may be higher or lower than the other without affecting the proper working of the engine. It will be seen that to successfully overcome these mechanical difficulties is no easy matter. In passing, it may be remarked that the mounting of chain-driven traction engines on springs is very easily accomplished. Fig. 122, in Chapter VI., shows how this can be done.

Some of the methods in use for mounting road locomotives on springs will now be noticed. One of the arrangements for effecting this purpose is that introduced by Messrs. Aveling and Porter. Fig. 131 is a transverse section of a road locomotive; Fig. 132

# Traction Engines

is a section on line A, B; Fig. 133 is a side elevation, with the right-hand driving-wheel removed to show the driving-disc, etc. The intermediate shaft has the third-motion pinion keyed on the end, which gears into the main spur-wheel; this wheel revolves on a strong steel tube, the large flange of which is firmly secured to the right-hand side horn-plate. By this means the main gearing is kept properly in pitch under all circumstances, and no motion of the axle can in any way affect its proper action. Between the main spur-wheel and the driving-disc there is fitted a steel plate, which is provided with two strong projections, which enter recesses in the spur-wheel; while two more projections at right angles with the above enter the driving-disc. This arrangement transmits the power from the spur-wheel to the driving-disc independent of the position

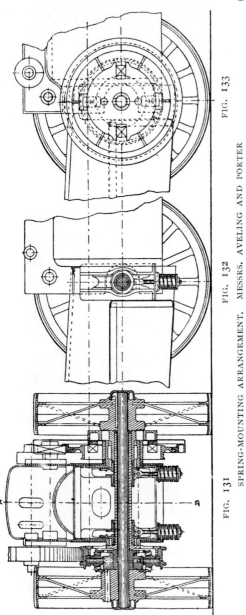

FIG. 133

FIG. 132

FIG. 131

SPRING-MOUNTING ARRANGEMENT. MESSRS. AVELING AND PORTER

of the axle. It will be seen from Fig. 131 that the driving-disc is keyed to a long cannon, which forms the boss of the compensating gear centre, thereby passing the power from one side of the axle to the other. The right-hand side driving-wheel and right-hand side bevel-wheel are both keyed to the main axle ; the left-hand bevel-wheel is bolted to the boss of the left-hand side driving-wheel, and thereby secures the proper action of the compensating apparatus. The main axle-bearings are provided with slides secured to the inside of the horn-plates ; the bearings are coupled to the square steel springs by links as shown. It will be noticed also that the sides of the main axle-bearings nearest the horn-plates are slightly rounded so as to allow the axle to assume a position out of line with the rest of the engine, so that the driving-wheels can follow the irregularities of the road. The springs on either side work independently the one of the other, and therefore come into action at whatever position the road wheels may be in. The full weight of the hind part of the engine rests evenly on the springs in the usual manner, but the details are worked out in the stiffest possible way. It will be seen that a wrought-iron plate fits in between the horn-plates and beneath the flanges of the axle-slides. The brake rim is cast on the main spur-wheel. The horn-plates are stiffened by an angle-iron frame fitted above the main axle-slides.[1]

MESSRS. CHARLES BURRELL AND SONS' patented arrangement of spring mounting for their road loco-motives is illustrated in the author's work, *Steam Locomotion on Common Roads*, so it need not be referred to in this place. It may be said, however, that engines fitted

---

[1] We learn that Messrs. Aveling and Porter are using a simpler plan of spring mounting, by allowing the up-and-down motion to be taken by the main gearing, longer cogs being adopted.

# Traction Engines

with their system of springs run smoothly at fairly high speeds on ordinary roads. Messrs. Burrell and Sons have adopted plate-springs at the hind and front axles of their most recent traction engines.

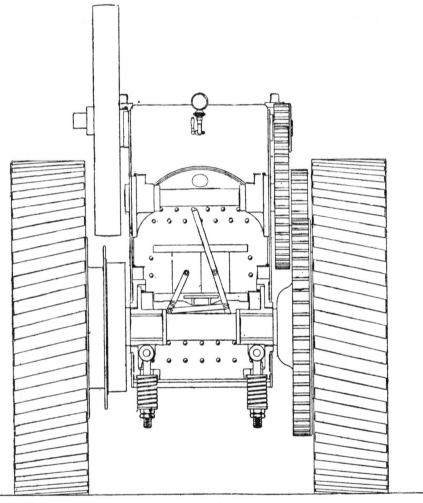

FIG. 134. SPRING-MOUNTING ARRANGEMENT
MESSRS. CLAYTON AND SHUTTLEWORTH

MESSRS. CLAYTON AND SHUTTLEWORTHS' arrangement of spring mounting is represented by Fig. 134, which is a cross-section of a road locomotive through the main

# Spring-mounted Traction Engines

axle with the tender removed. It will be seen that the main axle-boxes are made in two parts, the outer one is bolted to the horn-plate on each side, the inner box slides up and down and carries the axle; the inner boxes are kept rigidly in place by means of a cannon or distance-piece threaded on the axle. The two strong spiral springs carry the hind part of the engine as shown. Another distance-piece extends across the outer fire-box at the bottom; for stiffening the horn-plates, this distance-piece is bolted to the bottom of the fixed axle-box. Very little up-and-down movement is given, as little is required. Messrs. Clayton and Shuttleworth also use another arrangement, in which the gearing is not affected by the movement of the axle : plate springs are used ; it is a thoroughly efficient plan in all respects.

MESSRS. FODEN'S early spring-mounting arrangement

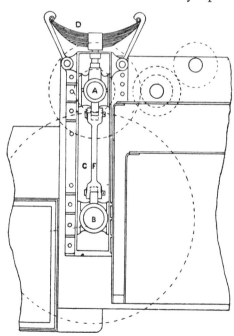

is illustrated and described in the author's work, *Steam Locomotion on Common Roads*, p. 249. Their present plan is shown by Figs. 135 and 136. From the part-sectional elevation, it will be seen that the bearings of the main axle and the second countershaft A and B, are connected by two levers F, the whole sliding in the two axle-boxes C C, shown in both the illustrations, preparation being made

FIG. 135. SPRING-MOUNTING ARRANGEMENT
MESSRS. FODEN AND CO.

# Traction Engines

on the two upper bearings for the suspension of the plate springs D D. The bearings E E, of the main axle and the third motion-shaft, are of extra length and

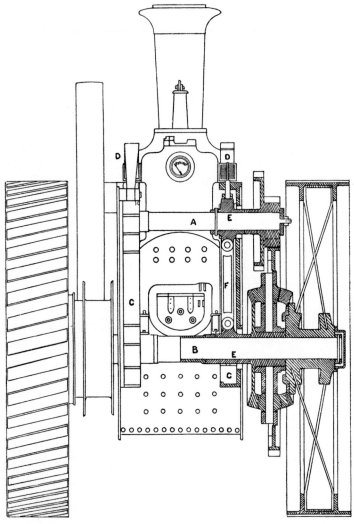

FIG. 136.  SPRING MOUNTING BY MESSRS. FODEN AND CO.

parallel, and being coupled by the levers F, having joints at each end, the necessary oscillating or vertical motion is allowed to take place without locking or strain.

# Spring-mounted Traction Engines

The third motion-shaft A, which moves up and down, is fixed slightly below a horizontal line drawn through the centre of the second motion-shaft, which is not affected by the springs, being fixed in bearings carried by the box bracket, therefore the up-and-down movement, which, at·the most, is only half an inch, viz. one quarter of an inch on each side of the centre, does not practically alter the depth in gear of the two spur-wheels, shown in dotted lines on the longitudinal section Fig. 135. It will be seen how the weight of the hind part of the engine is carried by the strong laminated springs D D. The front part of the engine is carried on springs also.

Messrs. Foden say : " This perfect spring arrangement materially reduces the effect of shocks or vibrations caused by passing over rough roads, and it is conducive to the reduction of the wear and tear arising from such causes in ordinary traction engines, as leaky fire-boxes, tubes and joints, strained frames, and the jolting to pieces of the motion work throughout. Moreover, this spring-mounting arrangement adds very considerably to the comfort of the engine-driver and steersman."

MESSRS. JOHN FOWLER AND CO.—The spring arrange ment patented in 1892 by Messrs. Fowler has stood the test for years, and many close imitations have appeared from time to time ; some of these could be illustrated if any useful purpose were served. Fig. 137 shows a section through the driving-axle of one of the Leeds road locomotives, by which it will be seen that the weight of the hind part of the engine rests on a very strong plate spring. The chief improvement consists in the equalising arrangement by means of which they have obviated the wear caused by the shafts not moving parallel with each other, and the excessive strains on

# Traction Engines

the shafts (due to the action of the springs being continually reversed), the arms connecting the shafts affected by the springs being always in tension, and the shafts always moving parallel to each other. By referring to

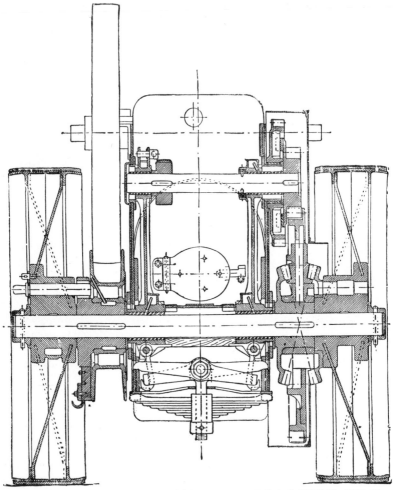

FIG. 137. SPRING-MOUNTING ARRANGEMENT. MESSRS. J. FOWLER AND CO.

the illustration it will be seen that the main pinion is driven through a driving-plate having large bearing surfaces, and long leverage from the wheel which transmits the motion, the said wheel running on a fixed

# Spring-mounted Traction Engines

bracket. The pitch circles of the driving-gear always roll truly together. Solid arms between the third motion-shaft and the hind axle are provided (one on each side), which carry suspension hooks and equalising levers, so arranged that any upward or downward move-

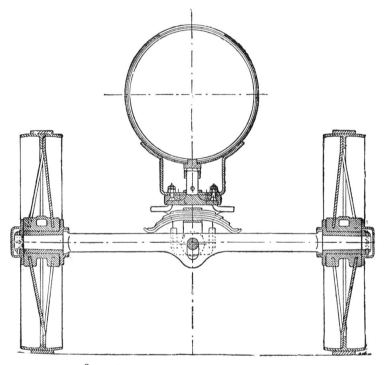

FIG. 138. FRONT AXLE. MESSRS. JOHN FOWLER AND CO.

ment of the engine is always at right angles to the hind axle.

Fig. 138 represents the front axle of Messrs. Fowlers' engines, the laminated spring shown allows free movement of the front wheels in all directions, to suit the inequalities of the road.

MESSRS. W. FOSTER AND CO.—The three illustrations, Figs. 139, 140, and 141, show the newly designed hind-axle spring-mounting plan patented by Messrs. Foster.

# Traction Engines

To the sides of the boiler L L are secured the axle brackets M M, provided with flat-sided holes. These brackets have also projecting arms in which the fulcrum pins N N are fitted. The inside axle brackets O O are free to move in the fixed brackets M M; the movable brackets are provided with forked joints on the lower sides, and fitted with pins at P P. The equalising levers O O are shown in Figs. 139, 140, and 141, the levers engaging in pins N N on the fixed bracket, and P P on the moving bracket; the levers are jointed together in the buckle of the plate-spring R, at S. T is a bar suspended from the fixed brackets M M by the adjusting nuts U U; the compression of the spring can be varied to suit the load. It will thus be seen how the weight of the engine is passed through the equalising levers from one bracket to the other, and then through the spring. Should one driving-wheel fall into a hollow place in the road the levers come into play, allowing the axle to be out of level, the suspension links holding the countershaft parallel with the axle, and keeping the last motion-wheels in gear. In order to allow the countershaft to vibrate without much affecting the second motion gearing, the countershaft bracket moves in a slide set at an angle as shown. It will be interesting to compare this countershaft bracket with Taskers', as illustrated in a subsequent page of this chapter.[1]

MESSRS. J. AND H. McLAREN.—Mr. John McLaren describes their method of spring mounting as under in a paper which he read before the Institution of Civil Engineers, 1890, to which we are indebted for the illustrations, Figs. 142, 143, and 144, and the particulars as

[1] Some of the above particulars and the illustrations are extracted from *The Engineer* for August 7th, 1903.

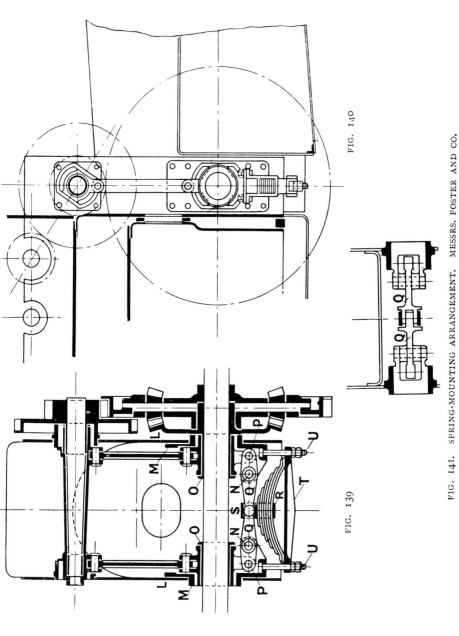

FIG. 140

FIG. 139

FIG. 141. SPRING-MOUNTING ARRANGEMENT. MESSRS. FOSTER AND CO.

# Traction Engines

under. " For many years the mounting of these engines upon springs formed an almost insuperable difficulty. This has now been overcome. Messrs. McLaren mount

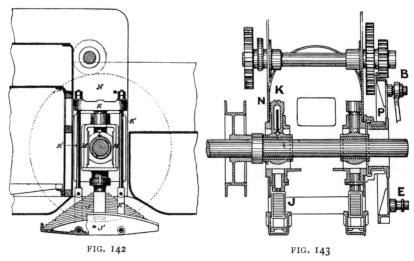

FIG. 142                    FIG. 143

most of their engines upon strong laminated springs, similar to those used on railway locomotives. The main source of wear and tear in the engine is occasioned by

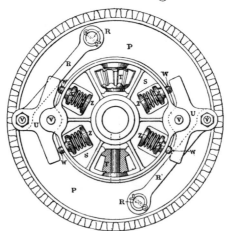

FIG. 144.    SPRING MOUNTING BY MESSRS. J. AND H. McLAREN

the shocks to which it is subjected in passing over rough and uneven roads. Pavements are especially trying and destructive. The McLaren and Boulton wood-block wheels obviate this to some extent. But for lighter engines an arrangement, as illustrated on opposite page, has been found to work successfully.

"Each spring, which is suspended under the axles through vertical links and a crosshead, takes a bearing K K upon the axle-boxes L L, which are free to slide up and down in the guides M M. These guides are fixed to the side plate of the fire-box N N, which is carried backwards for the purpose, as already described. The axle-box L L consists of a bushed casting, having two slippers O O trunnioned into it, and turned in a circular form to slide vertically in the guides M M, which are bored out hollow for the purpose. In the event of one wheel mounting an obstacle and causing the spring to act more on one side than on the other, the slippers still maintain their vertical position, while the bearing is free to accommodate itself to the angle taken by the axle. In order to admit of the axle thus moving vertically without the teeth of the spur-gearing being thrown out of pitch, the main spur driving-wheel P is not fixed on the axle, but is carried in a strong cast-steel bracket Q, fastened to the side-plate N of the fire-box. This is in the form of a clasp, bushed with brass, which grasps a large trunnion $P^1$, cast on the back of the main steel spur driving-wheel, which is thus maintained in pitch with the main driving-pinion. On the face of each driving-wheel are two strong crank-pins R R. Wrought-iron links $R^1 R^1$, Fig. 144, are coupled at one end to these pins respectively, and at the other end to the main driving-boss S, which carries the toothed pinions T T of the differential gear. It is evident, however, that if these links $R^1 R^1$ were coupled directly and rigidly to the driving-boss S, when the two points of connection

# Traction Engines

were in a horizontal position the springs on the main axle would become inoperative, the one link being in tension and the other in compression. The main driving-boss S is therefore driven through the two intermediary cross-shaped bell-cranks U U. These bell-cranks work on pins V V, which fix them to the main driving-boss S. The links $R^1 R^1$ take hold of each of them respectively by the outer end, through the pins $V^1 V^1$, and the two legs of each bell-crank rest on the pins W W. These pins pass through the rim of the main driving-boss S, and are screwed into washer-plates X X, which bear on the coil-springs Z Z. These plates and springs serve the double purpose of breaking the shock occasioned by suddenly starting the engine, and permit the carrying springs to act in any position of the driving-wheels."

In another place Mr. McLaren has said : " Sufficient movement is allowed to the action of the springs to take off all undue shocks from the engine, but the range is so limited that it has been found possible to dispense with the complicated mechanism for keeping the main driving-wheel and pinion in exact pitch, and in practice it is sufficient to make the teeth of these wheels somewhat longer, so as to admit of a slight in-and-out movement, corresponding with the travel or range of the axle-box permitted by the action of the springs."

There are several firms who are acting on the same lines ; they have discarded complex spring arrangements for keeping the last motion gearing in pitch, and have limited the range of motion, and allow the small movement to be transmitted to the gearing, the teeth being made longer to suit.

MESSRS. W. TASKER AND SONS.—The object of their invention is to enable the power of a spring-mounted

# Spring-mounted Traction Engines

traction engine to be transmitted directly through the gear-wheels to the main axle, and at the same time maintain a correct rolling of the pitch circles of the gearing, whatever may be the deflection of the springs through shocks and jars, and to provide an efficient parallel motion in the form of levers or sliding gear,

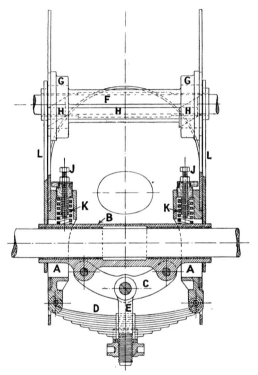

FIG. 145. SPRING MOUNTING BY MESSRS. TASKER AND SONS

to maintain the equilibrium of the engine and prevent oscillation. The invention consists essentially of an improved arrangement of bearings for the countershaft and the main axle, which permits the ends thereof to rise and fall equally, thereby ensuring that the gear-wheels of the shafts are maintained in constant and proper engagement.

Fig. 145 shows a cross-section of the hind part of a

traction engine for illustrating the spring arrangement. Fig. 146 shows a side view of the same. The main features of Messrs. Taskers' radial compensating bearings consist of two connected sleeves for the main axle and the countershaft, coupled to a pair of laminated springs placed transversely near the base of the horn-

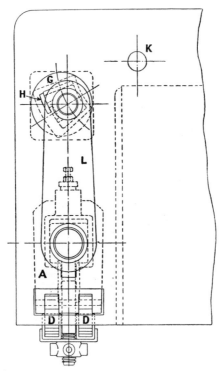

FIG. 146. SPRING MOUNTING BY MESSRS. TASKER AND SONS

plates. A pair of radial slides for the top bearings, working concentrically with the pinion on the first countershaft K, to maintain the proper relative position of the gearing pitch circles. There is a balancing or compensating slide H placed in a groove in the top sleeve F, and having diagonal enlarged ends fitting in corresponding recesses or spiral insets in the brackets to balance the boiler, and thus prevent the side roll or

# Spring-mounted Traction Engines

jamming of the teeth of the gearing when passing over rough roads. A pair of locking screws J are placed over the main axle-bearings A to be ready for any emergency, and around the screws are buffer-springs K to minimise very severe shocks, and prevent the breakage of the laminated mainsprings D. In order to make this device understood, the following is extracted from the specification of the patent. Now in order to keep the sleeve F containing the countershaft in a position

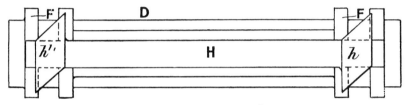

FIG. 147   DETAILS OF TASKERS' SPRINGS

parallel to the main axle when subjected to the shocks sustained by the driving-wheels of the engine, the sleeve is provided with a longitudinal groove or keyway at its ends with plates H set at an angle thereto, which slide in transverse grooves in the corresponding sides of the said radial slots. This bar sliding in the keyway, and guided by its plates in the transverse grooves, travels from side to side of the boiler horn-plates, that is to say,

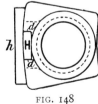

FIG. 148

across the longitudinal plane of the engine, and by reason of the inclination of its arms H also rises or falls, as the case may be. Therefore it will accurately guide the sleeve F carrying the countershaft, and effectually maintain the shaft in positions parallel to one another. The compensating slide or plate H consists of one steel casting, which when tooled and fitted only requires placing in position without pin or bolt, and is instantly ready for its work; its diagonal ends being

# Traction Engines

formed like a section of a coarse-pitched worm thread, and its radial action being identical with the sleeve, allows its large surfaces to fit and wear evenly both in the sleeve and insets in all positions of the slides. The two couplings L are of wrought-steel, their ends are bored to fit projecting spigots on each sleeve, and thus being outside of the horn-plates are readily removeable, pins and small surfaces being in this case also entirely avoided. The sleeve F and the compensating plate H are clearly shown in Figs. 147 and 148.

Messrs. Wallis and Steevens.—In some of the plans thus far dealt with, provisions have been made whereby the motion of the hind axle, due to the action of the springs, shall not interfere with the pitch circle of the spur driving-gear between the intermediate shaft and axle. In Messrs. Wallis and Steevens' arrangement, shown by Fig. 149, two springs are placed between the load of the engine and the hind axle. The intermediate shaft is fixed. The up-and-down motion of the axle, due to the play of the springs, is allowed for in the teeth of the spur-gearing; the cogs are longer than usual. The wheel has two pitch lines placed $\frac{3}{8}$ inch apart; between these two lines the cogs are practically flat, corresponding with the amount of vertical motion allowed. Of course this plan would be quite impracticable with a range such as is given by some makers to their spring engines. It is said by some practical men that "too much range is a decided disadvantage, making the engine dance, and causing a great wash of the water in the boiler." A range of about half an inch, they say, will be found sufficient to take off all the jar, and cause the engine to run smoothly on common roads.

It will be seen from the illustration that the two axle-

# Spring-mounted Traction Engines

bearings are connected together by a very strong distance-piece, so that the axle must always be parallel with the intermediate shaft when the springs are acting. The spring boxes are provided with set screws and nuts let into the castings, so that the amount of play allowed to the springs can be regulated. When the driving-

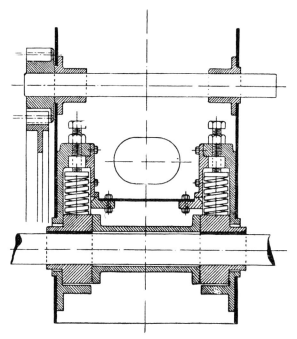

FIG. 149. SPRING MOUNTING BY MESSRS. WALLIS AND STEEVENS

wheels are subjected to an exceptional shock, the axle-bearings come in contact with suitable stops, to prevent the cogs of the spur-wheel and pinion entering too deeply into gear with each other. It is said that the up-and-down motion of the axle, causing the teeth of the gearing to ride in and out to the extent of such motion, works very well in practice, and the life of the gearing is not materially shortened by this sliding process.

The American builders of traction engines secure an

# Traction Engines

excellent arrangement of spring mounting, by placing the intermediate shaft on the same horizontal centre-line as the main axle. There are some serious drawbacks to the two shafts being placed in this manner, but this is not the time to mention them.

ADVANCE COMPANY. — The Advance Company's arrangement is shown by Fig. 150. The main axle is

FIG. 150. SPRING MOUNTING. ADVANCE CO.

attached to the bracket, which is pivoted to the casting shown; the casting and axle are capable of vertical movement sufficient to compress the spring, and relieve the boiler of jar and sudden strain. The free end of the bracket is broad and long, and slotted to take the two studs, with nuts which are tightened to allow the

# Spring-mounted Traction Engines

casting to move vertically between the plates. The upper casting supports the boiler on the mainspring. On the upper side of the abutment piece is another spring. The spring acts as a cushion to the upward movement of the boiler, and is independent of the spring. The boiler being suspended between two springs, its vertical movement must be brought to an elastic limit in either direction, thus wholly relieving the gearing of sudden jar, making it more pleasant for the engine-driver while travelling on the road, and preventing an amount of wear, and thereby prolonging the life of the engine.

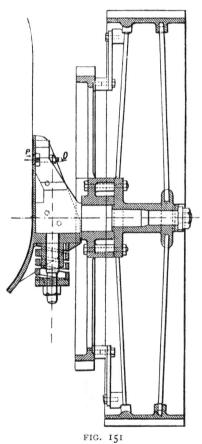

FIG. 151

RUSSELL AND CO.—In Russell's traction engine springs are adopted at both ends of the engine. Fig. .151 shows the hind axle-spring arrangement very clearly.

NICHOLS AND SHEPARD.— The main axle is placed about the centre of the fire-box; the method of mounting the engines on springs is nicely carried out, as shown by the illustrations (Figs. 152 and 153). The rear axle is square, forming a good seat for the spiral springs, which are kept in place by a bracket. The springs are hidden in the box above the axle. Over a square axle a sleeve is fitted for the hind road-wheel to run on.

O. S. KELLY COMPANY.—In the Springfield traction

engine the compensating centre-plate is provided with
an elastic connection. By means of this spring-drive

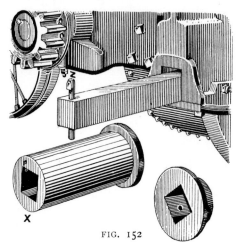

FIG. 152

the gearing is relieved of strain, and prevents the possibility of breaking any of the cogs. The only connection
between the outer circle and the arms is through six

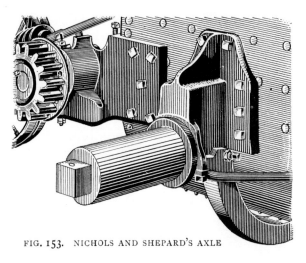

FIG. 153. NICHOLS AND SHEPARD'S AXLE

steel springs. Three of these springs are compressed in
a forward movement of the engine, and three in a backward movement.

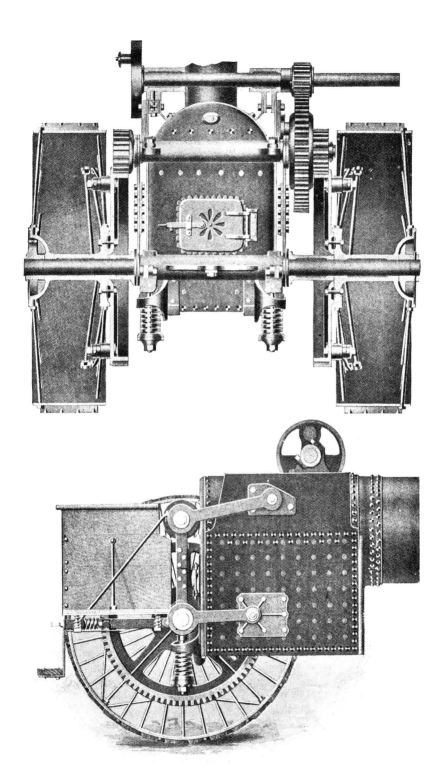

FIGS. 154, 155.  SPRING MOUNTING BY CASE CO.

# Spring-mounted Traction Engines

J. I. CASE COMPANY.—The most recent spring-mounting arrangement is the one carried out by the Case
Company. The accompanying illustrations (Figs. 154,
155, and 156) show the spring mounting. It is claimed
by the makers as an advance on anything that has been
attempted in the States. In the engine the whole weight
on the driving-wheels is suspended on double spiral

FIG. 156. DETAIL OF CASE'S SPRING MOUNTING.

springs. The method of accomplishing this is shown
by the illustrations. Two cast-iron brackets are bolted
to the corners of the fire-box shell, with pockets to
receive the springs on which the brackets rest. These
springs are seated in the sockets supported by eye-bolts,
which are attached to lugs on the axle-bearings by steel
pins. This construction permits the boiler to move
freely up and down on the springs, and yet by the
system of link connections the gearing is held in exact
mesh. The tension can be increased or decreased by

means of the nuts below the springs. The distance bars
shown in Fig. 154 serve the purpose of maintaining
an equal distance between the axle and countershaft
cannons ; the cannon bearings are equal in length to the
width of the boiler. They are connected to the boiler
and held in position by four radius links, two on each

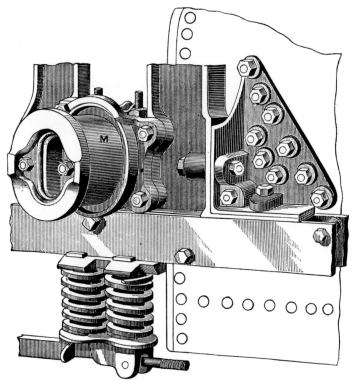

FIG. 157. THE GEISER ARRANGEMENT OF SPRINGS.

side of the boiler. The method of connecting the radius
links to the fire-box shell is illustrated. A cross link,
shown in Fig. 156, is supplied to prevent the upper part
of the boiler and countershaft from having any independent side-play ; also to keep the gearing in exact
alignment. This is accomplished by the cross link, which
connects the boiler from a steel bearing, bolted near the

# Spring-mounted Traction Engines

top of the fire-box, to a trunnion on upper cannon bearing. On the lower cannon bearing, next to the boiler, is cast a strong lug, which is fitted with a malleable slide; the slide is held in position between two steel brackets or guides bolted to the boiler under the fire-door to prevent side-play. Case's engine is also provided with springs in the centre plate of the compensating gear; to prevent the cogs being broken with the hammer-like blows, the gearing is required to give and take when the force of the engine is suddenly brought to bear on the inertia of the driving-wheels.

The GEISER COMPANY's arrangement is shown by Fig. 157, which explains itself.

# CHAPTER VIII

PROPOSED ROAD LOCOMOTIVE AND TRAIN FOR
PASSENGERS AND GOODS

WE have in the past seen some curious specimens
that were to eclipse all other engines—some
arranged vertically in the smoke-box, some placed on
the tender, others fixed beneath the boiler barrel, and
several types with all the wheels coupled. Road locomotive makers have often been urged to adopt the
railway locomotive as a model, thus several attempts
have been made to carry out this proposal. It would
be interesting to name other types of engines and
boilers, but these curiosities must not detain the reader.
All that need be said respecting coupled engines, underneath engines fixed to side frames, and others of a
similar character, is that as a rule only one engine was
made to the pattern. In the next chapter undertype
engines are dealt with. These experimental types have
given place to the modern road locomotive that we now
possess, and there can be no question that the best
remains.

The engine proposed for passenger service would
follow the lines of the modern road locomotive, with
modifications in construction to make it suitable for its
special work. It must have no experimental details in
its construction, all the vital parts must be of the well-
tried patterns. The engine would be mounted on the

# Proposed Road Locomotive and Train

top of the boiler, in the usual fashion, the cylinder occupying the position of the boiler barrel near the smoke-box. At the fire-box end the various shafts are carried by the horn-plates, stiffened by transverse plates forming the box brackets.· In this box the first motion gearing is placed, with the clutch lever for altering the speed. The working parts of the engine will be closed in. Every detail must be carefully studied as regards efficiency and wear, and no superfluous material retained in any detail. Wrought-iron and steel will be used frequently, so as to give the necessary strength, combined with the least possible weight.

The first consideration, and possibly the most important one, is the boiler. The well-tried locomotive type should be adopted. With fairly good water and careful attention, this boiler will give very little trouble. Steel has for some years been used for the shell, and this material is now in favour for the fire-boxes. At one time Lowmoor or Bowling iron was used. The working pressure is 150 lbs. per square inch ; the test pressure under water will be 240 lbs. The following are the thickness of the plates : Fire-box shell and barrel, $\frac{3}{8}$ in. ; fire-box front plate and saddle, $\frac{7}{16}$ in. ; sides of the fire-box carried up for supporting the crank-shaft, $\frac{5}{8}$ in. ; the internal fire-box, $\frac{3}{8}$ in. ; the fire-box and smoke-box tube plates are $\frac{5}{8}$ in.[1]

The stays for the fire-box sides and roof will be pitched 4 inches apart. Bridge bars·for staying the fire-box top cannot be recommended for several reasons, but the vertical screwed stays from the fire-box top to the arch plate, as used for some railway locomotives, are preferable. These stays are light, and the fire-box crown can be kept free from scale.

---

[1] For a compound engine, working at 180 lbs. steam pressure, the boiler-plates would be much thicker.

# Traction Engines

Solid iron fire-box foundation and fire-door rings should be used. The water space around the fire-box should not be less than $2\frac{1}{2}$ in. at the bottom and 3 in. at the top; the fire-hole ring is 2 in. square, the fire-box front plate being dished to suit. The longitudinal seams are double riveted, and so is the circumferential seam connecting the saddle-plate with the barrel. Some makers use 2-in. tubes, others $2\frac{1}{4}$-in. : the spaces between the tubes should not be less than $\frac{3}{4}$ in. ; both ends of the tubes should be expanded in the tube-plates and beaded. The boiler barrel must be made as short as possible, so as to reduce the amount of water carried, and the mean water-level will be less affected by the gradients of the road. A good-fitting ash-pan is an important item, with a damper door back and front; a swivel damper in the chimney base, below the exhaust nozzle, is useful. The chimney must be provided with a hinge, and facilities for lowering and raising it when low bridges have to be encountered. No sparks must be emitted, an effective spark catcher must be fitted, and the smoke-box door must be provided with a central handle that will pull the door tightly up to the smoke-box front. As far as possible the engine must be smokeless, coke must be mixed with good coal, and the damper arrangements such as to prevent the emittance of smoke. The fire-door will be of the sliding pattern. A good set of fire-bars is essential, the air spaces should be as narrow as possible, and all the spaces should be the same width. Unless the fire-bars are nicely made a waste of coal will ensue. Wrought-iron deep fire-bars, securely held in their places, are preferable. A manhole properly strengthened is placed in the barrel. The facilities for clearing out the boiler must be carefully studied ; in some instances the saddle-

# Proposed Road Locomotive and Train

plate is flanged under the hydraulic press to a large radius, so that two mudholes can be placed in the corners. Every part of the boiler will be riveted under the machine, and the very best workmanship must be bestowed upon it. For a single cylinder 9 in. diameter, and 12 in. stroke, 160 square feet of heating surface and 6 square feet of grate area would be required. For a compound engine with a high-pressure cylinder $6\frac{1}{2}$ in. diameter, a low-pressure cylinder of 10 in. diameter, both the pistons with 12 in. stroke, 145 square feet of heating surface and $5\frac{1}{2}$ square feet of grate area should be allowed. The noise from the exhaust must be suppressed. Two water-gauge fittings are essential, and they should be of such a safe character that the steam is shut off the moment a glass breaks.

The fire-box side plates are carried upward and backward so as to form the box brackets; there are two transverse plates firmly riveted between the sides, and held by angle-iron to the arch. Another plate will be placed at the top for further stiffening the whole structure; this top plate covers the gearing and forms a neat tray. The carriages for the crank-shaft, two countershafts, and the main axle, must be let into bored holes in the side plates, the rivets merely keeping the bearings up to their places. The carriages should be made of steel so as to reduce the weight. The box brackets must be machine-riveted. If the engine is mounted on springs, the above description must be modified.

The cylinder will be made in two parts, the shell or casing will be in one casting; the liner is made of hard metal and forced into the casing; the annular space around the liner is of ample capacity, in order to act as a steam dome and prevent priming. The jacket

# Traction Engines

steam-supply and drainage must be so carried out that the circulation of the steam in the annular space is maintained. At the highest part of this dome the stop-valve should draw its supply of steam for the working cylinder. All the passages for the steam should be of sufficient area to admit of a high piston-speed. The cylinder will be placed on the boiler as near to the smoke-box tube-plate as possible, and be provided with a strong flange all round the base, the bolts in which will be arranged about 4-inch pitch ; a sufficient amount of surface must be allowed so as to make a reliable joint between the foot of the cylinder and the boiler barrel ; this will prevent any springing of the barrel-plate. The cylinder may be mounted on a planed steel seating. It is usual to make the steam enter the cylinder as near to the smoke-box as possible. A double-spring Ramsbottom safety-valve is mounted on the top cover of the cylinder. The proper lubrication of the piston and the slide-valve is a very important matter, and must be well attended to. The greater part of the cylinder will be carefully lagged and covered with sheet steel.

The compound road locomotive is coming into more general use. It has its advantages—by its use the boiler can be reduced in size, a saving in coal and water is also effected, and the noise from the exhaust in the chimney is suppressed, which is a valuable feature in its favour. If a compound engine is selected the cylinders will be $6\frac{1}{2}$ in. and 10 in. diameter, and 12 in. stroke. It is usual to fit the compound cylinders of road loco-motives with an auxiliary valve, so that high-pressure steam can be made to enter the valve chest of the low-pressure cylinder, and both the cylinders exhaust into the common exhaust-pipe, the compound principle being

# Proposed Road Locomotive and Train

suspended for the moment when the engine has to start with a heavy load on an incline. As soon as the engine is running up to speed the auxiliary valve is closed. The steam chests should be placed outside so as to facilitate the examination of the slide-valves.[1] Compound road engines with tandem and Woolf cylinders are used, but a side-by-side double-crank compound engine should be specified. A relief-valve should be fixed on the low-pressure valve chest. A sleeve might be fitted on the exhaust pipe so as to further reduce the noise. As this engine is not intended for driving machinery from the flywheel, no governors need be provided.

The link-motion reversing-gear must be massive, with plenty of wearing surface, and deeply case-hardened. The lubrication of excentrics, the slide-valve, and link-motion must be properly carried out. Cast-iron excentric straps are mostly used, and when properly turned, with all the corners rounded off, with careful attention they will run almost without wear. Circular-bored guides are often used now for the crosshead in lieu of guide bars. Little more need be said about the engine work; the chief consideration rests with the wheels and the driving-gear. This brings us to the subject of the driving-wheels. In subsequent chapters the ordinary road wheels are illustrated, but these are not suitable for this purpose. The driving-wheels we should propose would be made of boiler plates and angle-iron, in much the same manner as the rubber-tired wheels were made a few years ago ; then spur-rings would be riveted near the rim or tire of the wheels ; both wheels would be driven from separate pinions on each end of the second

---

[1] In Clayton and Shuttleworths' road locomotives the slide-valves are placed on the top of the cylinders, actuated by radial gear, excentrics are therefore dispensed with.

# Traction Engines

countershaft. The main axle would in this case be fixed, the driving-wheels would run loosely on it; the axle might be lighter than usual, as no power would be transmitted through it. Wrought-iron, case-hardened bushes would be secured in the naves for the wheels to run on; the axle-ends would also be case-hardened. If these bushes are made a good length they will run for years without giving any trouble, provided they are well lubricated. This method of transmitting the power to the wheels is adopted for the sake of lightness. It will be necessary for the compensating gear to be made from small patterns, and be mounted upon the second counter-shaft; the rest of the gearing will be dealt with presently. The remaining part of the driving-wheels will be made of india-rubber and wood. Possibly no driving-wheels have answered so well for quick running as the rubber-tired ones, but as this type of wheel is too costly we must use less india-rubber, and place it around the cast-iron nave of the driving-wheel, as suggested by Mr. Pendred, also illustrated in Mr. McLaren's paper.[1] Impinging upon the rubber will be blocks of wood end-ways of the grain, with iron hoops on the edges, with suitable provision for allowing the wood blocks to move endways, but securely kept in their places circumferen-tially. No driving stress would pass through these wheels, as the spur-rings would be riveted near the rims. A wheel of this form, if properly made, would answer for light road locomotives.

If Boulton's wheels could be made of wrought-iron they would answer. A small amount of elasticity in the wheels would be sufficient to take off the concussion and give greater adhesion; the disc-wheels would afford the

[1] "Steam on Common Roads," by John McLaren. Excerpt, *Minutes of Proceedings* of Institution of Civil Engineers, Session 1890-91.

# Proposed Road Locomotive and Train

same flat surface on the road as the rubber-tired wheel. In addition to an ordinary strap-brake on the compensating gear, it may be advisable to fit a pair of brake-blocks to rings on the wheels for hilly districts, to be used in cases of emergency. The driving-wheels would be 6 ft. 4 in. diameter, and 1 ft. 4 in. on face.

The gearing will be made entirely of cast steel, the cogs will be carefully pitched and trimmed or machine-cut, and the teeth must not be of a very coarse pitch. The first and second motion gearing will be arranged between the bearings of the crank-shaft and counter-shafts, inside the box brackets. If a compound engine is employed, the gearing cannot be so nicely arranged, as the two cranks and four excentrics occupy too much room.[1] The inside gear engines possess several advantages : the gearing runs with little noise ; the engine can be made narrower than usual ; the bearings are more fairly worn ; and, what is of the greatest importance, the gearing is maintained rigidly in truth. All the gearing will be covered in with guards, so as to protect it from dust and suppress the noise. Two travelling speeds will be provided for. A ratio of 6 to 1 for the fast gear, and 10 to 1 for the slow gear, is decided upon. As a general rule the quick-travelling speed would be used, the slow gear being intended for cases of emergency, such as mounting inclines, traversing bad roads, or passing through crowded thoroughfares. These ratios will give a speed of six miles an hour, and ten miles, the engine running at 280 revolutions per minute ; of course, any speed lower than these could be run when required. If necessary, three speeds can be provided.

We must now deal with the method of mounting this

---

[1] In Clayton and Shuttleworths' compound engine the difficulty has been overcome by discarding excentrics.

# Traction Engines

spur-geared engine on springs. It is very evident that a small amount of movement, due to the action of the springs, will be required for an engine running at the speeds named, particularly as we have provided a certain amount of elasticity in the driving-wheels. The springs must be so arranged that they can be adjusted to give the required range for taking off the concussion. If more than $\frac{3}{4}$-inch play is given, the swaying of the passenger engine on some roads would become unpleasant. Several different methods of mounting engines on springs are already shown; these, however, are designed for heavy engines, in which the driving power passes through the main axle. It has already been said that the compensating gear will be fixed on the second countershaft, but the spring arrangement can be carried out on fairly simple lines. Good provisions for driving the winding-drum on the axle can be made without complication.

The usual tender and extra tank under the boiler barrel are shown in the sketch of passenger train, Fig. 158, but if necessary, a separate tender could be mounted on a pair of wheels and attached to the foot-plate of the engine. A spare tender, with tank filled and fuel replenished, could be taken on quickly, and the empty one left behind; this would save time on the road, clean water could be secured, and the total weight of the engine would be reduced by 30 cwt. The draw-bar would be attached to the horn-plates of the boiler. A spring draught-iron is very useful for taking off all jolting when the engine starts with a load. In addition to the feed-pump, driven by an excentric on the crank-shaft, an injector should be supplied, so that the boiler could be fed while the engine was standing. A steam-pump might be applied in lieu of the injector. Both

# Proposed Road Locomotive and Train

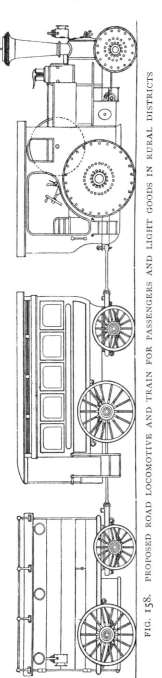

these appliances would be within the reach of the engine-driver. A large water-lifter and hose-pipe is an essential appendage for the kind of tender shown on the drawing. The steerage will be actuated from the foot-plate, but instead of the usual chains and chain barrel, we should recommend a large worm and rack under the boiler barrel. The rack would be guided and thus kept properly in gear with the worm. The connection between the rack and the front axle must be of a ball-and-socket arrangement, to allow for the up-and-down movement of the front axle. The front of the engine would be mounted on springs. A footboard would be provided on the side of the boiler for gaining access to the engine for oiling, cleaning, and adjustment. A neat cab is erected over the tender and the shaft end of the engine; the windows are arranged so that a good look-out can be obtained. The head-lamp must cast a good light on the road in front of the engine. All the handles for starting, stopping, and reversing the engine, for opening and closing the cylinder cocks, for starting the pump or the injector, for opening the sliding fire-door, for putting the

237

road-gear pinions in and out of gear, for opening and closing the ash-pan doors, for applying the brake, for sounding the whistle, and for starting the water-lifter, should be placed as conveniently as possible within reach of the engine-driver. Two men will control the engine, one as driver and one as steersman. Another man will be required to take charge of the omnibus.

The details of importance composing the road locomotive proposed for the running of light road trains have been touched upon. A drawing in side elevation is given of the train, Fig. 158. It will be seen that the working parts of the engine are hidden from view; the flywheel is of the disc pattern, of small diameter, and every possible thought will be taken to remove any objectionable features that are liable to frighten horses. Care will be taken that the road train cannot truthfully be termed a nuisance by persons who object to the use of machinery on roads. The engine is shown drawing an omnibus mounted on springs, which will seat twenty to thirty passengers; there is shown also a light spring four-wheeled van for carrying market produce, parcels, etc., to the railway station or market town. The engine will not vary much in appearance for different districts. It is believed the character of the train will often differ; it may be altered to suit the requirements of the neighbourhood through which the train shall run. The omnibus may give place to a light-covered wagonette, so that more room and power would be available for hauling merchandise.

Mr. McLaren has referred to the legal restrictions relating to road locomotives,[1] but more may be said on the subject, as the laws affect us to such an extent that

---

[1] "Steam on Common Roads," by John McLaren. Excerpt, *Minutes of Proceedings* of the Institution of Civil Engineers.

# Proposed Road Locomotive and Train

the traction engine proposed for the conveyance of passengers and light goods would not be permitted to run except at a crawling speed. The time has surely arrived for these Acts of Parliament to be modified or removed altogether. Instead of giving the simple road locomotive fair play, engineers are at the present time discussing a far more costly means of transport, viz. light railways or tramways. This is one of the proposals which has been suggested for helping the farmer to tide over the depression. Such railways may be required in some districts. It has been said, however, that their adoption will only add to the farmer's burdens. It has been urged that they never can be remunerative. The advantages of light railways have been over-estimated, and, without question, the means of transport now being dealt with has been entirely overlooked.

We do not for one moment believe that the road locomotive can compete with the light railway for speed and long distances, but we do believe that if it were freed from the all but prohibitive laws its utility would be surprisingly increased. So many people entertain the idea that road locomotives are only suitable for drawing heavy loads at very slow speeds. It must be remembered that the law compels them to travel along the roads at this tedious pace, and because of this enactment they are made exceptionally heavy so as to draw as much weight as possible.

Our legislators, and not our engineers, are to blame for some of the greatest disadvantages of the present road locomotives. We cannot stop to enumerate them, but one is the extreme weight of the engine and the trucks, and another is the great width of the train. If quicker speeds had been permitted, smaller engines and trucks would have been used in preference to the heavy

# Traction Engines

ones. With smaller and lighter road locomotives there would have been less risk of breaking bridges, reduced wear and tear to the roads, less risk of damaging old buildings near the road, and the road train would have been narrower, thus allowing more room for passing vehicles. Engineers and owners would gladly introduce a smaller road locomotive and train if they were allowed to run them at six or eight miles an hour in the open country.

Very few people know what a properly constructed road locomotive can do in the way of quick running, as such engines have been rarely tried in England. The arguments raised against their use for this purpose are based on our present engines that are built for, and used for, a totally different service. Our remarks made in favour of quick-running traction engines are mostly based on experience. Messrs. McLaren's parcel service in France shows what can be done. Lyons and Grenoble are nearly seventy miles apart. Each engine covered this distance in the night, and ran for hours together at eight miles an hour, over the worst possible roads and up some steep gradients.[1]

Undoubtedly the road locomotive and train that have been described would in many cases answer all the requirements for the conveyance of passengers and goods at economical rates in sparsely populated districts out of the reach of the main railway line. The roads are ready, and we have the engines,[2] so that this means of communication could be put into operation as soon as the laws are altered, without costing an extra penny to the ratepayers of the district through which it would

[1] "Steam on Common Roads," by John McLaren. Excerpt, *Minutes of Proceedings* of the Institution of Civil Engineers. Session 1890–91.
[2] Such engines are now made for the Colonies.

# Proposed Road Locomotive and Train

travel. The engines would be narrow, light, noiseless, and constructed so as to travel on any ordinary road, mount steep inclines, turn sharp corners, and run close to the farmyard gate. If a light railway or a tramway was to run through a parish or village containing a number of farms in the neighbourhood, it would only touch a small number of these homesteads; the greater number, to reach the railway, must use their horses, carts, and men. Whereas a road locomotive could enter the field or farmyard, take or deliver produce, and could serve any number of farms in the district.

Supposing two road trains were running regularly between a group of villages: on certain days of the week a different route could be taken, so as to put every doorstep in touch with the nearest market town and its main line railway station. A number of light road trucks would be left at any point of the journey, to be called for after they had been filled or emptied, so as not to keep the engine waiting. Such road engines are now helping the farmer, and working satisfactorily under the present fierce opposition and restrictions, doing such work as just described.

Road locomotives are appreciated on the Continent and in the Colonies. Our military authorities have proved the advantages of the engines when running at four miles an hour, and would gladly avail themselves of a greater number of engines if they were allowed to travel at eight miles an hour. It may safely be predicted that if the hindrances were removed, and the road locomotive were given fair play, this cheap and efficient means of transport would not only convey goods as at present, but passengers would be conveyed also. Many road trains would spring into existence, and bring life and activity to many a remote hamlet and farm. Other

# Traction Engines

advantages would accrue that are not thought of.
Many of our main roads are not suitable for tramways ;
to adapt them for laying the rails would entail an enormous expenditure of money.   No one would think of
allowing light railways to run on any of the roads, and
to use valuable land for such a scheme appears to be a
wasteful procedure.   Instead of laying tram lines, let a
tithe of the amount be expended in making and keeping
our highways in thorough repair.

It appears to be so unreasonable to place every
hindrance in the way of a simple system of communication which is ready to hand, and at the same time seek
the means to build up an extravagant system that.
farmers cannot pay for.   If Mr. Price Williams' esti-
mate is correct, the cost of each mile of light railway
would purchase two road locomotives, two omnibuses
to carry twenty or thirty passengers, two covered vans,
and four light waggons, all mounted on springs and
connected by spring draw-bars.

It must be remembered that the large railway companies will construct some light railways.   Not only so,
but light railways that are constructed by private companies, many of them will probably come into the hands
of the great railway companies.   Both these contingencies
must be resisted, otherwise no advantage would be gained
by any number of light railways.

The railway interest is very powerful in the country,
and this gigantic system is gaining possession of water-
ways, and is seeking to gain power over the roads.   One
large railway has already forbidden traction engines to
run over their bridges.   The roads were free for all
kinds of traffic before the railways came into existence.
If the railway company cut one of these roads, they
must provide a bridge strong enough to carry all loads,

# Proposed Road Locomotive and Train

and they must not interfere with any vehicle that has occasion to travel along the road and cross the bridge. The railway companies surely possess no right to interfere with the users of the roads; their duty is to carry freight and passengers, and not to interfere with pre-existing rights, as they are now endeavouring to do. We must retain our roads for the free use of the people, and not allow the railway companies to have any control over them whatever.

There are at least 8,000 traction engines at work in this country. They are sufficiently harassed by the injurious laws that are in force, without the railway companies seeking to add another burden. Can the railway companies forbid us to use a bridge over the railway, or canal, that is part of a main road, or even a level crossing that answers a similar purpose?

This much has been said respecting the railway interference with the traffic over the public roads, in the hope that this unjust proceeding may be nipped in the bud.

The main roads of this country are practically free, and must remain so. The engine and train that are proposed to run on these roads will be mounted on springs, and will come under the term of ordinary traffic, as they will not injure any well-made macadam road. Let every effort be used to remove the burdensome road-engine laws, and before two or three years have elapsed the problem of cheap transport will have become an accomplished fact, brought about by private enterprise and private money.

# CHAPTER IX

## UNDERTYPE ROAD LOCOMOTIVES

IN previous chapters a number of road locomotives are described which have been used for quick transport on common roads. A lighter type of road engine and train was proposed as being suitable for meeting the wants of the farmer and the inhabitants of sparsely populated neighbourhoods out of the reach of the main line of railway. It was said, "If such a road locomotive and train were allowed to run at six to ten miles an hour, the much-discussed and costly light railway would not be needed in hundreds of rural districts."

The engines dealt with were mostly of the ordinary pattern, with the working parts on the top of the loco-motive form of boiler. It is a well-known fact that *The Engineer* has for thirty years advocated another type of hauling engine, which appears to possess some com-mendable features.[1] The proposed road engine is to follow the railway locomotive engine as far as possible. There is every likelihood of common road haulage being more extensively employed in the near future. It is very important, therefore, that the engine adopted for the purpose shall be of the most suitable pattern.

In the present chapter it is proposed to give a few particulars, with outline drawings of the engines which

[1] *The Engineer*, August 23rd, 1867.

# Undertype Road Locomotives

have been built on somewhat similar lines to those laid down by *The Engineer*; after which an attempt will be made to ascertain the real value of the road locomotive of the proposed type, against the common form of traction engine made by all the recognised manufacturers of these engines. This is a very important question, and the present is a fitting time to introduce the subject.

For the last twenty-five years the writer has been taking a deep interest in all matters pertaining to traction engines, and has given some thought to the designing of road locomotives specially built for hauling purposes, with the engines placed between side plates underneath the boiler barrel. In order to obtain a clear conception of the subject, a few particulars from a recent article entitled "Traction on Highways"[1] may be quoted. After referring to the engines illustrated in *The Engineer*, January 17th, 24th, and 31st, 1896,[2] the writer says: " But the high-speed common road locomotive will not be like any of these ; it will, on the contrary, resemble very closely the railway locomotive. There will be a pair of inside cylinders between side frames under the boiler ; the fore carriage will answer to the bogie ; the driving-wheels may be driven by gearing or a chain. In any case, the engine will be carried on long laminated springs. We suggest nothing that has not been done. Such a design presents nothing offensive to horses, for the whole of the machinery may be enclosed, and it runs very silently. For obvious reasons, on which we need not enter, weight can be saved in many directions, and a locomotive can be produced which will be close to the ground, quite unobtrusive and handsome in appearance."

[1] *The Engineer*, February 28th, 1896.
[2] The articles in *The Engineer* of January 17th, 24th, and 31st, 1896, were contributed by the author.

# Traction Engines

In another article the following occurs : "We have adopted on the railroad a type of engine embodying the results of years of experience and invention, and this type, with certain modifications, is admirably adapted for common road work—better adapted, indeed, than any other."[1]

The following is quoted from another article : "Instead of the portable engine, we must take the railway locomotive as our model. We must provide a rectangular frame of iron, supported on wheels—preferably of wood. The crank-shaft must be driven by a pair of pistons in order to get rid almost or altogether of the flywheel —an unnecessary and objectionable excrescence, which should have no more place on a traction engine than it has on a locomotive."[2]

In another article it is said : "If the locomotive type of boiler be employed, the cylinders must be put under the boiler in the smoke-box ; they are to be kept as high as ·possible. The driving-wheel axle is to be placed under about the middle of the boiler barrel. The engine will run fire-box first. A glance at Fig. 172 will show what is meant. The slide bars must be carried over the shaft, inclined cylinders being strictly inadmissible. The crank-shaft will be placed well up to the fire-box."[3]

This is the last quotation that will be made : "If a satisfactory design for a four-coupled road locomotive could be produced, something worth having would be gained. Various devices for securing the required end have been proposed, but none are, in our opinion, satisfactory, all involving the use of gearing, and being more

[1] "Steam on the Highway," *The Engineer*, August 23rd, 1867.
[2] "Traction Engines," *The Engineer*, May 14th, 1869.
[3] "On the Construction of Traction Engines," *The Engineer*, July 28th, 1871, and succeeding numbers.

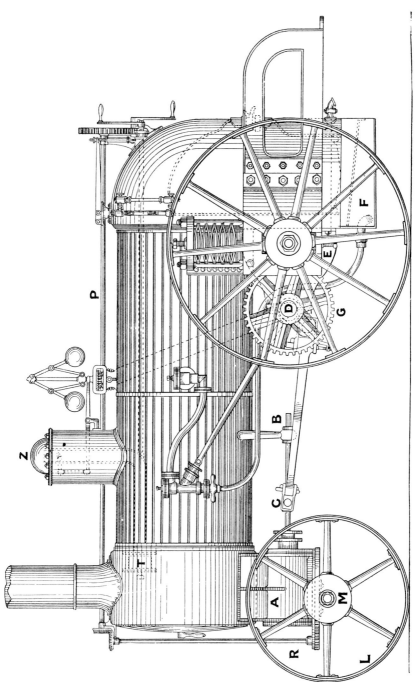

FIG. 159. SIDE VIEW OF "FARMER'S ENGINE"

# Traction Engines

or less, but generally more, complicated and objection-able."[1]

A considerable number of road locomotives more or less in harmony with these extracts have been produced ; the engines following the railway locomotive type will be described. No reference will be made to steam carriages ; the illustrations will represent road locomotives having the engine placed beneath the boiler.

It is interesting to note that one of the first traction engines ever made was of the undertype pattern. The two cylinders were placed beneath the smoke-box, the engine working below the boiler barrel. This was termed the " Farmer's Engine," it was designed by Mr. Robert Willis, of the establishment of Messrs. E. B. Wilson and Co., of the Railway Foundry, Leeds, in 1849.[2] Referring at once to our illustrations : Fig. 159 is a side elevation of the engine, Fig. 160 is a cross-section, and Fig. 161 is a half-sectional plan. The cylinders A A are attached to the smoke-box end of the boiler ; they are $6\frac{1}{4}$ inches diameter, having a stroke of 10 inches. The piston-rod is prolonged to reach the guide B, whilst a short crosshead, keyed on the rod at C, furnishes joint pins, to carry the ends of the forked connecting-rod of the crank D. This crank runs in bearings carried by wrought-iron brackets E E, bolted to the front end of the fire-box. It gives motion to the driving-axle F, through the spur-wheels, which admits of the obtainment of two speeds. On one side of the engine, the crank-shaft D carries a spur-wheel G, driving a pinion H on the main axle ; whilst at the opposite side the movement is reversed, the pinion being on the crank-shaft. In this way, by sliding the crank-shaft

---

[1] "Traction Engines," *The Engineer*, August 13th, 1875.
[2] *Practical Mechanics Journal*, vol. ii., April, 1849, to March, 1850.

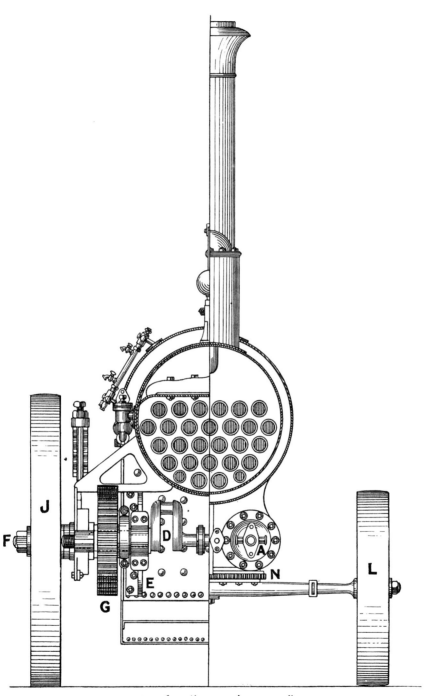

FIG. 160. "FARMER'S ENGINE"

wheel and pinion shown, the two ratios obtained are $2\frac{1}{4}$ to 1 and 1 to $2\frac{1}{4}$. The driving-axle F runs in bearings formed in curved wrought-iron brackets I I, bolted to the sides of the fire-box ; its pair of driving-wheels J J, of 4 ft. diameter, are entirely of wrought-iron, with round spokes riveted to a thin rim. The boiler was a fine example of workmanship, presenting a perfect novelty in its longitudinal joints of the barrel, as well as at the junction of the barrel-ends with the smoke-box and fire-box. It is 5 ft. 6 in. long and 2 ft. in diameter, and has 28 tubes $2\frac{1}{2}$ in. diameter. It has two plates in its length, riveted transversely in the usual way,—whilst *the longitudinal joint is a weld from end to end.* This peculiarity has excited considerable attention, as well from its novelty as its excellency of execution. The smoke and fire box are riveted to the barrel *without the use of angle-iron*, the angle-holding pieces being formed upon the barrel-ends, to rivet to corresponding angles on the attached parts. The front carrying-wheels L L are 2 ft. 8 in. diameter ; they run loose on their axle, which swivels on a central pin carried by a wrought-iron plate at M, bolted to a flange on the lower sides of the cylinders. The central portion of the axle is flattened on its upper side for bolting against the lower surface of a wrought-iron segmental toothed wheel N for steering. The steering handle is at O, close by the regulator handle : its stud-shaft carries a small pinion, gearing with a wheel on the rod P running along the top of the barrel of the boiler, and communicating motion by the pair of bevel pinions Q to a vertical shaft passing down the front of the smoke-box, and having a spur-pinion R at its lower end gearing with the wheel N on the axle. As the proper mode of steering common road locomotives has afforded much food for discussion,

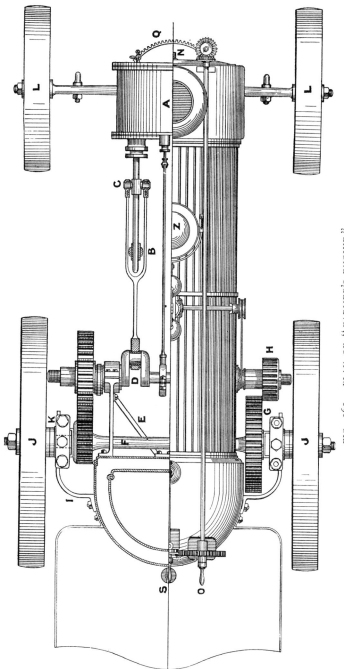

FIG. 161. PLAN OF "FARMER'S ENGINE"

it may be remarked here, that this arrangement of Mr. Willis has been found to answer perfectly.

The regulator handle is in the usual place S at the front of the fire-box, from which a handle passes along the boiler to the regulator T in the smoke-box. The regulator is explained in detail by the detached views, Figs. 162, 163. Fig. 162 is a longitudinal section of the regulator, and Fig. 163 a plan; looking on the disc valve-plate, U is the brass valve-disc, with two steam apertures V V corresponding to similar apertures in the cast-iron face W, leading into the back of the valve-chest, whence pipes pass at X to the cylinders. The face-piece W is kept

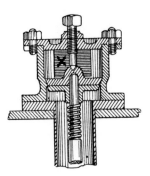

FIG. 162. DETAIL OF WILLIS'S ENGINE

up to its bearing in the valve-case by a set-screw passing through from the back; and when the steam pressure is low, the helix coiled on the regulator shaft keeps up the valve to its face. In this engine, the regulator shaft passes into the supply steam-pipe Y at the bend, where it is made steam-tight by a conical collar on the rod

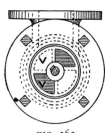

FIG. 163

ground into a seat in the pipe, and kept in its place by the pressure of the packing against another collar at the fire-box end. In fitting this class of regulator into a locomotive engine, the pipe Y is made to extend along the whole length of the boiler, having a longitudinal slit $\frac{1}{16}$ inch wide along the top to receive the steam, and to obviate the risk of priming, a strip of sheet-iron is laid over it as a loose cover. This arrangement does away with the necessity of a dome or steam receiver.

In the present engine a dome Z is used to receive

# Undertype Road Locomotives

the bent-up end of the steam-pipe, at the top of which a common throttle-valve A is placed, being set on a transverse spindle passing through the dome, and linked by a short lever connection to the end of the lever B of the governor, carried on a stud on the side of the dome, to the curvature of which it is bent to pass round to the valve spindle. The governor is supported in an appropriate brass bracket, bolted on the top of the boiler. It is driven from a small cord-pulley C on the crank-shaft close to the driving-pinion, and from this, a cord passes to a similar pulley D on the end of a short horizontal shaft driving the pair of bevel-wheels of the governor. When travelling on the road the governor is disengaged, and the throttle-valve is opened to its full extent, the ordinary regulator only being then used to control the movements of the engine. The force-pump for the boiler supply is bolted at E to the side of the boiler; it takes its supply from a water-cistern F placed beneath the ash-pan of the fire-box, from which a considerable amount of heat is derived, so that the water passes into the boiler in a warm state by the entrance clack at G. An excentric H on the crank-axle works the pump-plunger by the connecting-rod K in the usual manner.

Such is the general detail of this "farmer's engine," which, we are sure, only requires to be known to be pretty universally introduced. Being locomotive, it is easily transferable from one part of a large farm to another, so that whilst to-day it is thrashing corn in one quarter, to-morrow it may be pumping water or grinding in another. It was exhibited at the Norwich Show in 1849. At the Leeds meeting of the Yorkshire Agricultural Society, it evidenced its standing by carrying off the first prize of its class, not solely, it may be added, on account of its appearance, but for what it has proved itself capable of doing. Some weeks' work in Ipswich, Norwich, and the neighbourhood has tried its powers very fully. Here it was driven about the country by Mr. J. C. Wilson—from the builders' establishment —from farm to farm, and thus received both a locomotive and a stationary test. At Mr. Mumford's, of Bramford, it thrashed for two days, and another at Mr. Wood's farm, in the same district; as also at Mr. Frost's, near Freston; and, on the way to this place, it ascended Freston Hill, an inclination of 1 in 11. This it performed at a brisk walking pace, having, as is usual in travelling on the road, the slow motion in gear. On a level, it performed twelve miles within the hour easily.

When stationary, for driving any piece of machinery, the power may be taken from it three different ways. First, by a universal joint and coupling-rod screwed upon the end of the crank-axle, whilst the engine itself remains standing on its wheels, the spur-gearing being entirely disconnected; second, by the same, screwed on to the driving-axle; and third, by a belt passed over one or both driving-wheels, which, in both the latter cases, are to be elevated from the ground by the axle-springs, with a prop beneath the fire-box.

With 41 lbs. of coal, steam is got up to a pressure of 45 lbs. in three-quarters of an hour. In thrashing, its consumption of fuel is from 50 to 55 lbs. of coke per hour, evaporating in that time 41 gallons of water, driving two 4-horse thrashing machines, and, at a man's usual rate of feeding of 13 coombs per hour, thrashing 260 coombs of grain per day of 10 hours. Its usual rate of working is 70 strokes per minute; but this, of course, depends upon the nature of its work. Its entire weight, with fuel and water-supply, is 2 tons 10 cwt.

For large farms, we conceive that this engine will be

# Undertype Road Locomotives

a most effective assistant ; and even on those of limited extent, if at all conveniently located, its powers of locomotion on a common road will render it quite available, as it can be quickly taken from one farm to another.[1]

Nine years later Mr. John Smith, jun., of Coven, near Wolverhampton, patented the road locomotive that has been several times referred to by *The Engineer*.[2] This engine certainly deserves a full description. The patent is dated 1858, No. 1,799. Fig. 164 shows a side elevation, Fig. 165 gives an end view of the engine, while Fig. 166 illustrates the trunnion on which the boiler rested. An old engraving has the following description : "The engraving represents Smith and Higgs' patent locomotive steam engine, to travel on the ordinary roads without horses. It has been practically tested for three years, and is fully appreciated by those who have been saved much horse labour. It consists of an eight horse-power locomotive steam engine, fitted with patent adjusting boiler, so constructed as to keep the water always on a level when going on hilly roads, thereby preventing priming or burning the fire-box or tubes. It is also fitted with frictional straps for actuating one or both of the hind road wheels."

It will be seen from Fig. 164 that two deep side plates of wrought-iron run the whole length of the engine and tender. The two cylinders, $6\frac{1}{2}$ in. diameter and 10 in. stroke, are bolted between these plates beneath the smoke-box. The crank-shaft is placed as near to the saddle-plate of the boiler as possible, so as to obtain long connecting-rods ; the bearings for the crank-shaft are let into the side plates. On one end of

---

[1] The above particulars of this interesting relic appeared in *Practical Mechanics Journal* for 1849 and 1850.

[2] August 23rd, 1867 ; December 8th, 1876 ; February 28th, 1896.

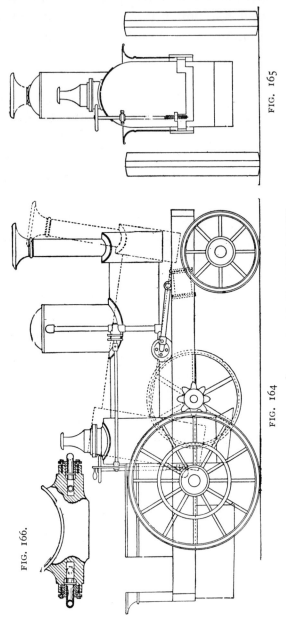

FIG. 165

FIG. 164

FIG. 166.

SMITH'S UNDERTYPE TRACTION ENGINE

the crank-shaft a small chain pinion is keyed, which drives a large chain wheel keyed to the axle; the ratio of the chain driving-gear is 9 to 1.

The axle is fixed beneath the fire-hole door, and is mounted on a pair of good springs carried by the side plates. Strong wood wheels are shown; the drivers are 6 ft. diameter, having twelve spokes, connected together in the centre of their length by a wrought-iron ring. The leading-wheels and under-carriage are made of wood. Here are the three commendable features which produce a silent-running engine—wood wheels, chain driving-gear, and a good arrangement of springs. The silent manner in which some of the old chain-driven traction engines passed along ordinary roads was very creditable.

Unless you happened to see the engine you would not know that a road locomotive was passing your dwelling. If a modern road locomotive engine traverses the same road, at the same speed, the noise and vibration, it must be admitted, are anything but pleasant, and to many persons are a real source of irritation. We trust, however, that the coming road engines will be no more a nuisance than were the old types referred to. Mr. Smith introduced the frictional straps, by means of which the axle would drive one or both of the main wheels; these straps were very extensively used on ploughing engines until quite recently. From the illustrations it will be seen that the boiler is pivoted on a casting carried by the side plates. The boiler could be maintained in a horizontal position by means of a screw and hand wheel while the engine was traversing hilly roads; it was found, however, that this arrangement was not needed in practice. A large dome is adopted, from the top of which the steam is conducted to the trunnion, and from thence to the cylinder. The trunnion on the opposite side served as the feed-water supply pipe. Fig. 166 illustrates this detail. The admission of the steam is controlled by a gland-cock. A flywheel is keyed on the overhanging end of the crank-shaft; the engine is fitted with link-motion reversing-gear and a set of governors. The steersman is provided with a seat in close proximity to the chimney and the hot smoke-box, as seen in the old engraving referred to, but judging by the expression on the face of the individual who occupies this responsible seat, no discomfiture is realised. The weight of the engine and boiler is exceedingly well distributed fore and aft. A door is provided for ready access to a roomy foot-plate; beneath this foot-plate is the feed-water tank. The boiler is of the raised fire-box locomotive type, and the working pressure is 100 lbs. per square inch. It is stated that a countershaft was added to one of the engines made by Mr. Smith, with spur-gearing between the crank-shaft and the intermediate shaft. The engine is reported to have travelled six miles at the rate of twenty miles an hour, and was eventually sent into the neighbourhood of Bristol. "Such an engine was built by the late Mr. Smith, and was perfectly successful." Considering the date when this engine was built, it is a most creditable piece of designing, and perfectly fulfilled some of the vital requirements of road locomotive engines.

Fig. 167 shows a side elevation of Bray's road locomotive, designed by the late Mr. D. K. Clark, for use in the Woolwich Dockyard, and was sent to the 1862 Exhibition.

Fig. 168 is a side elevation of a type of road locomotive patented by Messrs. Hornsby, Bonnel, and

# Undertype Road Locomotives

Astbury, in 1863. The engines had two cylinders, placed between side plates, and beneath the smoke-box of a locomotive multitubular boiler. The cylinders were

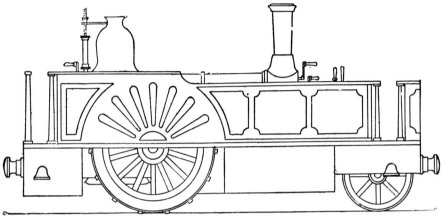

FIG. 167. BRAY'S ROAD LOCOMOTIVE

arranged with trunks, or hollow piston-rods, which passed through the back and front cylinder covers. The small ends of the connecting-rods were attached in the

FIG. 168. HORNSBY'S ROAD LOCOMOTIVE

middle of the trunks.  No slide bars were required, and long connecting-rods could be adopted, and at the same time allow the cylinders to be fairly near to the crank-shaft.  By this arrangement of engine, the cylinders, crank-shaft gearing, and countershaft could be nicely accommodated beneath a short boiler barrel.  The carriages for the two above-named shafts were let into the deep wrought-iron side plates in railway locomotion fashion.  Motion was communicated from the crank-shaft to the countershaft by spur-gearing, and from the countershaft to the driving-axle by a pitch-chain of

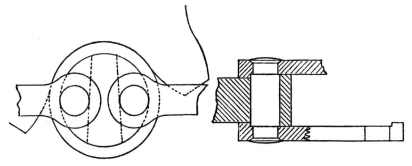

FIG. 169.  PITCH-CHAIN FOR HORNSBY'S ROAD LOCOMOTIVE

novel construction, as shown by Fig. 169.  The main axle was placed across the boiler beneath the fire-hole, and neatly mounted on volute springs, in a similar manner to some of the modern plans.  The working parts of the engine were all neatly boxed in, to protect the wearing surfaces from the dust.  A flywheel was keyed on the crank-shaft, a brake provided on the axle.  This engine possessed many commendable features ; it moreover presented a neat and trim appearance.  An engine of this type made by Messrs. Hornsby and Sons was shipped to Natal.[1]

[1] *Steam Locomotion on Common Roads*, E. and F. N. Spon, 1891.

# Undertype Road Locomotives

In 1866, Mr. D. K. Clark patented a form of road locomotive, as per Figs. 170 and 171. From these illustrations it will be seen that the principal framing

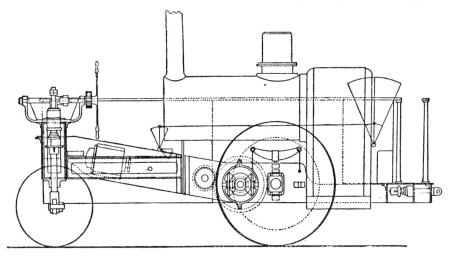

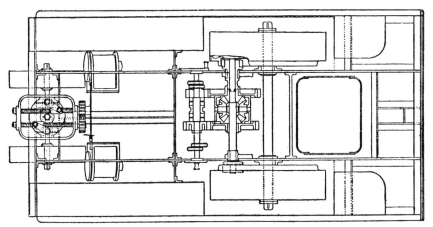

FIGS. 170, 171. CLARK'S ROAD LOCOMOTIVE

is composed of two parallel longitudinal horn-plates, of iron or steel, with suitable transverse plates. At the front end of the engine a light upright frame carries the steering-gear; the two screw shafts, nuts, and links are shown. The main axle is near the saddle-plate of the

# Traction Engines

fire-box. The two cylinders are placed on the outside of the main plates. Two travelling speeds are fitted ; between the two spur-wheels a frame is provided for carrying the compensating gear. The boiler, framing, engine, tanks, and other parts connnected thereto are carried by the axle and driving-wheels through two plate springs, as shown ; the vertical play of the axle-boxes is controlled by blocks of india-rubber placed at the top and the bottom. The front end of the engine is carried by springs. The noise of the exhaust steam was suppressed by causing it to escape in a series of small jets. In some respects the engine is well worked out, but it could not have been a success ; the driving-wheels are too small in diameter and the width of the engine over the framing is excessive. The method of driving the pinions on the crank-shaft is objectionable.

The next engine to be noticed is one made by Messrs. John Fowler and Co., in 1868. Fig. 172 represents a side elevation partly in section, Fig. 173 a plan, and Fig. 174 gives a view from the front end. The illustrations show the engine so clearly that little description is needed. The cylinders are placed beneath the smoke-box, over the locking gear. Two travelling speeds are provided ; the quick-speed pinion and wheels are placed between the bearings ; the slow-gear wheels are outside the bearings, as shown in Fig. 173. A clutch on the countershaft puts the fast-speed wheels into action ; another clutch on the crank-shaft acts in a similar manner for the slow-speed wheels. It will be seen that when the fast-speed clutch is out of gear, the wheel revolves on the countershaft ; when the slow-gear clutch is out of use the crank-shaft revolves in the pinion; when the fast-speed clutch is in action the slow-speed pinion will be driven by the spur-wheel on the counter-

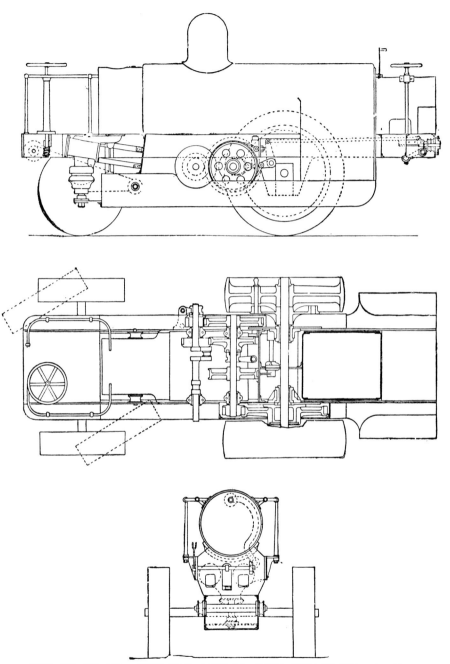

FIGS. 172, 173, 174. ROAD LOCOMOTIVE BY MESSRS. JOHN FOWLER AND CO.

shaft, an arrangement of gearing which cannot be recommended. The hind part of the engine is mounted on springs, which are not shown in the drawings. An efficient brake is keyed on the countershaft, and actuated from the foot-plate. The steering arrangement is shown clearly. It will be seen that the driving-wheels are made of cast-iron, 5 ft. 6 in. diameter, and 1 ft. 6 in. on face. The engine is considerably wider over the driving-wheels

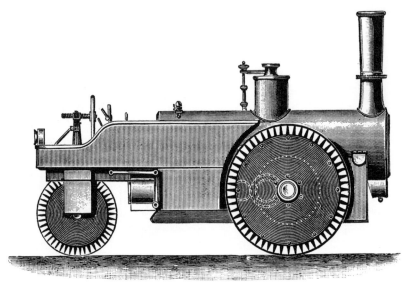

FIG. 175. ROAD LOCOMOTIVE. MESSRS. BURRELL AND SONS

than would be tolerated now. Taken as a whole, the engine presents a favourable example of the undertype road locomotive, with the engine arranged between side plates.

In 1871 Messrs. D. Greig and Max Eyth patented another type of road locomotive with the cylinders, crank-shaft, and gearing beneath a short boiler barrel. The engine travels fire-box foremost, the steersman and stoker occupying the same foot-plate.

Fig. 175 shows a road locomotive, designed by

# Undertype Road Locomotives

Messrs. Burrell and Sons. The engine is placed beneath the boiler; the fire-box travels foremost. This particular design was not carried out, but a goodly number of successful road locomotives were made, with the working parts on the top of the boiler; the main axle and the steering-gear being arranged in a similar manner to the illustration.

In the early part of 1872 the writer designed a road locomotive as per the sketch, Fig. 176, which explains

FIG. 176.   DESIGN FOR ROAD LOCOMOTIVE

itself. The front part of the engine frame was made much narrower than the hind part, but the front axle had to be somewhat longer than usual, in order to allow the engine to lock sufficiently for turning sharp corners.

Messrs. Archer and Hall patented a road locomotive in 1872, with the engine-work beneath the boiler barrel; the cylinders are placed near the fire-box, the crankshaft is beneath the smoke-box. The two trains of wheels representing the two speeds are so arranged that at whatever angle they may lie through the action of the springs, their surfaces of contact remain the same.

# Traction Engines

A saddle tank is placed over the boiler. The engine is mounted on three wheels; the single leading-wheel is at the fire-box end of the engine. The chief objection against the engine is its excessive width.

In 1872 Messrs. J. and T. Dale, of Kirkcaldy, constructed a road locomotive on Nain's patent, intended for running at six to eight miles an hour. It is mounted on three travelling wheels.

Messrs. Marshall, Sons, and Co. exhibited an under-type traction engine at the Smithfield Show, 1876. The single cylinder is bolted to the under side of the smoke-box and to the wrought-iron frame. Both the crank-shaft and countershaft brackets are bolted to the side plates beneath the boiler barrel. This engine was not built for hauling, but for ordinary farm purposes. A flywheel is provided for driving machinery by a belt. The engine having but one cylinder, it is necessary to have a flywheel which the engine-driver can reach, in order to pull the engine off the dead centre at times. Several engines of this type were built, and have given satisfaction. One has been used by the firm for many years for hauling goods to the railway station and for regular yard purposes. By the appearance of the smoke-box end, it would be thought that two cylinders occupied the space between the side frames, but a small water heater was made to correspond with the cylinder, giving to the engine a more symmetrical appearance. The engine is not mounted on springs, but is fitted with compensating gear on the main axle, and all the usual accessories for agricultural work.

A somewhat novel form of traction engine, invented by Mr. Willsher, was exhibited at the 1878 Smithfield Show. The single cylinder was bolted to the under side of the smoke-box. Side plates were only provided for

# Undertype Road Locomotives

carrying the bearings of the crank-shaft and the counter-shaft. The driving-wheels revolved on bosses secured to the horn-plates, the crank-shaft occupied the position of the main axle. The engine was mounted upon springs.

The latest and probably the best traction engine of the type under review was made by Messrs. John Fowler and Co., and exhibited at the Norwich Show of the Royal Agricultural Society, 1886. Fig. 177 shows a side view of the engine, Fig. 178 a plan, and Fig. 179 the clutch gear. From these illustrations it will be seen that the engine and gearing are placed beneath the boiler barrel, between two deep side plates. The boiler is mounted on these side plates at a considerable height to make room for the machinery below it. The compound cylinders are fixed at the smoke-box end, and the crank-shaft at the fire-box end of the frames. Two travelling speeds are provided, the pinions are slid in and out of gear by a lever, which is worked from the foot-plate ; no claw clutches are used, as in some of the earlier examples. The chief novelty of this engine arises from the fact that the fore wheels are driving-wheels, as well as the hind ones. Several engines have been made with all the wheels acting as drivers, which need not detain us, but the present arrangement appears to be the best. Power is transmitted to the leading wheels by Whittingham's patent gearing, which is well understood by traction-engine builders. The road wheels are 5 ft. 6 in. diameter and 1 ft. 6 in. wide. The total width over the hind wheels is 7 ft. 6 in., and the width over the fore wheels is 8 ft., this excessive width is a drawback. This engine, however, disposes of several of the imaginary difficulties of the undertype road locomotive.

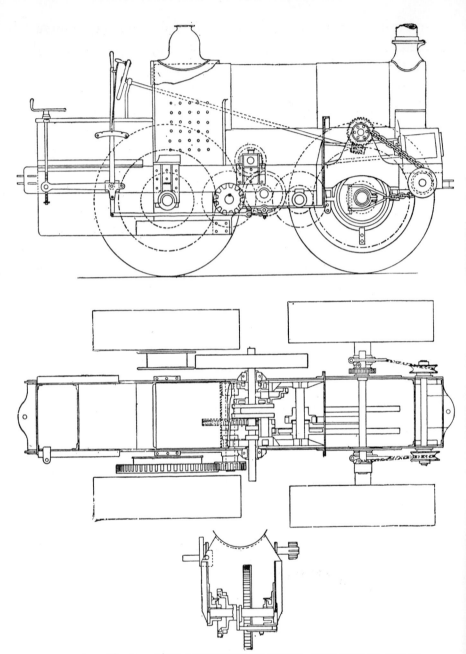

FIGS. 177, 178, 179. ROAD LOCOMOTIVE BY MESSRS. JOHN FOWLER AND CO

# Undertype Road Locomotives

Several other engines on the railway locomotive lines have been made, which are not included in the above descriptive remarks.

It is thought that no engine of this type has been turned out of any engineering works for the last ten years.[1]

At the present time there are more makers of road locomotives than ever before; there are a greater number of engines built per year, yet, as far as we are aware, not a single firm make hauling engines or light traction engines with the engines placed between side-plates, beneath the boiler barrel.

To account for this fact, we must relate the chief advantages claimed for the traction engine as now built, with inside gearing and all the latest improvements.

1. The principal working parts, mounted on the boiler, are all in sight, and can be examined and oiled by the driver without it being necessary for him to dismount.

2. When altering the gearing from fast to slow speed or *vice versâ*, the flywheel can be pulled round slightly to bring the teeth fair for entering ; the engine-driver can see when the wheels are right for sliding into gear.

3. The condensed steam from the jacket is returned to the boiler.

4. A good arrangement of gearing can be adopted by avoiding large differences in the diameter of the spur pinions and wheels.

5. Many of the engine details are used both for agricultural locomotives and hauling engines.

[1] Since the above was written Mr. Diplock has introduced a special road locomotive with the working parts beneath the boiler barrel. An experimental traction engine for the War Office, with the three-cylinder compound engine beneath the boiler barrel, is undergoing trials. We believe that neither of these engines has been put to actual everyday work.

# Traction Engines

6. A short fore axle can be adopted, rendering the engine more easily steered in contracted places.

The above are the advantages that are said to be wanting in the undertype engine. These drawbacks should be fairly tested—some admitted, others may be removed.

1. It is possible to arrange a foot-plate on the side-plate, and a neat handrail on the boiler, so as to give the necessary access for oiling, etc., without any need for the driver to dismount.

2. The changing of the speeds will be somewhat troublesome, as no jaw clutches must be used. In Fig. 173 the spur-wheels ran loosely on the shaft, and remained in gear. They were made to drive the shaft on which they were mounted, by means of claw clutches sliding on keys. This plan of driving is not very satisfactory, but in Fig. 179 the wheels are made to slide into gear ; the levers for actuating the movements are unfortunately somewhat complicated.

The teeth of the wheels must be lineable before they can be slid into gear ; in the overhead traction engine the flywheel is pulled round to bring them fair for each other. In the undertype no flywheel is used, and, if there had been one, it could not be reached from the foot-plate. A little steam must be admitted to move the engine slowly round for a turn or two, and by forcing the lever the wheel will slip into gear before the engine stops.

3. The loss of the condensed steam from the jackets is not a serious matter.

4. To obtain a proper distribution of the weight on the fore and hind wheels, it is essential that the main axle should be placed near the boiler front-plate beneath the fire-hole. The countershaft should be fixed as near

# Undertype Road Locomotives

the saddle-plate as possible. The length of the fire-box causes the centres of the two shafts to be too far apart for the correct train of gearing. In Fig. 177 the boiler is lifted so that one shaft passes beneath the fire-box, but this cannot be commended. There are two other methods of surmounting this difficulty, both of which will allow the boiler to be hung at a reasonable height above the ground, and there shall not be too great a difference between the pinions and wheels ; these plans will suggest themselves to engineers. A proper distribution of the weight can be obtained by an arrangement of engine somewhat after Fig. 175. The engine travels fire-box foremost, consequently when the driver is attending to the boiler, stoking, etc., he has his back turned towards the road to be traversed, which is not, however, a satisfactory arrangement of engine.

5. The necessity of keeping two types of boilers and cylinders in stock will be objectionable in some cases.

6. By a little scheming the front axle may be made considerably shorter than those shown in Figs. 174 and 178.

The principal objections raised against the undertype road locomotive have now been noticed, and when summed up they are not of a very serious nature. They are happily more than counterbalanced by the good points in the undertype arrangement.

The advantages in favour of the undertype engine for hauling purposes are valuable. The following are some of them :—

1. The countershaft and main axle being on the same horizontal centre line, a simple and perfect arrangement of springs can be secured.

2. The boiler is used as a steam generator only, and no engine parts are bolted to it.

# Traction Engines

3. The girder-frames are peculiarly adapted for a double-cylinder engine—preferably of the compound side-by-side type.

4. A copper steam-pipe in the smoke-box would help to dry the steam ; the cylinders can be well protected so as to further reduce the condensation of steam.

5. The exhaust nozzle can be placed in the best possible position for gaining a good blast.

6. A good steam dome can be adopted ; the steam being taken from the top, the tendency to prime will be entirely obviated.

7. For hauling purpose the side frames take all the strain ; the tender and the boiler being thus relieved, may be made lighter.

8. A simple and more engineering-like appearance can be obtained.

9. All the moving parts can be neatly enclosed.

As a light road locomotive for running at quick speeds silently and smoothly, the undertype engine is perfectly adapted. It offers more advantages as a light locomotive than for a heavy one, and no drawbacks would be encountered in a fast-speed road engine built on the railway locomotive lines. In previous chapters full particulars of the special details needed to adapt an engine for fast running are clearly set forth. Many of the features remain unaltered, no matter whether the engine is placed above or below the boiler. To repeat these essentials would be traversing the ground afresh to no purpose.

# CHAPTER X

## FESTIVE EXPERIENCES WITH EARLY TRACTION ENGINES

THE history of traction engines has been little more that a recital of failures. If the trial trips of some of the early specimens were written, they would be somewhat amusing. The first road engine ever made sadly misbehaved itself by knocking down a brick wall that happened to be in its way, and soon afterwards the same engine fell on its side with a crash while turning a sharp corner in the streets of Paris, for which offence the engine and its maker were at once locked up in prison, to prevent them from doing further mischief. Since Cugnot's little pioneer tumbled over, many others have followed its example. Many inventors have, during all periods of the traction engine's history, patented and constructed all sorts of abortions in the way of steam locomotives for common roads. Dozens of these schemes have never seen the light; others have been made for a very brief day and a sudden termination. Few firms have introduced their first traction engine without some mishap. In some cases, failure after failure has occurred previous to the perfecting of their number one; gratifying results were reported during the trials, but, curiously, no second engine was built to the same plans. The first traction engines made by two or three firms were never delivered to customers. One, at least, never emerged from the factory. The earliest performance on the road took place in a quiet corner of the yard, and was of too novel a character to admit of a repetition. Consequently, those few persons who viewed the eccentric movements of the number one may consider themselves favoured, for as soon as the performance was concluded, the engine was consigned to a dark corner of the shop and forgotten, or the boiler was stripped of its engine parts, and some of the details were utilised for other purposes. The shop engines of two firms were supplied with steam generated from traction engine boilers; the boilers were built for road-locomotive work, but neither the engine nor the boiler were allowed to leave the maker's hands. Two traction engines were tried in different parts of the country; both engines had a tendency to become restive, and each evinced a desire to soar aloft. One was loaded with pig-iron at the front end to keep its nose down. There was no means of loading the front axle of the second engine with pig-iron, so a heavy cable chain was wound many times round the boiler barrel, close to the smoke-box. After the engine had taken a short walk with this "muffler" round its neck, some other irritating defects showed themselves, which prevented its sale.

Here was a curious experience for a traction engine and the driver to be in. In the Argentine Republic a heavy traction engine was about to cross a railway line in the dark. There was a ditch on one side of the line; the bridge over the ditch gave way under the weight of the engine; the hind part fell into the ditch; the smoke-box projected on to the railway, when an express train was expected in a few minutes. The driver, fortunately, was a man of experience; he promptly put the spuds on the driving-wheels, and handled the engine with skill, so that he caused the engine to crawl up the ditch's bank, and thus managed to move the front part of the engine off the railway before the express dashed past. A few more revolutions of the engine in the same direction, hind foremost, placed it on solid ground, where the engine was left that night, so that the owner and driver might ponder over their miraculous escape.

A chain-driven traction engine had undergone repairs in a small engineer's shop in the south of England. A Saturday afternoon was the time fixed upon to have a trial run on the road. The foreman of fitters was to act as driver, another man as steersman, and a lad was appointed to walk in front with a red flag. The men on the engine were experienced mechanics, but they were new hands at traction engine driving. A good deal of time was spent in steaming the engine out of the works ; a considerable amount of plunging forward, shunting, and backing appeared to be necessary, in order to keep clear of the shop-corners and various door-posts, which stood provokingly in the way of the engine's progress. After breaking a window-sill, and splintering a wood column, the engine reached the road outside the works. All went well on the outward journey, beyond sundry damages to lamp-posts, house-corners, etc. The return of the engine was, however, attended with some difficulty. It was raining in torrents, and the travelling powers of the locomotive were anything but nimble. The country road was somewhat narrow ; the engine was run near a ditch, and stopped for a vehicle to pass ; the grass on the roadside was very slippery, and sloping towards the ditch. After starting, it was noticed that the engine was gradually sliding down the incline near the ditch ; the frantic efforts of the men in charge were unable to avert the sliding progress. The engine refused to answer to the steersman's wishes ; the driving-wheel nearest the ditch made a pit for itself ; the more the engine was

# Traction Engines

urged, the worse became the situation. Presently the fatal plunge was made, ending in the ditch. A detachment of labourers, armed with planks, jacks, and spades, were hired; an experienced driver was engaged. The men worked like navvies for an hour or two; the engine was raised to the road, and started for home. A mournful procession reached the works at dusk, drenched to the skin. The engine bore marks of her misadventure which were never effaced.

A new traction engine was being tested on the road by a thoughtless driver, who commenced to change the speed when the engine was on the summit of a steep incline; as soon as the spur-wheel was drawn out of gear, the engine began to run down the hill. A man on the road, taking in the situation, ran in front and shouted for the people to keep clear; at the foot of the hill was a row of palisades and a girls' school. The driver stuck to his post, and steered the engine into some immense balks of timber before the foot of the hill was reached. The collision with the timber caused a few breakages on the engine, but had it continued its rapid course to the bottom of the hill, the consequences would have been most serious. Other accidents have occurred when changing the speeds on inclines which need not be related. If it be really necessary to change the speeds on an incline, a wise driver will put on the brake, and scotch the wheels before throwing the pinion out of gear.

Other episodes and festive days could be given, but the trial trip of another traction engine will be related, which ended well. A few notes on how we tested our new traction engine follows.

The knowledge that some eminent engineers in the past had failed to produce a reliable traction engine,

# Festive Experiences

made the bringing-out of our first road engine a very important event; and particularly so because no one on the firm had received any experience in designing, making, or the management of such engines. In imagination the trial trip had been run many times over, broken axles and other mishaps, amid a gaping crowd, had been repeatedly pictured to the mind; and to avoid the possibility of witnessing such a scene in reality, it was decided to run the trial trip in the early morning, and pass through the town before the populace were out of bed. The twenty-first of June was the day pitched upon for the first run to take place, and all the necessary preparations were made before the men left on the preceding evening. The precise time for getting up steam in the night was only known to those who would take part in the trial, namely, the present writer, who designed the engine, and three of the foremen of the firm. Immediately the last man had left the works the doors were locked, the boiler was filled, the fire was lighted, and as soon as the steam was raised, the engine was run out of gear, then the gearing was run without the pins in for driving the travelling wheels. Coal and water were taken on board. At three o'clock in the morning, as it was already daylight, the driving-pins were inserted. The engine steamed out of the erecting shop, passed through a crowded and cramped yard, which was attended with some difficulty, there being very little room for turning. Moreover, those in charge of the engine were not experienced drivers; this was their first appointment as drivers and steersmen. At four o'clock the engine started to steam through the main streets of the town, It was a glorious midsummer's morning, and the engine and party were soon out in the open country, running along pleasantly without experiencing any drawback. The steering-gear was tried to ascertain the amount of room that was required for turning ; a measured mile in fast gear was run on a good level road in just under nine minutes, about seven miles an hour. A village was reached soon after five o'clock ; the engine was placed near the horse-pond, while the party procured bread and cheese and new milk from a farmhouse for breakfast. It was decided to return to the works by a longer route, making a journey of about ten miles. The engine travelled up a long hill having a gradient in places of 1 in 9 ; there was no priming of the boiler, the pressure being from 90 to 140 lbs. When coming down the hill the brake had ample power to check the speed, and stop the engine if necessary. The only mishap experienced during the run arose from the steering-barrel becoming fastened in its bearings, so that it could not be moved by the worm and wheel ; the slacking of the nuts of the brackets set the spindle at liberty. The heat of the boiler had caused the brackets to twist and bind the barrel, the bearings being too good a fit. This mishap caused some delay ; the cause of the seizure had to be discovered and remedied.

Our passage through the town homewards created some excitement among the inhabitants, many of them taking no small interest in our number one traction engine, and as the works were approached many of the men turned out to see us. No one knew, except those who planned the trip, what time we had started, nor where we had been ; the whole affair was a mystery to the masters and the men.

Many a consultation had been indulged in during the morning among the men, with a hope of solving the problem ; but all the evidence that could be produced was to the effect that when they came to the works at six o'clock that morning the engine had vanished, leaving its footprints on the surface of the road, and that it had not been seen by any one of them since the previous evening. No wonder that the return caused some commotion among the workmen, and since then reference has often been made to the trial of our first traction engine. The customer who had ordered the traction engine had arrived, but no engine was there for

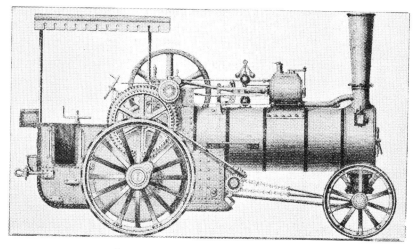

FIG. 180. A TRACTION ENGINE BY A NEW HAND

him to see; the master and he had to wait two hours for our return. This engine was afterwards finished and painted, not a single alteration of any moment made to it; and in a few days it steamed to the owner's farm with a thrashing-machine and straw-elevator behind it, and commenced work at once. Numerous engines were made from the same patterns, thereby showing that it was possible for a small firm without any previous experience in this class of machinery, by careful designing, combined with thoroughly good workmanship and

# Traction Engines

attention to all the little details, to introduce their first agricultural locomotive without any alteration being required. Fig. 180 represents the engine; it is not introduced as a modern specimen, but because some interest is attached to it.

The account of the trial trip of the number one traction engine appeared in *The Mechanical World*, October, 1882.

# CHAPTER XI

## MODERN ROAD LOCOMOTIVES AND TRACTION ENGINES[1]

THERE is probably no type of engine that is calculated to give more trouble and anxiety to both designer and builder than the traction engine; in fact, it has been said, "Anyone can make a steam engine, but only an engineer of special experience can build a successful traction engine." Many years of experience do not always furnish the requisite qualification, for some firms which have been longest in the trade are now anywhere but in the front rank, and the longer they live the less they appear to realise what will do and what will not do for modern road engines. On the other hand, some of the firms, which have more recently embarked in this trade, have already made their mark, and their productions give the impression of being of the right stamp. It is well known that the proportions and strengths of traction engines can only be arrived at by actual test; but failing that, mechanical instinct and good common-sense have often produced good results. It is impossible to calculate the strains to which the shafts and other details will be subjected.

At the outset, it may be well to enumerate some of the physical and mechanical difficulties that ordinary

---

[1] The introductory remarks were contributed by the writer to the American *Engineering News and Railway Journal*, 1892.

# Traction Engines

road locomotives have to surmount, after which little
surprise will be felt that many a firm's first traction
engine has proved to be a dead failure. The engines
must be suitably equipped for the complex duties they
have to perform, and, as far as possible, work in harmony
with the legislative restrictions under which they are
placed. They must be able to traverse all kinds of roads,
some of which are coated with loose metal, others are
paved with smooth and slippery materials, while still
others are so rotten that the wheels sink through the
thin crust into the ground beneath. Soft land has often
to be traversed, or the engines have to draw a thrashing
machine and place it in position for work in stack-yards
that are little better than swamps. The engines must
be able to draw their loads up grades ranging as high
as 1 in 6 in all kinds of weather, and must be constructed so that they will pass through narrow gateways,
and turn the most acute angles without disconnecting
the load. During wet weather the narrow lanes are so
soft that there is a strong probability of seeing the
engine gently slide into a country ditch, or suddenly
sink into a bog, the rest of a rainy day being often spent
by the men in charge in endeavouring to extricate the
engine by the aid of planks, screw-jacks, hurdles, and
anything available. All the parts must be strong enough
to bear the enormous strain of such an emergency as
the engine lifting itself out of this hole or ditch, so that
an ample margin of strength is absolutely necessary.
On the other hand, the engine must be so built that
little damage is caused to the wheels, machinery, etc.,
by the constant jarring and jolting on hard and rocky
roads, and that little damage will be done to the road.
Very often the engines are subjected to the roughest
treatment at the hands of negligent drivers, and in some

# Modern Traction Engines

districts nothing but the muddiest water can be procured for the boilers. The lubrication is lavished without stint on the accessible parts, and fearfully neglected on important parts which happen to be less easily accessible. But amid these adverse circumstances traction engines rarely give trouble. These considerations speak volumes in favour of modern road locomotives, as touching their simplicity of construction and non-likelihood of derangement, and the general suitability of the design for the multitudinous purposes to which they are now applied.

In addition to the mechanical difficulties there are, unfortunately, many annoying and unreasonable legal restrictions which are often enforced, to the owner's cost. In England there are numbers of individuals who are opposed to any but horse-power being employed on common roads, and are backed up in some cases, in their crusade against traction engines, by magistrates who entertain similar views, and these dignitaries are invested with the power to place almost insuperable impediments in the way of this important industry.

According to law, the engine must not run at more than four miles an hour in the open country, and two miles an hour when passing through villages and towns, and in each case a man must walk some yards in front to show what an evil thing is crawling behind him. The locomotive must consume its own smoke, and allow no steam to escape from the safety-valves. In many districts traction engines are prohibited from crossing the bridges, although they may be sufficiently strong to bear their weight. According to the Act, this anomaly exists at the present time: "If we send a boiler weighing 15 tons drawn by 15 horses over a country bridge, and that boiler breaks the bridge, we have nothing to pay, but if we send the same boiler over the bridge drawn

# Traction Engines

by an engine weighing 8 tons, and that boiler breaks through the bridge, we have the whole expenses to pay." Certain urban authorities may make by-laws regulating the use of traction engines on the highways, and in many instances road locomotives are only allowed to travel during the night. It is impossible to over-estimate the increased difficulties, dangers, and the excessive cost of working traction engines in the night. Many accidents have occurred owing to shortness of water, and lack of superintendence, while the men have been struggling against great odds and groping about with lanterns. Some of these accidents have ended fatally, and are clearly chargeable to the one-sided by-laws enforced by our local authorities. Many foolish objections are urged against the use of these engines, one of which is that spirited horses are frightened at their approach: such horses, however, should not be allowed on the roads until they are trained, for they are just as likely to shy at a wheelbarrow as an engine, and in either case disastrous results may occur.

The above are by no means all of the iniquitous laws; but it is time to turn to the design and construction of the locomotives. All the best road engines are marked by a great similarity of general design. The arrangement of the parts is carefully considered, with a view to secure a good mechanical design, and a symmetrical and neat appearance. Not only have the engines, as a whole, been neatly and compactly arranged, but the details in many instances are models of simplicity. It may be remarked that all attempts at so-called ornamentation, in the form of architectural mimicry so common a few years ago, have been abandoned, and in their place there is the true beauty of design, consisting of correct principles and graceful proportions worked out

# Modern Traction Engines

in the simplest and most pleasing manner, with due regard to their purpose.

The improvement in the design of these engines has been very marked during the last few years. It is not long since a paper spoke of traction engines as being ugly, noisy, and in very deed a nuisance : "We have an engine without springs, and with all the gearing exposed to the glare of day, thumping and clanking, and grinding and smoking along our highways. The thing is a nuisance, and it is folly to deny the fact." It is to be feared, however, that there are some engines made now which answer to the above description.

It has already been mentioned that the general arrangement of the engines made by the leading makers present a similarity of appearance. This arises from the fact that all the traction engine builders have adopted the locomotive multitubular type of boiler, and, by general consent, the horizontal cylinder is placed near the smoke-box end of the boiler, while the shafts and gearing are disposed in a type of box-bracket at the fire-box end of the boiler.

The boiler is of the flush-top locomotive multitubular type, with the shell made of steel plates, and the fire-box of Lowmoor iron or mild steel. It is particularly necessary that the boiler should be of the strongest form and construction, and well stayed for working safely and continuously at 140 to 180 lbs. steam pressure. A margin of strength must also be allowed to resist the strains arising from some of the engine parts being bolted down to it. In order to secure a narrow engine, which is always desirable, the boiler must be made somewhat small in diameter, and some difficulty will be experienced in providing in such a limited space (1) a proportionate amount of heating surface and grate area, so as to acquire rapid steam making, and (2) an abundance of steam room necessary to prevent priming. Unless the above important attributes are secured, it is impossible to have an efficient boiler.

The flanging and riveting of the boiler are done by hydraulic pressure, the longitudinal seams are double riveted, and the thick side-plates of the fire-box shell are carried upward and backward for supporting the bearings of the shafts and axle. Solid foundation and fire-hole rings are used instead of Z-iron for the water space around the fire-box. The full quantity of mud-holes and other provisions for washing out the boiler must be arranged in convenient positions. After completion the boiler is subjected to a water test up to 250 to 280 lbs. pressure per square inch. A sliding fire-door, two water-gauge glasses, and a smoke-box door that will tighten equally all around the outer edge should be furnished.

The cylinder should be steam-jacketed and well drained. It is usual to combine the cylinder casing, valve chest, and stop-valve chamber in one casting, made of cold blast iron. The working barrel or liner is cast separately, of special hardness, and afterwards tightly forced into the outer casing, thus forming an efficient steam-jacketed cylinder. The jacket space and stop-valve chamber are made of large capacity to constitute a dome, or reservoir, for the dry steam. The inlet into the jacket must be arranged as near to the smoke-box tube-plate as possible, for experience has shown that the engines are less likely to prime when the steam is taken from this part of the boiler. In order to present an ample bearing on the boiler barrel, the cylinder should be provided with a broad base, and a flange for foundation bolts all around. The stop-valve

# Modern Traction Engines

occupies the highest position in the cylinder, the opening is either V-shaped or round, so as to open gradually. The passages and steam ports should be of full area, to prevent any throttling. A double-spring weighted safety-valve is mounted on the top cover of the cylinder. Two displacement lubricators are fixed on the cylinder, one lubricates the slide valve, and the other supplies oil to the working barrel, to prevent the piston from scoring, which it is sure to do when muddy feed-water is used. For single-cylinder traction engines, it is usual to allow ten circular inches of piston area per nominal horse-power.

Stephenson's link-motion reversing-gear is the one most frequently used for single-cylinder traction engines. Other types have at various times been introduced, but the original valve gear when carefully designed gives satisfaction. The slip of the die may be reduced to the smallest amount, and the parts can be so arranged that an equal cut-off and release may be obtained at both ends of the cylinder, whether working in full gear, or notched up. The engine should exert the same power in forward or backward gear, and the cut-off should be as sharp as possible.

There are very few traction engines now made having cast-iron crank-shaft carriages, wrought-iron or steel-plate box-brackets having taken their places. Even when cast-iron crank-shaft brackets were used, the sides of the outer fire-box were generally carried backward for supporting the main axle, and occasionally for bearing the countershaft also. But it was reserved for Messrs. Aveling and Porter, in 1870, to carry these side plates upward as well as backward, so that all the shafts could be inserted in machined holes in the plates, making a most substantial job. This system of construction was

# Traction Engines

followed by most of the makers on the expiration of Aveling's patent. By referring to Fig. 181 it will be seen that the side plates are carried above the crown of the boiler, and holes are bored in them to receive the crank-shaft, countershaft, and main axle bearings. It may be stated here that traction engine makers are somewhat divided in opinion respecting the employment of one or two countershafts. Where two intermediate shafts are used, some of the gearing can be placed inside the box-brackets between the bearings. When one

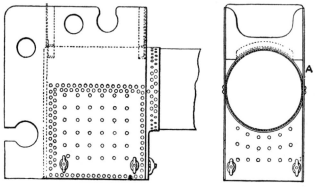

FIG. 181. SIDE PLATES OF TRACTION ENGINE

countershaft is adopted, all the gearing is placed outside the bearings. In Fig. 181 holes for two countershafts are shown in the side plates, and it will be noticed, also, that two plates, back and front, are inserted between the side plates, and riveted to them by means of angle-irons or flanges, these transverse stiffening plates being also attached to the shell of the boiler. A wedge-shaped strip of iron is inserted between the side plate and the arch plate at A to facilitate the caulking of this portion of the boiler. The longitudinal double seam of rivets passes through this wedge-plate, and forms a satisfactory piece of workmanship.

# Modern Traction Engines

The gearing plays a very important part in the construction of traction engines, but so many improvements have recently been made in the arrangement of the gearing, and in the quality of the steel of which it is cast, that little or no fear respecting the failure is entertained, and a breakdown in steel gearing is a rare occurrence. Many of the modern road engines are fitted with two countershafts, in which case the fast and

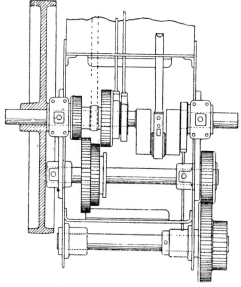

FIG. 182. GEARING IN BOX BRACKET

slow speed wheels and pinions can be placed inside the box-brackets. There is then no overhanging gearing on the crank-shaft, and the remaining wheels outside are placed as close to the bearing as possible. It is urged that the inside gearing wears more evenly, and the wheels are more rigidly maintained in truth ; another advantage is that the sizes of the pinions and wheels can be regulated to the exact requirements. One defect of all the outside gear engines, save Messrs. Burrell's, consists in causing the slow-speed pinion to slide inside the fast-gear pinion, for the purpose of keeping them as near to the bearing as possible, but this plan causes too much difference between the fast and slow travelling speeds, whereas in the inside gearing this defect is remedied. Engines having inside gearing make much less noise on the road than those with outside gearing. Fig. 182 shows in plan a neat arrangement of gearing within the box-brackets. The two pinions are keyed to the countershaft, and the two wheels slide on fixed keys on the countershaft. A lever, not shown, will place the

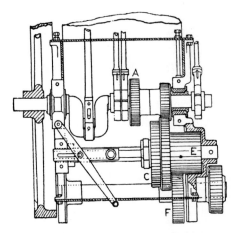

FIG. 183.   GEARING IN BOX BRACKET

wheels in any of the three positions for fast speed, out of gear, or slow speed. The wheels are now shown out of gear in the cut. The crank-shaft bearings and first countershaft bearings are combined in one casting, the remaining details are snugly placed in this box-bracket and explain themselves.

Fig. 183 represents another arrangement of gearing placed inside the box-bracket. The two pinions are keyed to the crank-shaft, the intermediate shaft is fixed, and the double-speed wheel and long pinion slide on it. In the position shown in the engraving, the engine is in

# Modern Traction Engines

slow gear. By means of the lever shown, the wheels and long pinion can be slid to the left so as to make the wheel C gear into the pinion A, and thus obtain a faster motion, the pinion E being of such a length that it remains in gear with the wheel F.

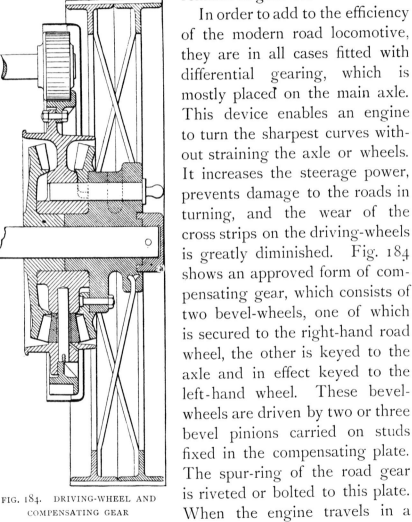

In order to add to the efficiency of the modern road locomotive, they are in all cases fitted with differential gearing, which is mostly placed on the main axle. This device enables an engine to turn the sharpest curves without straining the axle or wheels. It increases the steerage power, prevents damage to the roads in turning, and the wear of the cross strips on the driving-wheels is greatly diminished. Fig. 184 shows an approved form of compensating gear, which consists of two bevel-wheels, one of which is secured to the right-hand road wheel, the other is keyed to the axle and in effect keyed to the left-hand wheel. These bevel-wheels are driven by two or three bevel pinions carried on studs fixed in the compensating plate. The spur-ring of the road gear is riveted or bolted to this plate.

FIG. 184. DRIVING-WHEEL AND COMPENSATING GEAR

When the engine travels in a straight line, the teeth of the pinions act as drivers; the pinions do not revolve on their studs, but drive both the bevel-wheels at the same speed. When the

291

# Traction Engines

engine is required to turn to the right or the left hand, one driving-wheel having a tendency to travel faster than the other, the bevel pinions revolve on their studs to allow for this accelerated speed of one driving-wheel. In this instance the brake drum is cast with the compensating plate, as shown in the illustration. It is sometimes necessary to render the differential gearing inoperative, and this can readily be done by inserting the pin shown in one bevel-wheel and the central plate which carries the pinions. When the pin is inserted the gearing is locked. The winding-drum and compensating gear may be neatly combined, as shown by Fig. 223.

The winding-drum is generally placed on the left-hand side of the main axle. Fig. 185 shows the latest type of winding-drum, which can be disconnected from the driving-disc on which it revolves, for the purpose of paying out the steel wire rope as the engine travels forward. This effects a clear saving of time. With this form of loose drum the rope is secured to the waggon or thrashing machine at the bottom of the incline ; the engine travels forward to the top of the hill, the rope being paid out meanwhile. When it is necessary to commence winding, the driving-

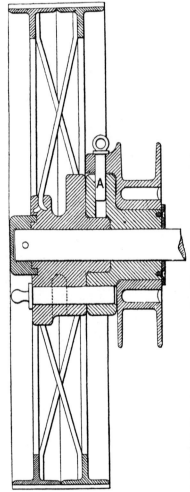

FIG. 185   DRIVING-WHEEL AND WINDING-DRUM

# Modern Traction Engines

pin is withdrawn, the small pin A is inserted in its place, and the waggon can then be pulled up the hill and connected to the drawbar of the engine for the purpose of being hauled in the usual manner. Before a fixed winding-drum could be used, the rope had to be drawn out by hand, which was unsatisfactory when compared with the improved plan.

All the handles for starting, stopping, and reversing the engine, for opening and closing the cylinder cocks, for starting the pump, for opening the sliding fire-door, for applying the brake, for testing the height of the water in the boiler, and for steering, are placed as handily as possible, so that one man may drive and steer the engine if required for short intervals.

The remarks thus far have dealt with single-cylinder traction engines, and engines not mounted on springs; but at the present day a large proportion of the traction engines manufactured are fitted with compound cylinders, and mounted on a good arrangement of springs.[1]

Nothing has been said respecting the large road locomotives built expressly for continuous hauling; to perform this severe work, week in and week out, with efficiency, the engines are made of stronger proportions than the ordinary traction engines intended for thrashing and general purposes.

In the road locomotives the shafts and axles are larger in diameter, the gearing is wider on the face and of a stronger pitch, the driving-wheels are larger in diameter, and very wide on face. Two tanks are provided; the brake acts on the rims of both the driving-wheels. They are usually mounted on a good arrangement of springs at the hind and front end of the engine.

[1] The method of mounting traction engines on springs has been dealt with in Chapter VII.

# Traction Engines

An awning, covering the driver and the tender, are usual accessories; the engine parts are screened from view by side plates, and the flywheel is of the disc type. A longer and stouter steel wire rope is provided on the slip winding-drum. Many such engines on the compound system are being built for traversing rough ground and hauling heavy loads in all parts of the world.

FIG. 186. TRACTION ENGINE BY MESSRS. ALLCHIN, NORTHAMPTON

Following these introductory remarks, the productions of the various English makers will be taken in alphabetical order.

### MESSRS. W. ALLCHIN AND CO.

Fig. 186 shows the gearing side of a single-cylinder general-purpose traction engine. The cylinder is steam-jacketed and efficiently drained, the liner is of special cast-iron to ensure durability. Some portion of the gearing is placed between the bearings of the side plates,

# Modern Traction Engines

thus avoiding overneck pinions on the crank-shaft. Most of the leading makers now use the inside gearing four-shaft type of traction engine, of which this is an example. The winding-drum contains sixty yards of steel wire rope, which can be run out as the engine travels forward. It will be seen from the illustration that the feed-pump is placed inside the horn-plate on the gearing side; the steerage is also arranged on the same side. A bored guide is adopted in lieu of slide bars. Some of the bearing brackets are riveted to the horn-plates; by this arrangement all the strain is taken by the plates, the rivets merely keeping the brackets in place.

It is a question whether hot-riveting the castings on is preferable to well-fitting bolts driven in with a heavy hammer. In some instances known to the writer rivets not being a good fit in the holes have worked loose; the only remedy under the circumstances was the removal of the rivets, and their places taken by bolts. No manhole is provided in the boiler barrel, but a filling hole is arranged in the cylinder-foot on the steam-chest side. Flat rods are used for the link-motion; the reversing lever and the brake are placed on the flywheel side as shown. A box is hung from the front axle for carrying loose tools. The working pressure is 140 lbs. to the square inch, while the hydraulic test pressure is 300 lbs. to the square inch.

### MESSRS. AVELING AND PORTER

The illustration, Fig. 187, represents a newly designed compound road locomotive mounted on laminated springs; the compound cylinders are placed side by side with outside valve chests. An auxiliary valve is fitted to admit high-pressure steam to the low-pressure steam chest for starting when the high-pressure crank is on the dead centre. The double-throw crank-shaft is cut from the solid ingot; some part of the gearing is placed between the side plates of the fire-box shell, which are carried upward and backward in one piece so as to support the crank-shaft, counter-shaft, and driving-axle in the most convenient position. Three pinions are employed in the compensating gear mounted on the driving-axle. A disc flywheel is provided. The wood-block brakes act on the insides of the tires of the driving-wheels, and are actuated from the foot-plate. An additional tank is carried beneath the barrel of the boiler, connected to the hind tank by means of a pipe of large diameter. On this tank a steam pump is mounted for feeding the boiler, as shown. A winding-drum is fitted on the hind axle, carrying 75 yards of steel wire rope, with brackets and guide rollers fitted on the tender. The water-lifter for filling the tanks is provided with 26 feet of india-rubber suction hose. The boiler is tested by hydraulic pressure to 300 lbs. per square inch for a working pressure of 180 lbs. The engine is fitted with two speeds. A rack is arranged round the coal bunker. The engine is mounted on an improved arrangement of laminated steel springs to both the hind and front axles, by which the springs come into operation at whatever position the road wheels may be in.[1] Sheet steel casing plates are placed round the working parts, as shown in the illustration.

Fig. 188 represents another road locomotive built by Messrs. Aveling and Porter, fitted with Boulton's wood-block wheels; these are illustrated in Figs. 189 and 190. The sections of the wheel show the construction clearly;

[1] The springs are illustrated in Chapter VII.

FIG. 187. COMPOUND ROAD LOCOMOTIVE BY MESSRS. AVELING AND PORTER, ROCHESTER

FIG. 188.  COMPOUND ROAD LOCOMOTIVE BY MESSRS. AVELING AND PORTER, ROCHESTER

# Modern Traction Engines

but the following description taken from Mr. McLaren's paper may be inserted :—

"The wheel has been brought out by Messrs. J. and H. McLaren and the late Mr. J. W. Boulton. It is being manufactured by Messrs. Aveling and Porter, and Messrs. J. and H. McLaren. It has a broad cast-iron rim $a$, with cells or slots $b$, about 6 inches square, cast

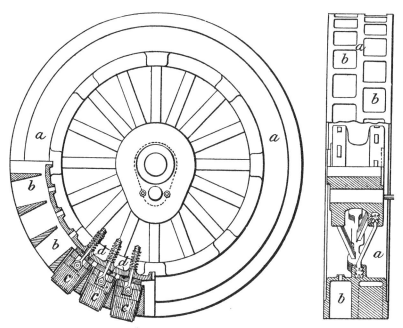

FIGS. 189, 190. BLOCK DRIVING-WHEEL

all round its circumference. These cells are 6 or 8 inches deep, closed at the bottom, but opened towards the outside of the periphery of the wheel. A hard wood block $c$ cut lengthwise of the grain, is fitted loosely into each cell, one end projecting a little beyond the rim of the wheel, and the other bearing upon an elastic pad or buffer $d$ between it and the bottom of the cell. A suitable provision is made to prevent the blocks from dropping out as the wheels revolve. When the engine is in motion the weight upon the rim of the wheel compresses the blocks so that those in the lowest and adjoining cells come in contact with the road at the same time, forming a large and continuous flat tread to the wheel, and so increasing its adhesion on the road. On paved streets the use of these wheels is specially advantageous, for not only is the tractive power of the engine enormously increased, but any possible damage to the paving setts, caused by the chipping action of ordinary wheels, is entirely avoided."

Respecting the compound engines it is said : " The additional cost is not a serious one, and is very soon repaid by the economy in fuel it ensures ; for in it the steam is used twice over, first in the high and afterwards in the low-pressure cylinder, and is not discharged through the exhaust until its pressure has been reduced almost to that of the atmosphere itself. In other words, there is more duty obtained from the steam in a compound engine than in a single-cylinder engine for the same expenditure of fuel. Another advantage of the compound engine is that of its subduing the noise of the exhaust when at work ; for perhaps in no class of engine is silent working more essential than for a road locomotive, seeing that their use is chiefly in towns or on busy suburban roads. The comparative noiselessness is due to the low pressure at which the steam is discharged into the atmosphere."

### MESSRS. CHAS. BURRELL AND SONS

Their single-crank compound general-purpose traction engine is illustrated by Fig. 191. The engine is mounted on the firm's patent system of springs under the hind axle. It will be seen that the high and low pressure cylinders are placed diagonally one above the other in the well-

# Modern Traction Engines

known arrangement. One connecting-rod and one crank are used; one set of link-motion reversing-gear is employed. The first-motion gearing is placed outside the horn-plate as shown; their patent clutch-gear is used for throwing the fast and slow speed pinions in and out of gear. A wood-lined brake band is applied to a flange cast on the double-speed wheel on the countershaft.

FIG. 191.   COMPOUND TRACTION ENGINE
MESSRS. CHAS. BURRELL AND SONS, THETFORD

Figs. 192 and 193 show two views of Messrs. Burrell's latest 10 horse-power nominal compound road loco-motive, mounted on laminated springs at the fore and hind parts of the engine. The cylinders are placed side by side; the pistons and connecting-rods transmit motion to a double-throw crank-shaft; the crank-pins are set at right angles to each other, 90 degs.

# Traction Engines

It will be seen that the slide-valves are placed outside so as to be easily accessible for adjustment and repairs. The governors of the high-speed type are placed in a cast-iron casing arranged on the top cover of the

FIG. 192.   COMPOUND ROAD LOCOMOTIVE
MESSRS. CHAS. BURRELL AND SONS, THETFORD

cylinder.   A Ramsbottom safety-valve is placed on the top cover also.   The double-speed gearing is arranged on the firm's well-known system, using their patent clutch-gear; the clutch-gear is illustrated on page 231 of *Steam Locomotion on Common Roads*.   The engine is

FIG. 193. COMPOUND ROAD LOCOMOTIVE. MESSRS. CHAS. BURRELL AND SONS, THETFORD

X

# Modern Traction Engines

mounted on plate springs ; it is fitted with side plates, a disc flywheel, an awning over the driver, and a coal-rack. A water-lifter is placed on the fore tank. Powerful block-brakes are fitted to the rims of the driving-wheels.

## MESSRS. CLAYTON AND SHUTTLEWORTH

The first illustration, Fig. 194, represents a general-purpose traction engine, in the design of which are embodied all the up-to-date improvements of the day. The

FIG. 194. TRACTION ENGINE
MESSRS. CLAYTON AND SHUTTLEWORTH, LINCOLN

boiler is made entirely of steel and stayed for a working pressure of 140 lbs. to the square inch. The top of the fire-box is stayed directly to the arch-plate of the outer shell ; it can be more easily kept clean than was the case with the roofing bars formerly used, which afford lodgment for scale and sediment. These roofing stays are placed vertically, and pitched four inches apart; they are screwed in the fire-box top and the arch-plate, the outside end is riveted over, the fire-box end is secured with a nut and a suitable joint between the nut and the plate. Boilers of this type have been used for many years with very good results. Figs. 195 and 196 represent a side view and an end view of a large compound road locomotive mounted on springs, intended for colonial purposes. The engine has been designed for hauling heavy loads for long distances without frequent stoppages for taking in water or fuel.

The high and low pressure cylinders are placed side by side, the slide-valves are arranged above the cylinders, and actuated by radial valve-gear, such as, or similar to Joy's, which produces an excellent distribution of steam to both cylinders. By the removal of the top cover of the cylinder, access can be gained to the high and low pressure slide-valves, the throttle-valve, and the stop-valve, for adjustment, etc. In this arrangement of engine, excentrics are dispensed with for working the slide-valves; the two-speed first-motion gearing can be placed inside the box-brackets in a four-shaft compound engine without crowding. The same gearing can be used throughout as for a single-cylinder traction engine. The slide-valve faces and valve-rods being parallel with the centre line of the cylinders, the slide-faces are more easily tooled and the valves are readily accessible for setting, examination, and repairs. By this patent system an economy of space on the crank-shaft is effected, which permits of the introduction of three-speed gearing when desired. High-pressure steam can be admitted to the low-pressure steam chest for starting, so that the engine for the time being will work the same as an ordinary double-cylinder engine. These

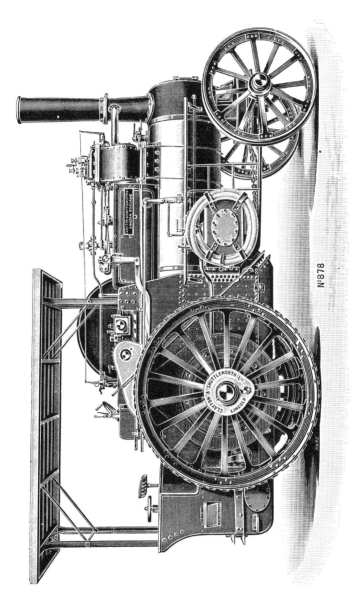

N°878

FIG. 195. PATENT COMPOUND ROAD LOCOMOTIVE MOUNTED ON SPRINGS

MESSRS. CLAYTON AND SHUTTLEWORTH, LINCOLN

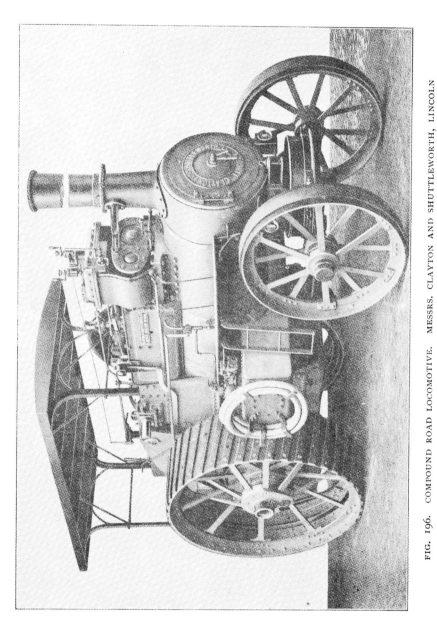

FIG. 196. COMPOUND ROAD LOCOMOTIVE. MESSRS. CLAYTON AND SHUTTLEWORTH, LINCOLN

# Modern Traction Engines

engines are made under Shuttleworth and Fletcher's patent.

The radial valve-gear is shown by Fig. 197. A section of the compound cylinder by Fig. 198, designed by the writer and patented in 1899. No. 16,668.

The engine is supplied with a supplementary tank beneath the boiler barrel, this tank is connected to the hind tank by means of a large pipe with a cock, which can be shut off to prevent the loss of water when travelling up steep hills. A Worthington or other steam pump is mounted on the tank, and draws water from the tank for feeding the boiler. An injector is also employed which draws its supply from the hind tank. On this fore tank is also mounted a water-lifter with 25 feet of hose pipe for drawing water from a river or wayside stream into the tanks; the work of filling both the tanks only takes a few minutes. A powerful block-brake acts on the periphery of both the hind driving-wheels. A slip winding-drum supplied with 75 yards of steel wire rope is mounted on the hind axle; the rope can be paid out as the engine travels forward, effecting a great saving of time and labour. The winding-drum offers the readiest means of pulling loads out of places inaccessible to the engine, or for hauling waggons up very steep inclines. As the engine travels up the steep bank the rope is drawn out during the ascent; when the engine reaches the top, the brakes are applied and the wheels are scotched; the engine proceeds to haul one or more waggons up the hill, or across a river, and then passes on the journey in the usual manner. The driving-wheels are 7 ft. diameter, and 2 ft. across the face; they are built up of three steel tee-rings with inside tire-plates and the usual diagonal cross strips. The leading-wheels are 4 ft. 6 in. diameter,

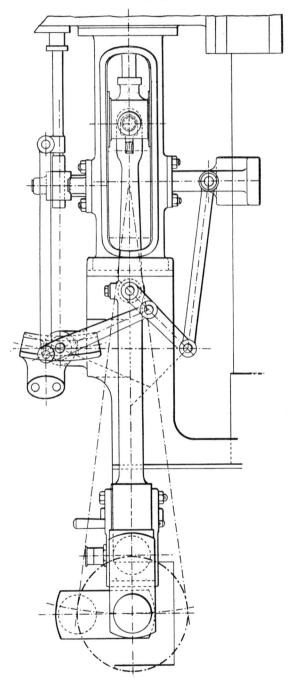

FIG. 197. RADIAL VALVE GEAR ON PATENT COMPOUND ROAD LOCOMOTIVES
MESSRS. CLAYTON AND SHUTTLEWORTH, LINCOLN

# Modern Traction Engines

and 9 inches on the face. An auxiliary valve-gear is applied to these compound engines for admitting a breath of high-pressure steam into the low-pressure valve-chest for starting, or for getting out of difficult

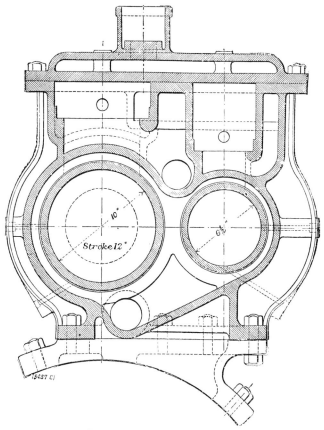

FIG. 198. SECTION OF COMPOUND CYLINDER
MESSRS. CLAYTON AND SHUTTLEWORTH, LINCOLN

places; the valve is closed by a spring as soon as it is released. A footboard extends along the boiler barrel for giving access to the engine for lubricating, cleaning, or adjusting the working parts; a ladder is also provided, as shown. A disc flywheel and side-plates are fitted so as to reduce the risk of frightening horses. The engine

# Traction Engines

is provided with a light awning over the foot-plate and the hind part of the engine. Two mudholes are provided in the corners of the saddle-plate which facilitate the raking out, as shown by the sketch, Fig. 199. There are three other mudholes, also arranged in suitable places. The steering-gear chain barrel is placed beneath the fore tank, and the chains lead off quite straight to the quadrant on the fore axle. The working pressure is 180 lbs. to the square inch, the hydraulic test pressure 300 lbs. The travelling speeds are three and five miles an hour. Many road locomotives are provided with three speeds—two, four, and six miles an hour. Some of the dimensions of the engine are given in the table below.

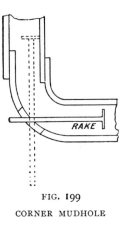

FIG. 199

CORNER MUDHOLE

### TABLE VII.

| | |
|---|---|
| Diameter of the high-pressure cylinder . . | 7 in. |
| Diameter of the low-pressure cylinder . . | 11 in. |
| Length of stroke . . . . | 12 in. |
| Diameter of crank-shaft . . . | 4 in. |
| Diameter of main axle . . . | 5½ in. |
| Diameter of driving-wheel . . . | 7 ft. 0 in. |
| Width of driving-wheel . . . | 2 ft. 0 in. |
| Diameter of leading-wheel . . . | 4 ft. 6 in. |
| Diameter of flywheel . . . | 4 ft. 6 in. |
| Number of boiler tubes . . . | 48. |
| Diameter of boiler tubes . . . | 2 in. |
| Grate area for inferior coal . . . | 7·5 sq. ft. |
| Heating surface for inferior coal . . | 176 sq. ft. |
| Tank capacity . . . . | 410 gall. |
| Total length of engine . . . | 19 ft. |
| Total width of engine . . . | 7 ft. 7 in. |
| Height to the top of the flywheel . . | 9 ft. 8 in. |

One of Messrs. Clayton and Shuttleworth's arrangements of spring-mounting is illustrated in Chapter VII.

FIG. 200. COMPOUND ROAD LOCOMOTIVE WITH AWNING. MESSRS. CLAYTON AND SHUTTLEWORTH, LINCOLN

# Modern Traction Engines

A second arrangement of spring mounting can be applied, in which the movement of the axle and the first countershaft in no way affect the mesh of the gearing.

Fig. 200 shows another compound road locomotive, provided with an awning from end to end. This engine is mounted on springs at the fire-box and also at the smoke-box end.

A considerable number of these road locomotives have been shipped to Australia, South Africa, New Zealand, Egypt, France, Spain, Portugal, etc. Several of them are used for ploughing by direct traction in Africa and Europe, special provision being made for attaching the ploughs to the tender of the engine. Quite recently, compound road locomotives have been shipped with ash-pans suitably made for the engines to cross rivers, three or four feet deep, without the water putting out the fires. Another 8 horse-power road locomotive in Russia, fitted with oil-burning apparatus, hauls loads of 27 tons up a mountain-side, over the worst possible roads, to a height of 300 feet, part of the incline being 1 in 9. An ordinary 8 horse-power traction engine is constantly hauling $33\frac{1}{2}$ tons gross in three trucks, at four miles an hour on the level, and up a rise of 1 in 15. The same engine travels sixteen miles on one filling of the tanks.

MESSRS. E. FODEN, SONS, AND CO., SANDBACH

The illustration, Fig. 201, shows a compound road locomotive, built for the British Government by Messrs. Foden. The advantages of the compound road locomotive are as follows. The strain on the gearing is reduced to a minimum, or less than half required to move the same load with a single engine. They can be moved at a slow rate—an important advantage in hooking on ;

# Traction Engines

they are able to start a heavy load gradually, whereas with a single engine the load is started with a jerk. The strain on the gearing, and therefore on the travelling-wheels, being uniform throughout the stroke of the engine, enables it to carry better over soft, greasy roads. Priming is practically done away with in the compound engine.

The boiler is made throughout of Siemens' mild steel; the barrel is $\frac{7}{16}$ in. thick, the fire-box $\frac{3}{8}$ in. thick, the tube and horn-plates are $\frac{1}{2}$ in. thick. A 6-horse compound road locomotive contains fifty-six $1\frac{3}{4}$ in. tubes ; the working pressure is 160 lbs. per square inch. The cylinders are steam–jacketed ; the steam chests are placed outside each cylinder, thus rendering the valves easy of access for refacing or adjustment. A double high-pressure arrangement is fitted to the compound cylinders, by means of which high-pressure steam can be admitted into both cylinders directly from the boiler, and each exhausts independently in the chimney. For starting heavy loads, getting out of soft places, or for ascending steep inclines, this auxiliary gear is of great advantage. Ramsbottom piston-rings are used, forming a steam-tight joint with the cylinder. The large end bearing of the connecting-rod is of phosphor-bronze ; the end of the rod is forged solid, and afterwards the space for the bearing is cut away, forming a fork-end ; the bearing is secured by dovetailed steel block and bolt, cottar, and pins. Balance weights are strapped to the crank sweeps. The compensating-gear centre is riveted to the main spur-ring by plug-fit rivets, supporting in position two strong steel pinions secured by large turned pins ; one of the bevel-wheels is keyed to the axle, and the other riveted to the travelling - wheel. Some of Messrs. Foden's driving-wheels are fitted with tough

FIG. 201. COMPOUND ROAD LOCOMOTIVE

Y

# Modern Traction Engines

cast-iron rims, but in the engine illustrated steel tee-rings are used of large diameter, with the usual cross strips ; the riveted holes are drilled in position, and the riveting done by pneumatic machinery ; the two webs of the tee-rings are held together sideways by means of large bolts, as shown. The fore wheels are made with cast - iron rims, hooped with mild - steel bands ; the bosses are fitted with phosphor-bronze bushes. Strong laminated springs carry the hind part of the engine. Two or three travelling speeds are fitted to suit the requirements of customers. A fore tank is provided under the boiler barrel, connected to the hind tank in the usual manner ; the pump draws its supply from the front tank as shown ; the pump-plunger is cased with brass. Side plates are fitted for screening the working parts from view ; a disc flywheel is also used for a similar purpose. An awning and a wood rack are included in the outfit. The high-speed governor acts on an equilibrium throttle-valve. A Ramsbottom safety-valve is mounted on the top of the cylinder. A winding-drum is keyed to the main axle. An efficient brake acts on the steel angles bolted to the rims of the driving-wheel. The main axle runs in phosphor-bronze bearings, and the gearing is all of crucible cast-steel from machine-cut patterns. Messrs. Foden's new spring arrangement has been dealt with in a previous chapter.

MESSRS. W. FOSTER AND CO.

A single-cylinder traction engine is illustrated by Fig. 202. The special feature consists of an awning covering the whole of the engine from end to end. The cylinder is cast from close-grained tough iron of special hardness ; the starting-valve is placed in the highest part of the cylinder casing. By removing the steam-chest cover, the slide-valve and the throttle-valve may be examined while steam is up. A Ramsbottom safety-valve is mounted on the top cover of the cylinder, as shown. It is a four-shaft type of engine, having the first-motion gearing between the side plates and the bearings. The sliding spur-wheels are fitted on keys cut out of the solid shaft. A brake is supplied, the sheave of which is cast with the hub of one of the driving-wheels. The cross-arm governors control the equilibrium throttle-valve. A platform is fixed on the side of the boiler barrel, which gives access for cleaning and oiling or adjusting the wearing parts. The driving and leading wheels are of the usual design, the former having steel cross strips $\frac{3}{4}$ inch thick; the feed-pump is placed on the boiler barrel. The starting and regulating can be done from the tender, as shown. All the details are clearly illustrated.

The next illustration, Fig. 203, shows a newly designed compound road locomotive fitted with three travelling speeds and mounted on springs.

The dimensions of the steam-jacketed cylinders are $6\frac{3}{4}$ in. and 10 in. diameter by 12 in. stroke. Siemens-Martin steel plates are employed in the construction of the boiler, which is suitably stayed and constructed for safely working at a pressure of 180 lbs. per square inch. The driving-wheels are 7 ft. diameter by 1 ft. 6 in. width on face, built up in the usual manner with cross strips to comply with the Acts of Parliament. All the shafts are of steel, the crank-shaft being 4 in. diameter; the dips are cut out of the solid forging; the second-motion shaft is $3\frac{3}{8}$ in. diameter; the third-motion shaft is $4\frac{1}{4}$ in. diameter, the main axle being 6 in. diameter. The cylinder is fitted with a converting-valve, by means

FIG. 202.   TRACTION ENGINE BY MESSRS. W. FOSTER AND CO., LINCOLN

FIG. 203. COMPOUND ROAD LOCOMOTIVE. MESSRS. FOSTER AND CO., LINCOLN

FIG. 204.   COMPOUND ROAD LOCOMOTIVE.   MESSRS. JOHN FOWLER AND CO., LEEDS

# Modern Traction Engines

of which the working of the engine can be changed from compound to a double-cylinder high-pressure engine, useful for starting with a heavy load behind, for mounting a steep gradient, or passing over rough ground. In order to make a change from compound to high-pressure working, both cylinders exhaust into one common exhaust-pipe. By means of the auxiliary valve it is possible to admit high-pressure steam to the low-pressure cylinder only, and thus work as a single-cylinder engine. The arrangement of the spring mounting is illustrated and described in Chapter VII. The gearing is proportioned for giving three speeds, of $2\frac{1}{2}$, 4, and 6 miles an hour, when the engine is running at 250 revolutions a minute. A single clutch lever puts any of the speeds out of gear, or into mesh, without the possibility of two sets of gearing being put into gear at the same time.

From the illustration it will be seen that the engine is supplied with a supplementary water-tank mounted beneath the boiler barrel, fitted with a filling pocket, a water-lifter, and a hose-pipe, and a Moore steam-pump as a duplicate feeding arrangement. The steering-chain barrel is placed beneath the tank; the chains are attached to an angle-iron ring on the front axle, to which a round box is hung. The front axle is provided with a plate spring. Side plates are fitted to the engine for screening the working parts; a disc flywheel and an awning form part of the equipment.

MESSRS. JOHN FOWLER AND CO.

The first illustration, Fig. 204, represents a type of road locomotive suitable for pioneer work. A similar one was sent to Uganda. It is a compound engine fitted with a fore tank, an awning, a disc flywheel, and all the

# Traction Engines

equipments for making long journeys without constant stoppages for taking in water, etc. Road locomotives of this type have been shipped to the Colonies. The following is a brief account of work done in Australia. "A load of wool was hauled 40 miles, part of the journey being across country without any road whatever. The engine crossed Lachlan River with banks 50 feet deep, and pulled the load after her with ease; the engine was sent up country 300 miles in a time of drought for irrigating purposes; the pump driven by the engine delivered 2,000 gallons per minute, and was kept running night and day."

Fig. 205 represents a compound general-purpose engine. The slide-valves are arranged near the top of the cylinder casing; the valve-rods are set at an angle to point to the centre of the crank-shaft. An auxiliary valve is provided for sending high-pressure steam into the low-pressure valve chest, so that for the time being the engine will work as a double-cylinder non-compound engine. The valve closes automatically when released by the driver. Stauffer's lubricators are used for the front and hind wheel naves. An inside tire is fitted in the driving-wheels; the front wheel spokes are all riveted to the same side of the tee steel ring; instead of being riveted on each side alternately as is usually done, the makers have some good reason for deviating from the general method of construction. A strong draw-back lug is fitted to the fore carriage locking-plate, a circular box is hung to the front axle, the chimney is of extra large diameter. Mudholes are provided in the corners of the saddle-plate; the horn-plates are double-riveted to the saddle-plate and arch-plate as shown. A cap covers the key end of the fly-wheel. The engine is provided with a winding-drum

FIG. 205.   COMPOUND TRACTION ENGINE BY MESSRS. JOHN FOWLER AND CO., LEEDS

# Modern Traction Engines

and wire rope, a water-lifter, and hose-pipe. During some trials of a 10-horse nominal road locomotive (not illustrated) about 7 cwt. of coal was sufficient for a journey of 30 miles, and 430 gallons of water was carried, a fresh supply of which was required every 12 to 15 miles. The engine hauled 33 tons gross up a continuous rise of 1½ miles, part of which is as steep as 1 in 13. The driving-wheels are 7 ft. diameter and 2 ft. wide on face, fitted with tee-iron cross strips. Three speeds are provided—the slow, 1½ to 3 miles an hour; the middle gear gives 2½ to 4½ miles an hour; and the fast gear from 6 to 8 miles an hour. Messrs. Fowler's spring-mounting arrangement has been described in Chapter VII. A large compound engine made by the firm, hauls five heavy vans containing the paraphernalia for a steam circus or roundabout. The engine draws the apparatus during the daytime; at night it also keeps the machine in full swing, and drives a dynamo for lighting up the whole show. On the road the engine hauls the five vans and water-cart at a good speed up some of the steepest hills in Kent, Surrey, Berks, Bucks, and Oxfordshire. An engine of this type started from Leeds on a journey of 88 miles with a load of 45 tons; the load consisted of 10 waggons of switchback machinery; the time occupied was 28 hours.

A considerable number of road locomotives are used in many districts for hauling huge boilers, machinery, and other commodities that the railways are unable to carry. By the employment of these road trains some traders are practically independent of the railway companies, and the economy of steam haulage is proved beyond doubt. *The Engineer* recently remarked : " Hitherto the transports for the Dover and Canterbury manœuvres have gone by rail ; they are now being taken by road by traction engines. It is suggested that traders and farmers might adopt the same system by judicious co-operation. Many classes of merchandise would suffer nothing from the longer time spent in conveyance. The military authorities reckon that they are making a saving of fifty per cent." As an instance of the economy secured by the employment of road locomotives, may be mentioned the removal of a large boiler which cost £1 15s. If horses had done the work, this would have cost over £5, occupying a much longer time, and taking up considerably more room.

FIG. 206.    TRACTION ENGINE.    MESSRS. R. GARRETT AND SONS, LEISTON

MESSRS. R. GARRETT AND SONS

The great demand which exists for a good traction engine has induced the above firm to devote special attention to the production of an engine in which are embodied all recent improvements. Fig. 206 represents a single-cylinder general-purpose traction engine. The chief characteristic feature is the corrugated fire-box, Fig. 207, introduced in 1876. This fire-box has been

# Modern Traction Engines

extensively used. The makers claim the following advantages for it:—

Elasticity of construction means durability, and as the crown of this fire-box, owing to its shape, requires no staying, it is free to expand and contract without fear of straining or cracking. Apart from durability, its camber or arch-like construction, is the source of far greater strength than is found in flat-topped fire-boxes.

GARRETT'S CORRUGATED FIREBOX.

FIG. 207

In addition to these two good points of increased durability and strength, this fire-box has also the advantage of extreme efficiency, as, owing to its form, it contains more heating surface than any other fire-box of equal grate area; and it must be remembered that the experiments of Monsieur Petiet have proved that about one half of the total evaporation of a boiler takes place in the immediate vicinity of the fire-box.

Besides strength, durability, and efficiency, absence of incrustation and freedom from the collection of mud on the crown are two very noticeable qualities of this fire-box, and must be experienced to be thoroughly appreciated. The natural expansion and contraction are alone sufficient to prevent incrustation, as any thin coating of mud or scale which may collect is immediately broken up on the next occasion of a change in temperature (with the consequent alteration in area and form of crown plate), and carried away by the violent ebullition which takes place above this—the hottest—region of the fire-box, to settle ultimately in a specially designed mud-pocket from which it is easily removed.

z

# Traction Engines

On the top of the cylinder are the starting-valve and the throttle-valve case, which are so arranged that the slide-valve can be examined whilst the engine is under steam. A Mollerup oil-press is provided, by means of which the oil is forced against the steam pressure into the valve chest, where it intermixes with the steam, and lubricates the valve faces and piston. The governors are of the Pickering type, acting direct upon a balanced cylindrical valve. The governor is fixed upon the cylinder: it and the equilibrium throttle-valve can be taken out for inspection while the steam is up. It will be seen that the engine is of the four-shaft type, the advantages of which have been explained. A winding-drum and steel rope are included; from the position of the rope rollers it will be seen that the rope is paid off from the top of the drum. The feed-pump inlet is bolted to a steel-faced connection, provided with a cock between the check valve and the boiler. A platform running the whole length of one side of the boiler barrel is supplied, whereby oiling and cleaning are greatly facilitated. Before leaving the works the engines are tried in the usual manner; the boilers are tested by hydraulic pressure to 240 lbs. per square inch, and by steam pressure to 150 lbs. for a regular working pressure of 135 lbs. per square inch.

MESSRS. J. AND H. McLAREN

Some road locomotives, similar to the one illustrated by Fig. 208, have been shipped by Messrs. McLaren to South Africa. The engine has compound side-by-side cylinders of 7 in. and 11 in. diameter; it has developed 70 horse-power on the brake, and in an actual test hauled a load of 55 tons up an incline of 1 in 12. The fire-box is of extra size for burning inferior fuel. A distance of

FIG. 208. ROAD LOCOMOTIVE BY MESSRS. J. AND H. MCLAREN, LEEDS

# Modern Traction Engines

12 miles can be traversed on bad roads with one tank full of water. The driving-wheels are of great width, so as to travel over soft ground without sinking. All the shafts are of great strength. The engine is mounted at the fire-box end on the spring arrangement as illustrated in Chapter VII. Laminated springs also carry the front end of the engine. The steerage of the front wheels is often effected by an arrangement of worm and rack, so as to be positive in its action, and without the back-lash inevitable with chain steerage. This renders it more reliable in travelling along roads which are frequently mere shelves on mountain-sides, and where an accident to the steering-gear might involve a most serious accident.

One of Messrs. McLaren's traction engines, built for colonial requirements, has been used for wool cartage in New Zealand, and has travelled nearly 70,000 miles without a crack in the fire-box or the breaking of a spring; this shows that they have succeeded in adapting the engine to the tasks it has to perform.

Figs. 209 and 210 show one of McLaren's traction-engine boilers of the multitubular type. It is an excellent generator, and forms a support upon which the engine parts are bolted. The employment of traction engines for industrial purposes is extending. Mr. John McLaren gives some interesting particulars of work done, which are quoted.

In the Sheffield district a number of men, who call themselves "contractors," have each acquired from three to half a dozen traction engines, and either let them out on hire by the day, or themselves undertake the moving of heavy loads. In this way large quantities of flour, coal, and other materials are daily sent to the outlying villages in the Peak district, which has hitherto been without any railway communication. One contractor is largely employed at iron and steel works, moving heavy articles such as armour-plates, hammerblocks, and other weights occasionally exceeding fifty tons. He is also employed in hauling by road boilers, spur-wheels, stern-posts, and other bulky articles which cannot be conveniently carried by rail. These are frequently taken long distances, such as to Newcastle, Liverpool, etc., without any hitch or trouble. Another contractor in the Peak district traverses a distance of

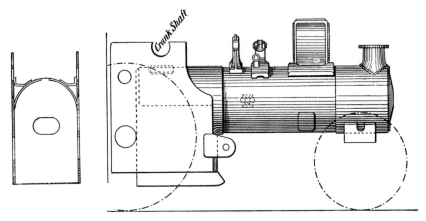

FIGS. 209, 210. TRACTION ENGINE BOILER BY MESSRS. McLAREN, LEEDS

32 miles daily, with an 8 horse-power engine. The trip consists of a 16-mile journey to the railway station with the empty waggons, returning the same distance with a load of 13 tons of coal. The weight of the two waggons is $5\frac{1}{2}$ tons, making a gross load of $18\frac{1}{2}$ tons, exclusive of the weight of the engine. This performance has been maintained for several years, making an average of 192 miles per week. In summer weather, with good roads, the outward journey has been frequently made with a load of about 12 tons of limestone for road repairs. This involved a detour of several miles, which

# Modern Traction Engines

brought the average distance travelled up to 205 miles per week.

As an instance of what may be done with traction engines, when intelligently worked, reference may be made to the experience of the Cliffe Hill Granite Company, Markfield, Leicester, where two 8-horse traction engines have been regularly worked for several years. The quarry is situated about three miles from the railway siding, and each of the engines makes about five trips per day, hauling an average load of about 13 tons

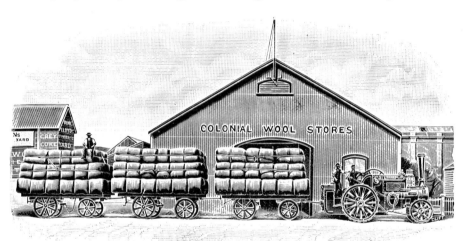

FIG. 211.   ROAD LOCOMOTIVE AND TRAIN.   MESSRS. McLAREN, LEEDS

per trip in two waggons. By this means about 40,000 tons per year are hauled out by the two engines, in addition to a large quantity of coal and other inward traffic brought home from the station. Except that the gradients, which are not very steep in any case, are generally in favour of the load, this may be taken as a fair average result, only it must be borne in mind that some trouble is taken to see that the engines are never stopped, either from snow or other obstacles. In winter when there is snow on the ground it is immediately

# Traction Engines

cleared off by a large squad of quarry employés, as in the event of the road becoming blocked the quarry would be laid idle, and all the workers temporarily thrown out of employment. When the engines were put on to this road at first, they cut through the soft country roads in several places. These places were filled up with waste from the quarry and covered with a thick coating of granite, and, though the original cost was rather heavy, the work was done thoroughly, and the advantage of this is now being felt in the reduced cost of maintenance.

Another illustration, Fig. 211, shows one of McLaren's compound spring traction engines on its arrival from an up-country station with about 20 tons of wool behind it. The journey of 150 miles in all was actually accomplished in $2\frac{1}{2}$ days from starting out to home again.

MESSRS. MARSHALL, SONS, AND CO.

One of this firm's general-purpose compound traction engines is illustrated by Fig. 212. The steam-jacketed cylinders are mounted on a steel-plate seating near the smoke-box end of the boiler, as shown; the ends of the guides are provided with a similar seating-block. The slide-valves are placed near the top of the cylinder casing; the valve faces are set at an angle, so that the valve-rods point to the centre of the crank-shaft; by this plan the valves are fairly easy of access for setting and adjustment and for scraping up the valve faces when worn. Guides for the valve-rods are mounted on the trunks, the governors also are provided with a seating on the bored guides near the valve-rods.

The sides of the fire-box shell are carried upward and backward for supporting the bearings of the crank-shaft, the counter-shafts, and axle in the usual manner.

FIG. 212.   COMPOUND TRACTION ENGINE BY MESSRS. MARSHALL, SONS, AND CO., GAINSBROUGH

# Modern Traction Engines

Flanged cross-plates connect the two side-plates together. The throat or saddle-plate is flanged to a large
radius, so that the mudholes can be placed at the
corners. The worm and worm-wheel of the steerage
gear are placed inside the chain-barrel brackets. The
next engine is illustrated by Fig. 213; it is a compound
traction engine fitted with a fore tank, and side-plates

FIG. 213. COMPOUND TRACTION ENGINE
MESSRS. MARSHALL, SONS, AND CO., GAINSBOROUGH

for screening the working parts. It will be seen that
the general details are similar to the one previously
illustrated. The steering-gear is fixed on the fore tank,
the stay bar is attached to the tank also. A wood rack
in the tender, and a box on the front axle, are included
in the outfit of the engine. The first-motion gearing is
placed between the bearings of the box brackets; the
rest of the gearing is well cased in to protect it from
mud and dust.

# Traction Engines

MESSRS. RANSOMES, SIMS, AND JEFFERIES

The agricultural locomotive illustrated by Fig. 214 is intended for driving a thrashing machine or for general hauling purposes on a farm, in fact for all the uses to which steam can be applied as a motive-power in farm work.

From the illustration it will be seen that the engine is of the four-shaft type, so that any advantages of the inside gearing and the two countershafts are secured in this example. The engine is fitted with four slide-bars, with cast-iron slipper blocks. An outside feed-pump is provided, which can be started or stopped from the tender. Most of the details are of the usual form now adopted by all the leading makers. It may be remarked that this engine was designed a few years ago by the writer.

The boiler is made entirely of steel, and is of the most approved locomotive design. It is of ample capacity, and of full strength for working continuously at 140 lbs. pressure per square inch, being tested by hydraulic pressure to 240 lbs. The longitudinal seams are double-riveted, and the edges of the plates planed. All riveting and flanging are done by hydraulic pressure. The fire-box is of special fire-box-quality steel, and is constructed to burn any description of coal, but if required for burning wood, shavings, or straw, it can be made of extra-large dimensions. The tops of the fire-box are stayed directly to the arch-plate, thus enabling the fire-box tops to be kept free from scale and sediment.

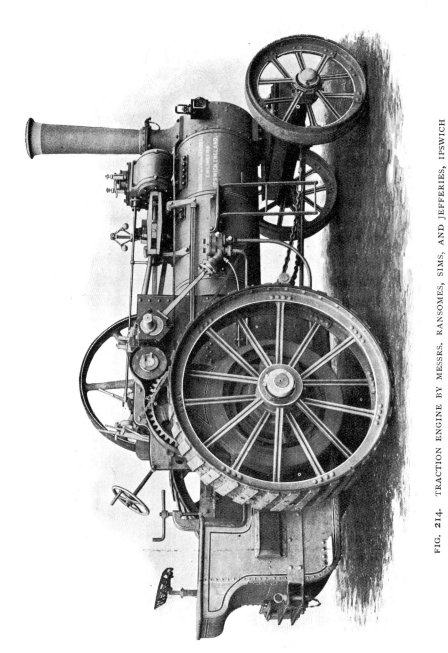

FIG. 214. TRACTION ENGINE BY MESSRS. RANSOMES, SIMS, AND JEFFERIES, IPSWICH

# Modern Traction Engines

The following table gives a few dimensions of the four sizes manufactured with single cylinders :—

TABLE VIII.

|  | 6 Nominal H.-P. | 7 Nominal H.-P. | 8 Nominal H.-P. | 10 Nominal H.-P. |
|---|---|---|---|---|
| Diameter of cylinders . . . | 8 in. | 8½ in. | 9 in. | 10 in. |
| Length of stroke . . . . | 10 in. | 12 in. | 12 in. | 12 in. |
| Diameter of flywheel . . . | 4 ft. 6 in. | 4 ft. 6 in. | 4 ft. 6 in. | 4 ft. 6 in. |
| Revolutions per minute . . | 160 rev. | 160 rev. | 160 rev. | 160 rev. |
| Diameter of driving-wheels . . | 5 ft. 9 in. | 5 ft. 9 in. | 6 ft. 3 in. | 6 ft. 6 in. |
| Width of driving-wheels . . | 1 ft. 4 in. | 1 ft. 4 in. | 1 ft. 4 in. | 1 ft. 6 in. |
| Extreme length of engine . . | 17 ft. 2 in. | 17 ft. 9 in. | 18 ft. 6 in. | 19 ft. 6 in. |
| Extreme width over axles . . | 6 ft. 6 in. | 6 ft. 11 in. | 6 ft. 11 in. | 7 ft. 6 in. |
| Height to top of flywheel . . | 8 ft. 6 in. | 8 ft. 9 in. | 9 ft. 0 in. | 9 ft. 2 in. |
| Weight of engine when empty . | 8 tons. | 9 tons. | 10 tons. | 11 tons. |
| Weight with coal and water ready for work . . . . | 8¾ tons. | 10 tons. | 11¼ tons. | 12½ tons. |
| Speeds per hour . . . . | 1½ & 3 m. | 1½ & 3 m. | 1½ & 3 m. | 1½ & 3 m. |

The next table gives the sizes of the compound engines :—

TABLE IX.

|  | 8 Nom. H.-P. Compound. | 10 Nom. H.-P. Compound. |
|---|---|---|
| Diameter of high-pressure cylinder . . . | 6¼ in. | 7 in. |
| ,, low-pressure ,, . . . | 10 in. | 11 in. |
| Length of stroke . . . . . . | 12 in. | 12 in. |
| Diameter of flywheel . . . . . | 4 ft. 6 in. | 4 ft. 6 in. |
| Revolutions per minute . . . . . | 160 rev. | 160 rev. |
| Diameter of driving-wheels . . . . | 6 ft. 3 in. | 6 ft. 6 in. |
| Width of driving-wheels . . . . . | 1 ft. 4 in. | 1 ft. 6 in. |
| Extreme length of engine . . . . | 18 ft. 6 in. | 19 ft. 6 in. |
| Extreme width over axles . . . . | 6 ft. 11 in. | 7 ft. 6 in. |
| Height to top of flywheel . . . . | 9 ft. | 9 ft. 2 in. |
| Weight of engine when empty . . . . | 10½ tons. | 11½ tons. |
| Weight with coal and water ready for work . | 11¾ tons. | 13 tons. |
| Speeds per hour . . . . . . | 1½ and 3 m. | 1½ and 3 m. |

The illustration, Fig. 215, represents a compound road locomotive fitted for continuous hauling purposes. It will be seen that the steam chests are placed outside; making the examination, adjustment, or repairs of the slide-valves or valve faces easily accessible. The fore tank is placed in the usual position beneath the pump, the pipes from which draw the feed and return into the

# Traction Engines

tank the water that is not sent into the boiler. A water-lifter is mounted on the tank; the suction-hose may be carried on the bracket provided. The driving-wheels are of large diameter and of extra strength. The advantages of the compound engines are as follows. A saving of thirty per cent. in coal and water is effected; they can be started in any position of the cranks by means of an auxiliary valve which admits high-pressure steam to the low-pressure valve chest; they are less noisy than the single-cylinder engines; the cylinders are so proportioned that the work done is equally divided between them, thus ensuring steady running; the shocks on the crank-pins are less severe; the calls of the engine upon the boiler for steam are reduced, therefore the wear and tear of the fire-box and tubes are much diminished, and the cost of repairs reduced.

The working parts generally are of extra strength for continuous hauling, this work being of a very severe nature that unless hauling engines are well made they will soon fail.

A table of the chief dimensions of these engines is given :—

TABLE X.

|  | 8 Nominal H.-P. | 10 Nominal H.-P. |
|---|---|---|
| Diameter of high-pressure cylinder . . . | 6½ in. | 7 in. |
| „ low-pressure „ . . . | 10 in. | 11 in. |
| Length of stroke . . . . . . | 12 in. | 12 in. |
| Diameter of flywheel . . . . . | 4 ft. 6 in. | 4 ft. 6 in. |
| Revolutions per minute . . . . . | 180 rev. | 180 rev. |
| Diameter of driving-wheels . . . . | 7 ft. | 7 ft. |
| Width of driving-wheels . . . . . | 18 in. | 18 in. |
| Extreme length of engine . . . . . | 18 ft. 6 in. | 19 ft. 6 in. |
| Extreme width over axles . . . . . | 7 ft. 3 in. | 7 ft. 6 in. |
| Height to top of flywheel . . . . . | 9 ft. 6 in. | 9 ft. 6 in. |
| Weight of engine when empty . . . . | 12½ tons. | 14 tons. |
| Weight with coal and water ready for work . | 13¾ tons. | 15½ tons. |
| Speeds per hour . . . . . . | 2 and 4 miles. | 2 and 4 miles. |

FIG. 215. COMPOUND ROAD LOCOMOTIVE. MESSRS. RANSOMES, SIMS, AND JEFFERIES, IPSWICH

# Modern Traction Engines

A few particulars are given of the firm's patent compound road locomotive specially adapted for haulage
work, mounted on springs and fitted with the radial
compensating bearings. The crown of the fire-box is
stayed with wrought-iron bridges; the boiler is tested
by hydraulic pressure and subsequently under steam,
the final test being the haulage of a heavy load over
a hill road with steep gradients.

FIG. 216. ROAD LOCOMOTIVE. MESSRS. TASKER AND SONS, ANDOVER

Fig. 216 shows the engine clearly. The gearing is
arranged for three travelling speeds on the road, the
changes being quickly effected by the speed-regulating
gear. It is impossible for two speeds to be in at the
same time. The starting-valve is placed as near the top

355

of the cylinder as possible, and admits hot, dry steam to the high-pressure cylinder. An auxiliary valve is also fitted for admitting high-pressure steam into the low-pressure cylinder for starting and for emergencies. This is worked from the foot-plate. The pistons are of the Ramsbottom type; the crank-shaft is accurately balanced. A front tank is fitted beneath the boiler barrel near the

FIG. 217. THE LITTLE GIANT. MESSRS. TASKER AND SONS, ANDOVER

throat-plate, the diagonal steering-rod passing through it, as shown. The engine is provided with an awning, side protecting plates, and a disc flywheel.

Messrs. Tasker are the makers of the Little Giant traction engine, constructed to come under the Motor-car Act of 1896. It is termed of four nominal horse-power; it will develop 16 horse-power on the brake.

# Modern Traction Engines

Fig. 217 shows the engine. The cylinder is cast in one piece with the steam chest and the steam jacket. To ensure perfect relative accuracy in the bearings and to minimise steam in the motor, the crank-shaft, intermediate shaft, and main axle are all carried on the horn-plates. The engine is geared to travel at two speeds. It is mounted on a complete arrangement of laminated and coil springs, which effectually control the jar and vibration while travelling on the road.

The Little Giant is adapted for all kinds of light haulage work at moderate speeds. Being constructed to come within the requirements of the Light Locomotive Act, it is free from a multitude of restrictions with which traction engine traffic is surrounded. No licenses are required for it, and no limits are fixed for working hours. It is more under control than horses, and the fuel is much cheaper than horse-keep. The boiler is adapted for burning coal or coke. It is neatly cased in, and is provided with a disc flywheel.

Dimensions of the Little Giant made by Messrs. Tasker and Sons :—

### TABLE XI.

| | |
|---|---|
| Diameter of cylinder | $5\frac{1}{4}$ in. |
| Length of stroke | 9 in. |
| Diameter of driving-wheels | 4 ft. 0 in. |
| Width of driving-wheels | 8 in. |
| Diameter of leading-wheels | 3 ft. 0 in. |
| Width of leading-wheels | 4 in. |
| Working pressure | 150 lbs. |
| Capacity of water-tank | 60 galls. |
| Capacity of coal bunker | $1\frac{1}{4}$ cwt. |
| Travelling speed, fast | 6 miles. |
| Travelling speed, slow | 3 miles. |
| Length over all | 11 ft. 3 in. |
| Width over all | 4 ft. 6 in. |
| Height to top of chimney | 8 ft. 3 in. |
| Hydraulic test pressure | 250 lbs. |
| Weight of engine, empty | 2 tons 18 cwt. |

# Traction Engines

The eight horse-power nominal single-cylinder road locomotive shown by Fig. 218 is of the three-shaft type. In the opening sentences of this chapter, mention was made of three-shaft and four-shaft traction engines; the makers claim some advantages for their system of construction—a saving of wearing parts, a stronger, simpler,

FIG. 218.   ROAD LOCOMOTIVE BY MESSRS. WALLIS AND STEEVENS, BASINGSTOKE

and handier engine.   The fast-speed pinion is the one furthest away from the crank-shaft bearing, and the small pinion slides inside the fast-speed pinion in the usual manner.  A steam-jacketed cylinder is placed at the smoke-box end of the boiler; the jacket is in direct communication with the steam space of the boiler.  The flywheel is fitted with a wrought-iron plate to form a disc, instead of the wheel being cast on a disc as is the general practice. The engine is mounted on springs, as illustrated in Chapter VII.   This arrangement, it is stated, is simple

358

# Modern Traction Engines

and efficient; the spring motion is taken on the main axle, which is only allowed to be actuated about three-eighths of an inch. The springs in no way affect the power of the engine, " as, in the makers' opinion, results if the wheels are made to spring, as with some arrangements produced by other firms."[1] By the turning of a screw the power of the spring can be adjusted,

FIG. 219. SMALL STEAM MOTOR BY MESSRS. WALLIS AND STEEVENS

and if desired, the springs can be put out of action altogether. The fore tank is shown with the water-lifter on the top. A Ramsbottom safety-valve is mounted on the cylinder-top, the governors, winding-drum brake; an awning over the driver and a coal rack are included in the outfit. The driving-wheels are constructed of tee-rings, joint strips, and steel treads, all riveted up by machinery under a pressure of 50 tons.

The next illustration, Fig. 219, shows the flywheel side

[1] Exception will be taken to this statement, probably; no opinion is expressed by the writer.

# Traction Engines

of a three horse-power traction engine, made sufficiently light so as to run under the Light Locomotive Act of 1896. The next, Fig. 220, represents a light locomotive or steam motor drawing a loaded waggon. Where there is much work to be done, the saving effected by using steam in lieu of horses is great. These motors are not designed for the purpose of conveying passengers, or for high-speed light parcel delivery, but are made to do the work of one, two, or more heavy draft horses. For this work the makers think it is far prefer-

FIG. 220. SMALL TRACTION ENGINE
MADE BY MESSRS. WALLIS AND STEEVENS, BASINGSTOKE

able for the motor to be independent of the vehicle to be drawn. The engine is easy to handle, divides the weight over eight instead of four wheels, *i.e.* the motor and the load in a waggon. Two travelling speeds are provided, enabling the motor to run from two to five miles an hour. The motor can be attached to any van, waggon, or trolley now in use with horses. It is constructed for hauling loads of from four to six tons, and works at a small expenditure of fuel and water. The working parts of the motor are all cased in, so as to be less liable to frighten horses; the brake acts on the rim of the driving-wheel, as shown. There is undoubtedly

# Modern Traction Engines

a great future for the small and light traction engine; the restrictions of the law have retarded progress, but now that motors can be built to comply with the Act of 1896, these restrictions are removed, and the little engines are as free on the road as any other vehicle.

TABLE XII.

DIMENSIONS OF MOTOR BY MESSRS. WALLIS AND STEEVENS.

| | |
|---|---|
| Diameter of cylinder . . . . | 6¼ in. |
| Length of stroke . . . . | 9 in. |
| Diameter of hind wheels . . . . | 4 ft. 6 in. |
| Width of hind wheels . . . | 9 in. |
| Diameter of front wheels . . . . | 3 ft. 4½ in. |
| Width of front wheels . . . . | 6 in. |
| Length over all . . . . . | 13 ft. 2 in. |
| Width over all . . . . . | 5 ft. 2 in. |

Will haul 12 tons up 1 in 12, and 23 tons on the level road. Requires 50 lbs. Welsh coal, and 45 gallons of water per hour.

FIG. 221. TRACTION ENGINE. THE WANTAGE ENGINEERING CO.

## THE WANTAGE ENGINEERING CO.

Fig. 221 represents an 8 horse-power general-purpose traction engine made by the Wantage firm. It is of the three-shaft type, with the fast and slow-speed pinions on the end of the crank-shaft outside the bearing; the slow-speed pinion slides inside the fast-speed or large pinion in the usual manner in three-shaft traction engines. The cross-head is of cast-iron, bored to fit the bored guide, which is supported by a bracket; this forms the governor stand,[1] and carries the reversing lay shaft. A cross-arm governor is adopted, which acts on an equilbrium throttle-valve. The winding-drum is on the gearing side of the engine; it carries fifty yards of $1\frac{1}{2}$-in. circumference steel-wire rope. It will be seen that the steering-gear is placed

FIG. 222.   ROAD LOCOMOTIVE.   THE WANTAGE ENGINEERING CO.

on the right-hand side (the gearing side), the reversing lever and the pump occupying the left-hand side.

Another illustration, Fig. 222, shows a single-cylinder road locomotive with outside gearing as the engine just described. A fore tank is fitted with the steerage bolted to the front. Side-plates for screening the working parts and a plated flywheel for a similar purpose is also shown. The winding-drum is combined with the compensating gear, and when so arranged, the axle does not revolve when the drum is used. This arrangement

[1] In the illustration, Fig. 221, two slide bars are shown; the bored guide has been introduced recently.

# Modern Traction Engines

was patented some years ago by Messrs. Charles Burrell and Sons. Fig. 223 shows the plan. The spur-ring is bolted to the compensating plate, in which the bevel-pinions are fitted ; one bevel-wheel is keyed to the axle, the other bevel-wheel used is fixed to the driving-wheel by the pin, and when the pin is withdrawn, the drum can revolve without the axle moving, by means of the pinions revolving on their gudgeons, as well as being turned by the spur-ring.

TABLE XIII.

DIMENSIONS OF 8-HORSE TRACTION ENGINE BY THE
WANTAGE ENGINEERING CO.

| | |
|---|---|
| Diameter of cylinder . . . | 9 in. |
| Length of stroke . . . . | $10\frac{1}{2}$ in. |
| Diameter of crank-shaft . . . | $3\frac{3}{8}$ in. |
| Diameter of flywheel . . . | 4 ft. 6 in. |
| Width on face of flywheel . . . | 6 in. |
| Revolutions per minute . . . | 160 |
| Diameter of main axle . . . | $5\frac{1}{4}$ in. |
| Ratio of gearing, slow . . . | 25 to 1 |
| Ratio of gearing, fast . . . | 13 to 1 |
| Speeds on road, slow . . . | $1\frac{1}{2}$ miles |
| Speeds on road, fast . . . | 3 miles |
| Diameter of front axle . . . | $3\frac{1}{2}$ in. |
| Diameter of driving-wheels . . . | 6 ft. |
| Width on face ,, . . . | 16 in. |
| Diameter of leading-wheels . . . | 4 ft. |
| Width on face ,, . . . | 8 in. |
| Boiler-barrel plate . . . . | $\frac{3}{8}$ in. |
| Tube plate . . . . | $\frac{5}{8}$ in. |
| Fire-box casing plates . . . | $\frac{3}{8}$ in. |
| Inside fire-box plates . . . | $\frac{3}{8}$ in. |
| Working pressure . . . . | 150 lbs. |
| Hydraulic pressure . . . . | 220 lbs. |
| Number of tubes and diameter of tubes . | 42—2 in. |
| Length of tubes . . . . | 5 ft. 5 in. |
| Length of fire-box . . . . | 2 ft. 9 in. |
| Width of fire-box . . . . | 2 ft. $1\frac{1}{4}$ in. |
| Height of fire-box . . . . | 2 ft. $8\frac{3}{4}$ in. |
| Capacity of tank . . . . | 135 galls. |
| Total length of engine . . . | 17 ft. 3 in. |
| Total width of engine . . . | 7 ft. 3 in. |
| Height of engine . . . . | 10 ft. 3 in. |
| Weight of engine . . . . | 10 tons |

# Traction Engines

Before we pass on to deal with the American engines, the question of small traction engines *versus* self-contained steam waggons must be touched upon. The

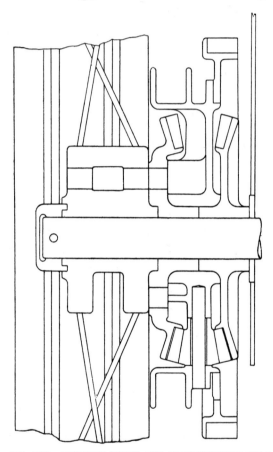

FIG. 223. WINDING-DRUM AND COMPENSATING GEAR

author is a firm believer in the engine and the load being independent of each other ; a small traction engine, working under the 1896 Act of Parliament, with two or three sets of small trucks, must be more useful than the steam lorry. The engine need never be kept waiting

# Modern Traction Engines

for loading or unloading. If any accident occurs, or any difficult position has to be scaled, the separate engine can be uncoupled and then pull the load over the bad place or up a bank. If a motor waggon gets into a difficulty, the entire machine must be unloaded, at a great waste of time and expense; and after the difficulty has been surmounted the load must be carted to the lorry, or taken by other means, and reloaded. The cost of transport is much less when a traction engine is in constant use, and is not kept waiting for loading and unloading. Motor waggons require three hours to do what a small traction, with a supply of trucks, would do in an hour. The trucks could be made to suit a varying load; they need not be to the same pattern. A small traction engine can be yoked to any van or waggon intended for horse haulage. If one of these tiny road engines was hauling two trucks loaded with three tons each, no hill nor any bad piece of road would hinder its progress. The total load is distributed over eight or twelve wheels instead of four. Traction engines are well-tested servants, and rarely break down; they have years ago passed the experimental stage. If necessary the trucks could be made to tip up the load. For all industrial concerns, where plenty of vans are available, it would be much cheaper to purchase a traction engine suitable for coupling to any or all of the vans in turn, rather than to buy a steam lorry and leave the existing vans lying idle.

# CHAPTER XII

## LATEST TYPES OF AMERICAN TRACTION ENGINES

A CAREFUL and prolonged study of recent American traction engine practice reveals some advantageous features which are worthy of attention. Some of their characteristics are passed over in silence because they cannot be commended. First, the American traction engine has not much tendency to prime in spite of a small steam capacity in the boiler. This is partly obviated by the adoption of a steam drum of large capacity, from the top of which the steam for the cylinder is collected. In many cases the steam is also slightly superheated by the pipe being made to pass through the top of the smoke-box on its way to the cylinder. In England all the cylinders are steam-jacketed. The jacket space is of liberal capacity, and acts as a steam dome, so that nowadays priming is almost unknown, and some traction engines are made that are not given to this vice in the least. As arranged, the American cylinders cannot be steam-jacketed; if this useful appendage were added, further economy would be secured. Secondly, it is generally supposed that the American traction engines are considerably lighter than the English engines. But when compared power for power there is little difference in the large sizes. For instance, the large ploughing engine made by the Buffalo Pitts Company, rated at 35 horse-power,

# American Traction Engines

with a 9-in. by 12-in. cylinder, weighs, fully equipped, 26,000 lbs., or over 11½ tons. An engine of English build of 35 actual horse-power, with a 9-in. by 12-in. cylinder, weighs, fully equipped, 26,880 lbs.

It will be seen, therefore, that there is little difference in the weight of these two engines. In the smaller sizes of engines the American are lighter than the English engines of the same power. The reason for this is not far to seek. The American engines, as a rule, are built for driving and hauling light thrashing outfits, are supplied with one speed, have light boilers, shafts, axles, and road wheels. The English engines, on the other hand, are intended for general purposes; they work and haul heavy thrashing machines and stackers; but in addition to this they are repeatedly made to haul farm produce over bad roads and soft headlands. The advantages of light traction engines are well known and appreciated. In special situations the slimly built engines do excellent service, but are of no use for general purposes. The English owners are satisfied with nothing less than excessive loads. Here is an instance. A 9-in. diameter and 12-in. stroke road engine draws easily 24 tons up an incline of 1 in 12, at four miles an hour; the same engine hauls 34 tons up the same gradient at three miles an hour, and on fairly level roads it will haul a load of 45 tons at four miles an hour. Of late years, however, it may be noticed that the American traction engines are being made heavier than formerly.

In the third place, most of the American traction engine makers place the compensating gear on the countershaft. This secures a reduction in the weight of the apparatus itself; but it possesses other advantages. It admits of the main driving-gear being fixed on both sides of the engine, therefore no power is transmitted through the main axle.   As the pinions on each end of the intermediate shaft gear into spur-rings bolted near the periphery of the road wheels, the stresses are evenly distributed, the axle, the gearing, and the driving-wheels may be much reduced in weight, ample strength is secured without excessive proportions.

Fourthly, the advantage of a high piston-speed goes without saying.   Most of the American engines run about 400 ft. per minute, enabling a small engine to develop as much power from the flywheel as a larger engine running at 300 ft. per minute.   Most of the American engines travel at a slower rate than the English engines.   The former rarely exceed three miles an hour, the latter always run up to four or five miles an hour in the open country.

Fifthly, by placing the intermediate shaft on the same horizontal centre line, the American builders secure an excellent arrangement of spring mounting.   To obtain an efficient arrangement of springs for traction engines driven by spur-gearing is no easy problem when the countershaft is placed above the main axle, as in the English style of engine.   But when the countershaft is placed on the horizontal centre line, as adopted by the American builders, the proper arrangement of springs is easily secured, and can be therefore included without extra charge in the engines of most of the makers. There is, however, one drawback to the placing of the intermediate shaft as mentioned above, viz. when secured at the front of the fire-box beneath the boiler barrel.   In order to obtain the proper distribution of the weight on the road wheels it is essential that the main axle should be placed at the rear of the fire-box. Having arranged the position of the two shafts in this manner, the centres are too wide apart for the correctly proportioned pinion and wheel. It is therefore necessary to move the main axle nearer the centre of the fire-box to suit the gearing. The result is that the engine rears in front when hauling.

To prevent this rearing propensity a water-tank is placed at the smoke-box end, and the bottom of the tank in some instances is made of cast-iron as much as 2 in. to 5 in. thick, to secure the necessary weight for the purpose.[1]

Reference may be made here to the method of riveting pursued in one of the American shops, and it is surprising to find hand riveting is recommended as being better than steam riveting. Experience teaches us that the very best hand riveting will not do for English traction engine boilers. All the best makers use hydraulic riveting machinery for closing every rivet in the boiler, the box brackets, the steel gearing, and the wrought-iron road wheels, under a pressure of not less than 60 tons. No other system of riveting will compare with this ; no other will stand the heavy work to which British traction engines are subjected. Most of the steam riveting machinery has long ago been sent to the scrap-heap to make room for more modern tools. The boilers are so designed that no hand rivets are needed, all are put in by the hydraulic machine. The

---

[1] Since writing the above I have been in correspondence with a practical engineer, who has handled many types of American traction engines. Bearing upon the subject of rearing he says, "The writer has handled a 7½-in. by 10-in., weighing about 12,000 lbs. It was found to be taxed to its utmost to draw a load of six tons over a very small gradient on account of its rearing proclivities. This is a fault which some American engines are prone to, on account of the faulty distribution of the weight on the ground wheels. The driving-wheels in this engine were pivoted on the side of the fire-box. Had it not been for this engine rearing, it is possible for it to have drawn about 15 tons."

# Traction Engines

following are extracts from American catalogues: "English engine builders commonly build some parts of their traction engines heavy enough to stand the strains which, by reason of the weakness of other parts, they will not be called upon to bear. It takes increased power to move those heavy parts without adding anything to the efficiency of the engine." The beauty of design, exact proportions, and high efficiency of the English traction engines are only known to those who use them in all parts of the world, and they are holding their own against all comers in every country.

It will be noticed that the American makers do not produce large road locomotives for hauling purposes; the engines described are all built for thrashing-machine work. One maker, some years ago, used power-steerage on their traction engines; this appears to have been discontinued.

Some of the American traction engine makers are very careful to say that the boilers are made on their own works. Many of the American boilers are built by firms engaged chiefly in boiler work. Some English firms are occasionally asked to quote prices for American traction engine boilers, because of the superior work produced in Great Britain. The following table of dimensions was sent round to some of the leading English makers, who were asked to state prices, delivery dates, etc., in 1903. It may be that the order for these boilers was given out to an English firm. An American maker says: "Several years ago we bought ready-made boilers, as do many, including some of the largest builders of traction engines to-day."

Leaving the boilers, the chief characteristics of the American traction engines are: The Corliss or some other massive engine frame is supported by the boiler; this

# American Traction Engines

frame is rendered necessary because of the employment of thin sheets in the boiler. The boiler is saved from some of the racking strains of the engine, but some far heavier strains are passed through it without any misgiving; for instance, the gearing, and very much of it too, is bolted to the boiler; the excessive strains of this gearing are passed through the thin shell of the boiler. A balanced disc, and an overneck crank-pin, are nearly universal; this device was used in England on portable engines thirty years ago. Cast-iron gearing and steel pinions are used. One travelling speed only is provided, as a rule. A friction-clutch cannot be dispensed with on American traction engines. Heavy castings for gearing, with light-driving road wheels and engine parts prevail. Unlagged boilers and many naked steam pipes are evident on nearly all the American traction engines.

### TABLE XIV.
#### DIMENSIONS OF AMERICAN TRACTION ENGINE BOILERS

| Size | 1 | 2 | 3 | 4 |
|---|---|---|---|---|
| Diameter of shell outside | $27\frac{1}{2}$ in. | $29\frac{1}{2}$ in. | $30\frac{3}{4}$ in. | 32 in. |
| Number of tubes | 36 | 41 | 46 | 54 |
| Diameter of tubes | 2 in. | 2 in. | 2 in. | 2 in. |
| Length of tubes | 64 in. | 64 in. | 64 in. | 64 in. |
| Smoke-box length | $31\frac{1}{8}$ in. | $33\frac{1}{4}$ in. | $31\frac{1}{2}$ in. | 34 in. |
| Width of fire-box | 23 in. | $24\frac{1}{2}$ in. | 26 in. | 27 in. |
| Length of fire-box | $37\frac{3}{16}$ in. | $43\frac{3}{16}$ in. | $43\frac{3}{16}$ in. | $43\frac{3}{16}$ in. |
| Height of fire-box | 40 in. | 40 in. | 42 in. | 42 in. |
| Fire-door | $10\frac{1}{4} \times 14$ in. | $11 \times 15$ in. | $11 \times 15$ in. | $11 \times 15$ in. |
| Draught-door | $6 \times 11$ in. | $6\frac{3}{4} \times 15$ in. | $6\frac{3}{4} \times 15$ in. | $6\frac{3}{4} \times 15$ in. |
| Diameter of dome | 15 in. | 15 in. | 15 in. | 15 in. |
| Height of dome | 20 in. | 20 in. | 20 in. | 20 in. |
| Fire-box tube-plate | $\frac{1}{2}$ in. | $\frac{1}{2}$ in. | $\frac{1}{2}$ in. | $\frac{1}{2}$ in. |
| Fire-box plates . | $\frac{3}{8}$ in. | $\frac{3}{8}$ in. | $\frac{3}{8}$ in. | $\frac{3}{8}$ in. |
| Straw-burner door | — | $6\frac{3}{4} \times 15$ in. | $6\frac{3}{4} \times 15$ in. | $6\frac{3}{4} \times 15$ in. |

Longitudinal seams, $2\frac{1}{2}$-in. pitch; $1\frac{1}{2}$ in. apart; $\frac{5}{8}$-in. rivets.
Six longitudinal stays, $\frac{7}{8}$ in. diameter.
Fire-box roofstays pitch, $4\frac{1}{4} \times 4\frac{13}{16}$ in.
Water-bottom type of boilers.

# Traction Engines

The engines will be taken in alphabetical order. The first is made by

The makers affirm that Fig. 224 "is the most beautiful engine manufactured, graceful in design and simple in construction." Respecting the beauty of design, they say : " This important feature is seen in every line and curve, while simplicity marks it as a whole. Compare it

FIG. 224. THE ADVANCE CO.'S TRACTION ENGINE

with any make of engine in the market, and your first and last opinion will be that in beauty and simplicity of design, the Advance engine is beyond each and every one." Our readers will form their own opinion respecting the engine and the claims made for it. The engine frame is bolted to the boiler at the crank and cylinder end; the overneck crank-disc is used. Steam is taken from a dome placed in the centre of the boiler barrel. Most of the weight of the engine is placed forward, and on the front wheels ; unless this were done, the engine would rear, owing to the driving-axle being fixed in the centre of the fire-box, as shown. The driving-wheels have cast-iron naves, a long bearing for the axle, and steel spokes, with cast-iron tires with cross strips cast on.

The makers recommend their compound· traction engine, which they say effects a saving of 28 per cent. in fuel and water over the simple engine. An illustration is given, Fig. 225, of the tandem cylinder which explains itself. The simple engines have a working pressure of

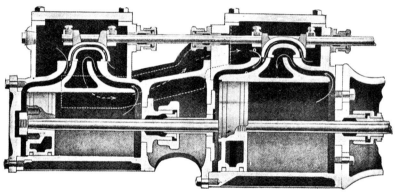

FIG. 225. TANDEM COMPOUND CYLINDER. ADVANCE CO.

120 lbs. per square inch, and the compound engines 150 lbs. per square inch. In the saving recorded above, the boiler of the compound engine was lagged during the trial, while the simple engine had a naked boiler, so that a good proportion of the gain is due to the clothing of the compound boiler. The Advance spring-mounting arrangement is illustrated in Chapter VII. Compared with some of the American makers, the Advance Company give few particulars of their traction engines. Two tables of dimensions are appended on the following pages.

## TABLE XV.

## DIMENSIONS OF ADVANCE COMPANY'S TRACTION ENGINES

*WOOD AND COAL BURNERS*

| | 6-Horse. | 10-Horse. | 12-Horse. | 15 Compound. | 16-Horse. | 18 Compound. |
|---|---|---|---|---|---|---|
| | Inches. | Inches. | Inches. | Inches. | Inches. | Inches. |
| Diameter of cylinder . | 6¼ | 7¼ | 7⅝ | 6¼ and 9 | 8½ | 7¼ and 10¼ |
| Stroke of cylinder | 8 | 10 | 10 | 9 | 10 | 9 |
| Diameter of boiler . | 22½ | 25½ | 27½ | 27½ | 29½ | 29½ |
| Length of fire-box . | 28 | 34½ | 36½ | 36½ | 40 | 40 |
| Width of fire-box . | 18 | 21 | 23 | 23 | 24 | 24 |
| Height of fire-box . | 31 | 34 | 35½ | 35½ | 39 | 39 |
| Diameter of flues | 1¾ | 1¾ | 2 | 2 | 2 | 2 |
| Length of flues . | 59½ | 69½ | 79 | 79 | 77¾ | 77¾ |
| Width of flywheel . | 7 | 8 | 10 | 10 | 10½ | 10½ |
| Diameter of flywheel . | 32 | 36 | 36 | 36 | 40 | 36 |
| Diameter of traction wheel | 54 | 60 | 62 | 62 | 64½ | 64½ |
| Width of traction wheel . | 10 | 12 | 15 | 15 | 17 | 17 |
| Number of flues . | 30 | 40 | 38 | 38 | 40 | 40 |
| Speed (revolutions) . | 240 | 225 | 225 | 244 | 225 | 244 |

374

TABLE XVI.

DIMENSIONS OF ADVANCE COMPANY'S TRACTION ENGINES

*STRAW BURNERS*

| | 16-Horse. | 18 Compound. | 22-Horse. | 26 Compound. |
|---|---|---|---|---|
| | Inches. | Inches. | Inches. | Inches. |
| Diameter of cylinder | 8½ | 7¼ and 10¼ | 9 | 9 and 12 |
| Stroke of cylinder | 10 | 9 | 11 | 10 |
| Diameter of shell | 29½ | 29½ | 33½ | 33½ |
| Length of fire-box | 41½ | 41½ | 54¼ | 54¼ |
| Width of fire-box | 24 | 24 | 28 | 28 |
| Diameter of flues | 2¼ | 2½ | 3 | 3 |
| Length of flues | 93 | 93 | 99½ | 99½ |
| Width of flywheel | 10½ | 10½ | 12½ | 12½ |
| Diameter of flywheel | 40 | 36 | 44 | 44 |
| Diameter of traction wheel | 62½ | 62½ | 72 | 72 |
| Width of traction wheel | 17 | 17 | 20 | 20 |
| Number of flues | 24 | 24 | 24 | 24 |
| Speed (revolutions) | 225 | 244 | 220 | 220 |

# Traction Engines

The makers assert "their traction engine has far out-stripped its rivals in the race for public favour." In the present engine the hind axle is placed beneath the fire-hole, mounted on cast-iron brackets bolted to the front of the fire-box shell; the countershaft is arranged directly over it as in English practice. It will be noticed that

FIG. 226.   TRACTION ENGINE.   THE CASE THRESHING CO.

horn-plates are provided for carrying the crank-shaft plummer blocks; this again is following English design.

Owing to the axle being placed in this position, the engine can be mounted on the boiler with the crank-shaft near the driver, without any fear of the engine rearing. Fig. 226 represents a Case traction engine The driving-wheels have square-headed steel spokes, held in position by lock-nuts to prevent their working loose in the hub. At the tire-ends the spokes are held by nuts, not cast in as is usual; the cross strips are of malleable iron riveted on the tires. A section of the boiler is given by Fig. 227, from which it will be seen it has a brick arch in the fire-box. Experience has taught the makers that water-legs and baffle-plates are poor substitutes compared with the brick arch, which, becoming incandescent, materially aids the combustion of straw, the only fuel available. Messrs. Case are compounding their traction engines like the rest of the American makers; they have adopted the tandem

FIG. 227. TRACTION ENGINE BOILER. CASE THRESHING CO.

arrangement, using a single-balanced slide-valve for the distribution of steam to both the high and low pressure cylinders. The working pressure for the simple and compound traction engines is 130 lbs. per square inch.

### THE FRICK COMPANY

" The ' Eclipse ' traction engine is the standard engine of to-day," and, as the makers state, "represents the most advanced practice in this special department in steam engineering."

It is a general-purpose engine, intended for driving a thrashing machine or for road locomotive work. In this road engine the axle is placed in the front of the fire-box. The independent system of mounting the machinery at

# Traction Engines

the fire-box end of the boiler is clearly shown in the illustration, Fig. 229. The boiler is relieved of all the working strains of the machinery, and instead of carrying the engine it is mounted on a frame, as shown. The driving-wheel and spring-drive for the compensating bevel-wheel is shown by Fig. 228. It will be seen that

FIG. 228. DRIVING-WHEEL. THE FRICK CO.

flat iron spokes are used riveted to the tire ; the cross-strips are made of cast-steel and riveted on.

A very good drawing is given, Fig. 230, of the Frick engine in plan. The overneck disc-crank is discarded with advantage for the counterbalanced dip-crank ; the counterbalance weights are placed in the most efficient position ; the crank-shaft bearings are of great length. A single excentric reversing-gear is shown. The friction

FIG. 229. TRACTION ENGINE. THE FRICK CO.

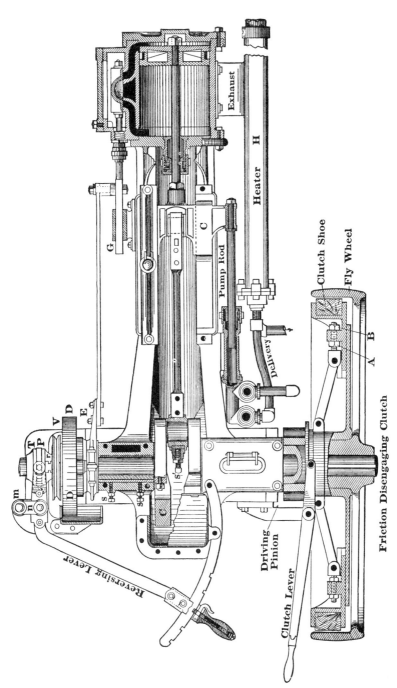

Reversing Lever

Pump Rod

Exhaust

Heater H

Delivery

Clutch Shoe

Fly Wheel

A   B

Driving Pinion

Clutch Lever

Friction Disengaging Clutch

FIG. 230.   PLAN OF TRACTION ENGINE.   THE FRICK CO.

# Traction Engines

disengaging clutch is an important feature on all American traction engines, and is never used in England; the want of it is not experienced in practice. The front and hind parts of the engine are carried on springs, not very clearly shown in the illustrations. A long-stroke feed-pump delivers the water into a heater, through which the exhaust steam passes to the smoke-box. There is no cast-iron used in the construction of the boiler, the plates are all of steel. The boiler is made with a circulating water-bottom and water-front.

GAAR SCOTT AND CO.

Fig. 231 represents a single-cylinder traction engine. The driving-wheels are cast solid, or practically in one piece; the segment side of the wheel shows the large diameter of the segment, and its strong attachment to the lugs cast with the tire. The face of the wheel as well as the cross strips are chilled; the spokes are cast in two rows from the nave to the tire of the wheels. A Corliss type of frame is adopted by the firm, with the usual counterbalanced disc. The steam pipe is led from the dome to the cylinder in the steam space of the boiler, an advantage over many of the exposed steam pipes in vogue. It will be seen that the driving-wheels are stationed in the centre of the fire-box shell, and to prevent the engine from rearing, a large water-tank is fixed beyond the smoke-box, as shown. The bed-plate or frame, the cylinder, guides, and pillow-blocks are all cast in one piece; they are bored at one operation; the valve-rod gland is bored at the same time, so that these parts are always in perfect alignment. Spiral rolls are used for the steering chains, and the chains are always fairly tight, the slack is taken up by the roller. A Pickering governor is mounted on the throttle-valve box. Gaar Scott make compound

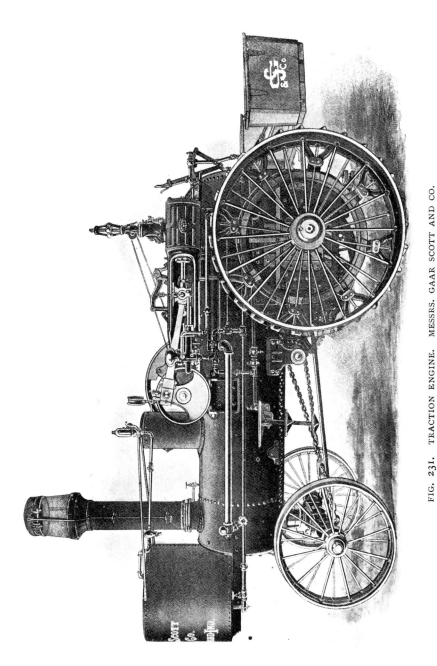

FIG. 231. TRACTION ENGINE. MESSRS. GAAR SCOTT AND CO.

## TABLE XVII.—SPECIFICATIONS FOR GAAR SCOTT TRACTION ENGINES

(Dimensions are given in Inches)

| Tractions. Coal and Wood Burners. | Cylinder. Diameter. | Cylinder. Length of Stroke. | Boiler. Shell. Diam. | Boiler. Shell. Length over all. | Boiler. Fire-Box. Length. | Boiler. Fire-Box. Width. | Boiler. Fire-Box. Height. | Boiler. Flues. Diam. | Boiler. Flues. Length. | Boiler. Flues. No. | Band Wheel. Diameter. | Band Wheel. Width of Face. | Band Wheel. Revolutions per Minute. | Front Ground Wheels. Diameter. | Front Ground Wheels. Width of Face. | Drive Ground Wheels. Diameter. | Drive Ground Wheels. Width of Face. |
|---|---|---|---|---|---|---|---|---|---|---|---|---|---|---|---|---|---|
| 10-H. Simple . . . . . | 7 | 11 | 27½ | 124¾ | 32¾ | 24¼ | 36 | 2½ | 70 | 23 | 42 | 8 | 228 | 40 | 6 | 62 | 12 |
| 13-H. ,, . . . . . | 8 | 10 | 29½ | 131 | 38¾ | 26 | 37¾ | 2½ | 70 | 28 | 38 | 10 | 252 | 40 | 6 | 62 | 14 |
| 16-H. ,, . . . . . | 8¼ | 11 | 32½ | 131 | 38¾ | 28 | 38 | 2½ | 70 | 32 | 42 | 10 | 228 | 40 | 9 | 62 | 16 |
| 18-H. ,, . . . . . | 8½ | 11 | 34½ | 131 | 38¾ | 29½ | 39½ | 2½ | 70 | 38 | 42 | 12 | 228 | 44 | 11 | 66 | 18 |
| 22-H. ,, . . . . . | 9 | 11 | 34½ | 153 | 44¾ | 29½ | 39½ | 2 | 86 | 56 | 42 | 12 | 228 | 44 | 11 | 66 | 20 |

| Tractions. Straw, Coal, and Wood Burners. | Cylinders. High-pressure. | Cylinders. Low-pressure. | Cylinders. Length of Stroke. | Boiler. Fire-Box. Height. | Boiler. Fire-Box. Length. | Boiler. Fire-Box. Width. | Boiler. Waist. Diam. | Boiler. Return Flues. No. | Boiler. Return Flues. Diam. | Boiler. Return Flues. Length. | Boiler. Small Direct Flues. No. | Boiler. Small Direct Flues. Diam. | Boiler. Small Direct Flues. Length. | Boiler. Main Direct Flues. Diam. | Boiler. Main Direct Flues. Length. | Band Wheel. Diameter. | Band Wheel. Revolutions per Minute. | Front Ground Wheels. Diameter. | Front Ground Wheels. Width of Face. | Drive Ground Wheels. Diameter. | Drive Ground Wheels. Width of Face. |
|---|---|---|---|---|---|---|---|---|---|---|---|---|---|---|---|---|---|---|---|---|---|
| 16-H. Simple . . . . | 8¼ | — | 11 | 36½ | 37½ | 27¾ | 32½ | 19 | 2½ | 96 | 4 | 2½ | 57 | 12 | 55 | 42 | 257 | 40 | 9 | 62 | 16 |
| 18-H. ,, . . . . | 8½ | — | 11 | 38 | 39¼ | 30½ | 35½ | 21 | 2½ | 107 | 6 | 2½ | 65 | 14 | 63 | 42 | 257 | 44 | 11 | 66 | 18 |
| 22-H. ,, . . . . | 9 | — | 11 | 38 | 39¼ | 32¾ | 36½ | 22 | 2½ | 113 | 6 | 2½ | 71 | 14 | 69 | 42 | 257 | 44 | 11 | 66 | 20 |
| 25-H. ,, . . . . | 9½ | — | 11 | 38 | 39¼ | 32¾ | 36½ | 22 | 2½ | 125 | 6 | 2½ | 83 | 14 | 81 | 42 | 257 | 44 | 11 | 66 | 20 |
| 20-H. Compound . . | 6½ | 9¾ | 10 | 38 | 39¼ | 30½ | 35½ | 21 | 2½ | 107 | 6 | 2½ | 65 | 14 | 63 | 42 | 257 | 44 | 11 | 66 | 18 |
| 25-H. ,, . . | 7¼ | 10½ | 10 | 38 | 39¼ | 32¾ | 36½ | 22 | 2½ | 113 | 6 | 2½ | 61 | 14 | 69 | 42 | 257 | 44 | 11 | 66 | 20 |
| 30-H. ,, . . | 8 | 11½ | 11 | 38 | 39¼ | 32¾ | 36½ | 22 | 2½ | 125 | 6 | 2½ | 83 | 14 | 81 | 42 | 257 | 44 | 11 | 66 | 20 |

# Traction Engines

traction engines with tandem cylinders; the high-pressure cylinder and the low-pressure cylinders are directly and strongly attached to each other, without any open space between them; a metallic packing-ring is employed between the cylinders for the piston-rod. With many thrashermen, however, it is still an open question whether there is enough advantage gained in compound engines over simple engines to compensate for the extra cost of the former. It is understood this firm make their own boilers for their traction engines; they use two types: for straw burning they recommend a return flue boiler with the chimney at the fire-box end. A table of dimensions is given on page 385.

## THE GEISER MANUFACTURING CO.

It is stated that these makers "produce the best-designed, best-constructed, and best-adapted line of machinery of its kind in this or any other country." The engine frame is of the Corliss pattern, with a disc-crank, the main axle is placed behind the fire-box beneath the firehole, the right position for preventing any rearing propensity. The driving-wheels are constructed of steel and malleable iron, the spokes are steel tubes; they are provided with wedges at one end, they can therefore be tightened when required. All spur-wheels are used for the compensating gear, and by the use of steel springs is made elastic. This not only ensures the gearing against sudden jars, but it also causes an equal bearing on all the pinions. An illustration, Fig. 232, shows the piston-valve. By the use of this valve the power of the engine is increased, better control of the engine is secured, and the engine is more easily reversed. The valve and its seat are made of hard chilled metal, ground truly; there is therefore practically no wear; the valve

# American Traction Engines

and parts are interchangeable. The method of spring mounting is illustrated in Chapter VII. A brick arch is used in the fire-box of the boiler for burning straw; the horn-plates of the boiler are carried backward for

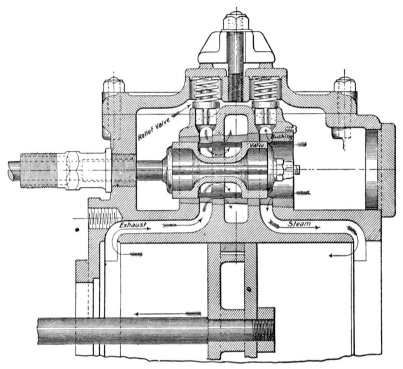

FIG. 232.   THE PISTON-VALVE.   THE GEISER CO.

supporting the main-axle carriages. The platform of the engine is short, which makes it convenient to fire the boiler from the ground when thrashing.

## THE O. S. KELLY MANUFACTURING CO.

The traction engines made by this firm differ from all the American examples which we have thus far described. They have advantages not possessed by the others; for instance, the heavy Corliss frame has been dispensed with; the cylinders are bolted to a steel-plate bracket;

they are three-shaft engines; the horn-plates of the boilers are carried upward and backward for supporting the bearings of the crank-shaft, the counter-shaft, and the main axle.

The aim of the makers has been to make a more powerful engine without increasing the weight, because the strength of the bridges has not kept pace with the times in the United States as well as in Great Britain. An engine, built as Fig. 233, has very few studs or bolts in the boiler to work loose and cause leakage; the barrel of the boiler and the smoke-box is made in one plate; the fire-box is stayed at $4\frac{1}{2}$ in. pitch with stays $\frac{7}{8}$ in. diameter. All the bearings are lined with phosphor-bronze. The power is transmitted from the crank-shaft to the main axle by means of two pairs of gear wheels: a great reduction in the gearing compared with many other engines. The compensating gearing is mounted on the main axle. An end view of the engine is given by Fig. 234 to show the simplicity of the arrangement. The driving-wheels have flat steel spokes; the tires are also of steel; the bosses are of cast-iron. The larger traction engines are fitted with suitable gearing for travelling at two speeds; the smaller engines are fitted with a single-speed train of gearing; the ratio of the fast-speed gearing is $22\frac{1}{2}$ to 1. A single excentric reversing-gear is adopted; the lever is shown. The pipe conducting the steam to the throttle-valve, and thence to the cylinder, is seen. The flywheel is 40 inches diameter and 10 inches wide on face.

FIG. 233. TRACTION ENGINE. THE O. S. KELLY CO.

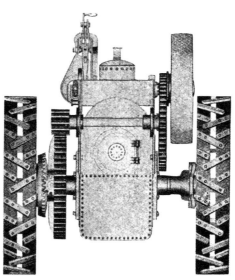

FIG. 234. END VIEW OF THE KELLY TRACTION ENGINE

# American Traction Engines

The new Huber traction engine is fitted with a return-flue boiler. The makers claim for this boiler superior steaming qualities, and an advantage in the cylindrical shape, which means an equal distribution of the weight of the boiler on the front and hind axles. The boiler is raised further from the ground, so that the engine can

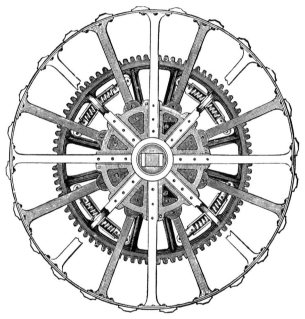

FIG. 235. THE HUBER CUSHION GEAR

pass through streams without putting the fire out, and when travelling over mud and soft land the fire-box cannot rest on the ground and allow the wheels to spin round for lack of solid ground to rest upon. A large tank is hung on the smoke-box door ; and when it is necessary to sweep the tubes the tank has to be swung around, being hung on the door. The Huber cushion-gear driving-wheel is shown by Fig. 235 ; the wheel does not revolve on the axle, neither does the axle turn; but the wheel revolves around the trunnion, which extends up and down from the centre of the hub, forming a five-inch bearing for the bracket, which is fastened to the axle, holding the wheel at right angles with the axle, but free to slide up

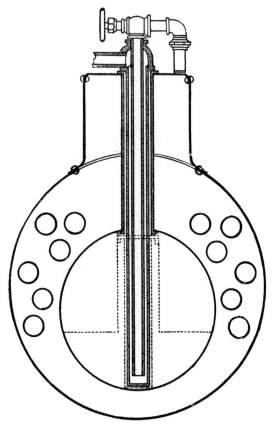

FIG. 236.   THE HUBER SUPERHEATER

and down in the slotted trunnions.   Fig. 236 shows the superheater.   The steam passes from the boiler into a small pipe, down through the boiler to the bottom of the fire-flue.   The end of the pipe is open, and it is encased in a large pipe, so that the steam passes through the fire between the outer and inner pipes before being delivered to the engine. This double pipe is encased in a heavy cast-iron sleeve, which protects it from damage from the great heat, and dries the steam, causing some economy. Fig. 237 illustrates the gearing. The pinions on the countershaft are interchangeable, and are made of steel.

FIG. 237. SPRING DRIVING-GEAR. THE HUBER CO.

Instead of using a key to fasten them, a clutch, as shown on the pinion on the crank-shaft, is used. The ratio of the gearing is given in the table of dimensions on the following page.

### THE NEW BIRDSALL CO.

The work required of a traction engine is so much greater than it was a few years ago that manufacturers have been obliged, from year to year, to build stronger and heavier engines. The result is that many of them

## TABLE XVIII.
## TABLE OF DIMENSIONS OF THE NEW HUBER TRACTION ENGINES

| Rated Horse-power, Engines, and Boilers. | Diameter of cylinder. | Length of stroke. | Size of band-pulley. | Speed of band-pulley. | Face of band-pulley. | Length of boiler including breeching. | Diameter of boiler. | Length of fire-flue. | Rear diameter of fire-flue. | Front diameter of fire-flue. | Thickness of shell—inches. | Thickness of fire-flue. | Thickness of heads. | Number of return flues. | Size of return flues. | Diameter of front wheels. | Diameter of rear wheels. | Width of tire—front wheels. | Width of tire—rear wheels. | Thickness of tire—front wheels. | Thickness of tire—rear wheels. | Revolutions of band-pulley to one of drive-wheels. | Actual horse-power—brake test. |
|---|---|---|---|---|---|---|---|---|---|---|---|---|---|---|---|---|---|---|---|---|---|---|---|
| 8 H.-P. Loco. | 7 | 8 | 33 | 300 | 9 | 87 | 33 | 69 | 21 | $18\frac{1}{2}$ | $\frac{1}{4}$ | $\frac{5}{16}$ | $\frac{3}{8}$ | 10 | 3 | $33\frac{1}{2}$ | 50 | $6\frac{1}{2}$ | 11 | $\frac{5}{16}$ | $\frac{1}{2}$ | 17 | 20 |
| 10 " | $7\frac{1}{2}$ | 8 | 37 | 250 | 11 | 87 | 36 | 69 | 22 | $20\frac{1}{2}$ | $\frac{9}{32}$ | $\frac{5}{16}$ | $\frac{3}{8}$ | 12 | 3 | $42\frac{1}{2}$ | $56\frac{1}{2}$ | 8 | 14 | $\frac{3}{8}$ |  | 20 | 25 |
| 12 " | 8 | 8 | 37 | 250 | 11 | 98 | 36 | 82 | 22 | $20\frac{1}{2}$ | $\frac{9}{32}$ | $\frac{5}{16}$ | $\frac{3}{8}$ | 12 | 3 | $42\frac{1}{2}$ | $58\frac{3}{4}$ | 8 | 14 | $\frac{3}{8}$ | $\frac{1}{2}$ | 22 | 28 |
| 16 " | $8\frac{1}{2}$ | 10 | 40 | 240 | 11 | 111 | 38 | 93 | 25 | $21\frac{1}{2}$ | $\frac{9}{32}$ | $\frac{3}{8}$ | $\frac{3}{8}$ | 14 | 3 | $42\frac{1}{2}$ | $58\frac{3}{4}$ | 8 | 16 | $\frac{3}{8}$ | $\frac{1}{2}$ | 17 | 38 |
| 18 " | 9 | 11 | 42 | 230 | 12 | 116 | 41 | 94 | 26 | 23 | $\frac{9}{32}$ | $\frac{7}{16}$ | $\frac{7}{16}$ | 18 | 3 | 45 | 61 | 10 | 18 | $\frac{3}{8}$ | $\frac{1}{2}$ | 21 | 41 |
| 20 " | $9\frac{1}{2}$ | 11 | 42 | 230 | 12 | 116 | 44 | 94 | 28 | $23\frac{1}{2}$ | $\frac{9}{32}$ | $\frac{7}{16}$ | $\frac{1}{2}$ | 20 | 3 | 45 | 64 | 10 | 20 | $\frac{3}{8}$ | $\frac{1}{2}$ | 18 | 44 |
| 25 " | $9\frac{1}{2}$ | 12 | 44 | 220 | 12 | 128 | 44 | 106 | 28 | $23\frac{1}{2}$ | $\frac{9}{32}$ | $\frac{7}{16}$ | $\frac{1}{2}$ | 20 | 3 | 45 | 66 | 12 | 24 | $\frac{3}{8}$ | $\frac{1}{2}$ | 18 | 52 |

# American Traction Engines

are so very heavy, making it impossible to use them where the ordinary country bridge has to be contended with. Many of the American traction engines are much heavier than is really necessary, but the Birdsall Co. assert that their traction engine is equally serviceable in the mountains of Tennessee as on the great plains of the North West, and as serviceable in thickly populated New York and the New England States, where good roads and bridges are protected by State laws limiting the amount of load on the highways. A Corliss frame is used, and an overneck crank with a balanced disc. Motion is transmitted from the crank-shaft to a counter-

FIG. 238.  DRIVING-WHEEL.  BIRDSALL CO.

shaft by means of a diagonal shaft; the countershaft and the axle are placed on the boiler front. Fig. 238 shows one of the driving-wheels. They are formed of angle-iron rings riveted to the open-faced tire, which allows the mud and sand to pass through; the spokes are crossed and riveted together; they are riveted to the bars and to the angle-iron rings also. A very large boiler is used; the makers state that the boilers are made on their own works under their supervision. Figs. 239 and 240 give sections of the boiler, showing the steam-pipe, the engine frame, and the steam-dome. The firm make double-cylinder engines, but not of the compound type, a rather unusual practice now. The engine is mounted on springs, and a spring-driving arrangement is used. A large tank is suspended beneath the boiler barrel. The makers say:

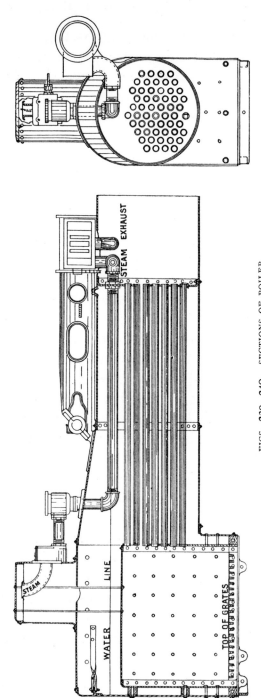

FIGS. 239, 240. SECTIONS OF BOILER

SHOWING THE ENGINE-FRAME, DOME, AND STEAM-PIPE. BIRDSALL CO.

# American Traction Engines

" The Birdsall traction engine is constructed on different lines from those of any other manufacturer, and cost more than many of the other types to build." They have had twenty years' experience, and have reason for making this particular style of engine.

## THE NICHOLS AND SHEPARD CO.

The makers say: "If you don't buy your engine of us, you don't buy your engine right. We build our engines on honour, for we know our reputation is at stake— a reputation flawless and progressive for over half a century." Fig. 242 shows one of the firm's traction engines with a water-tank on the smoke-box. The axle is arranged near the centre of the fire-box shell; the countershaft is placed beneath the boiler barrel near the saddle-plate. The Corliss frame is used on this engine, but it is partly combined with a massive water-heater. It will be seen from Figs. 152 and 153, Chapter VII., that the hind axle passes beneath the boiler fire-box shell, and is made square its entire length. Over the square end a large sleeve is used, which gives greater wearing surface to the hub of the driving-wheel. The sleeve and driving-wheel are held in place by a nut and pin. The traction gearing is strong, and the pinions are made of steel. Round spokes are used for the driving-wheels cast into the hub and tire; the spoke-ends are riveted to the rim also. The cross strips are of malleable cast-iron, and specially formed for preventing sticky soils from filling them up. The crank-disc is forced on to the crank-shaft by screw-pressure.[1] A long-stroke pump is worked from the crosshead. A good form of copper thimble, as

---

[1] It is usual to force details of this kind on to the shaft by hydraulic pressure.

shown in Fig. 241, is used for securing the boiler-tubes at the fire-box end.

The Nichols-Shepard 13 horse-power traction engine, when running 225 revolutions per minute of the crank-shaft, travels at about three miles an hour. The weight of the engine in working trim is about 11,500 lbs. (5·166 tons). The engine will haul 20 tons on smooth, hard roads, working at 125 lbs. pressure per square inch. Compound traction engines are not listed by this firm.

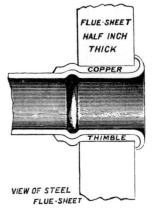

FIG. 241.   COPPER THIMBLE

### PITTS COMPANY

There are certain qualities which a traction engine should possess. Under the term strength — driving, hauling, and traction power; durability — superiority of material, workmanship, and construction; under the word efficiency — quick steaming qualities, economy in fuel and water. The Pitts' factories have been enlarged; a building with 35,000 square feet of floor space has been constructed. The foundry has been enlarged by an addition of 10,000 square feet; a third cupola has been added of 25 tons per hour capacity, and the entire plant has been equipped with electric power from the Niagara Falls. Fig. 243 shows a Pitts' traction engine. The engine frame is of the square box pattern, which is a strong form of construction; the box acts as a feed-water heater, as is pretty generally used by the American makers; the feed-water from the injector or steam-pump passes through the heater on its way to the boiler. The cylinder and bored

FIG. 242.  TRACTION ENGINE.  THE NICHOLS AND SHEPARD CO.

guide are cast with the box-shaped heater. A large round tank is supported on channel bars in front of the smoke-box, the position of the main axle renders this necessary. The driving-wheels have flat steel spokes bolted or riveted to the nave, at one end, and to the tire at the other, as shown. On the 22 horse-power engine the main gearing is five inches on the face of the

FIG. 243. TRACTION ENGINE BY BUFFALO PITTS CO.

cogs, and the driving-wheels are 6 ft. 6 in. diameter. Both ends of the connecting-rod are of the solid type. Pitts' universal direct-flue locomotive boiler is illustrated by Fig. 244. A fire-brick arch is adopted for burning straw; the fire-box has a water-bottom, as shown; ash-pan doors are fitted to both ends of the fire-box; suitable hand-holes are provided for cleaning purposes. A sloping fire-box top stayed direct to the shell is shown. Some of the larger sizes of traction engines have double

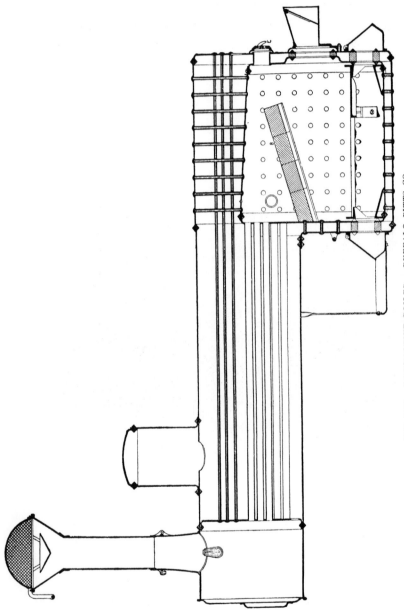

FIG. 244. LOCOMOTIVE BOILER. BUFFALO PITTS CO.

# American Traction Engines

side-by-side cylinders (non-compound); dip-cranks, of course, are used. Double-cylinder traction engines have some disadvantages which need not be named, but they are well known to experts.

## THE PORT HURON ENGINE AND THRESHER CO.

Their neatly got up catalogue commences as under: "There are three classes of traction engines. Heavy Weight, as English makes.—Built much heavier in some

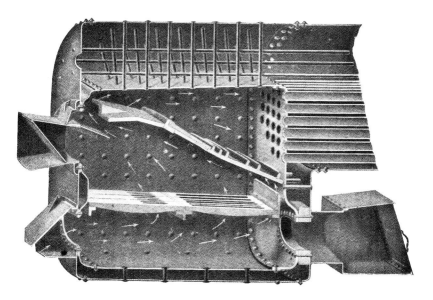

FIG. 245.  STRAW-BURNING FIRE-BOX.  PORT HURON CO.

parts than necessary for the work they have to do. Middle Weight.—Port Huron, correctly proportioned. Each part designed especially for the work it has to do and the strain it has to stand. Light Weight.—Those American and Canadian makes built with the sole idea of making them of light weight without regard to correct proportions." Our readers will form their own opinions respecting the above remarks. The Port Huron traction engines are speeded to run at 220 revolutions per minute; this gives a travelling speed of 2·1 miles an hour. A round-bottom locomotive boiler is used. The round-bottom fire-box is most convenient for cleaning,. as the mud all settles in one place, where it is easily removed; the flat fire-box top is stayed to the shell, as shown; longitudinal stays are also employed.

The straw-burning fire-box is shown by Fig. 245. The straw is fed through a funnel of the ordinary shape. A deflecting plate is shown inside the fire-box, which

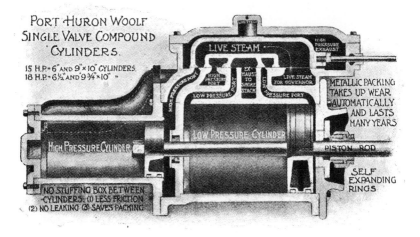

FIG. 246.

directs the straw and draught from the door in a downward direction, which aids combustion and prevents the chaff from being drawn up by the draught around the deflecting plate towards the tubes. The compound cylinder is illustrated by Fig. 246. One valve admits steam to both cylinders. It will be seen that there are only two stuffing-boxes; metallic packing is used between the two cylinders.

Fig. 247 shows a compound traction engine fitted with a cab and canopy; the cylinders are placed well

# American Traction Engines

## TABLE XIX.

## TABLE RELATING TO PORT HURON TRACTION ENGINES

The weight of the engine is included in the table showing tons hauled, and should be deducted for comparisons with animals.

Travelling speeds on the road :—220 revolutions of the engine per minute gives 2·1 miles an hour ; 275 revolutions=2·6 miles an hour ; 300 revolutions=2·8 miles an hour ; 350 revolutions=3·3 miles an hour.

The figures in the table show .pounds pulled by the flywheel on the main driving-belt, also pounds pulled on the draw-bar ; but the weight of the engine must be deducted to obtain the net hauling power on the load behind the engine.

The figures in the table show the number of feet and fractions the engine will lift itself per minute.

| HORSE-POWER. | | | CYLINDER. | PISTON. | | PULL. | LIFT. | TONS ENGINE WILL HAUL ON GRADES. (Deduct Engine Weight.) | | | | WEIGHT OF ENGINE. |
|---|---|---|---|---|---|---|---|---|---|---|---|---|
| Traction Rating. | Stationary Rating. | Indicated. | Size, Inches. | Area, Sq. inches. | Pressure, lbs. | On Road, lbs. | Itself, Ft. per Min. | 5 in 100. | 10 in 100. | 15 in 100. | 20 in 100. | |
| 12 S. | 23 | 25 | 7½ × 10 | 44·18 | 2,075 | 4,138 | 52·76 | 41 | 20 | 15 | 10 | 13,375 |
| 14 S. | 28 | 30 | 7¾ × 10 | 47·17 | 2,520 | 5,038 | 60·5 | 50 | 25 | 18 | 12 | 13,950 |
| 16 S. | 31 | 33 | 8 × 10 | 50·27 | 2,790 | 5,577 | 63·4 | 55 | 27 | 20 | 13 | 14,175 |
| 15 C. | 34 | 36 | { 6 × 10, 9 × 10 } | { 28·27, 63·62 } | 3,060 | 6,117 | 77·2 | 61 | 30 | 22 | 15 | 13,900 |
| 18 C. | 40 | 42 | { 6½ × 10, 9¼ × 10 } | { 33·18, 74·62 } | 3,600 | 7,197 | 85·5 | 71 | 35 | 26 | 17 | 14,426 |
| 20 C. | 44 | 46 | { 6½ × 10, 9¼ × 10 } | { 33·18, 74·62 } | 3,960 | 7,917 | 89· | 79 | 39 | 29 | 19 | 14,675 |
| 30 C. | 62 | 65 | { 8½ × 10, 13¾ × 10 } | { 56·74, 137·89 } | 5,590 | 11,071 | 99·8 | 110 | 55 | 37 | 27 | 20,500 |

TABLE XX.

TABLE RELATING TO PORT HURON TRACTION ENGINES.

| Traction Rating, Horse-Power. | Boiler. Fire-box (Inside Measurements). Width, Inches. | Length, Inches. | Height, Inches. | Door (Elliptical), Inches. | Draught (Elliptical), Inches. | Shell. Outside Diameter, Inches. | Tubes. Number. | Length, Inches. | Diameter, Inches. | Heating Surface, Square Feet. Fire-box. | Tubes. | Smoke-box. | Total. | Grate Area, Square Feet. | Smoke-box. Length, Inches. |
|---|---|---|---|---|---|---|---|---|---|---|---|---|---|---|---|
| 12 S. | 23 | $37\frac{3}{16}$ | 40 | $10\frac{1}{2} \times 14$ | $6 \times 11$ | $27\frac{1}{2}$ | 36 | 72 | 2 | 40 | 114 | 3 | 157 | 5·9 | $31\frac{3}{8}$ |
| 14 S. | $24\frac{1}{2}$ | $43\frac{3}{16}$ | 37 | $10\frac{1}{2} \times 14$ | $5\frac{3}{4} \times 15$ | $29\frac{1}{2}$ | 41 | 72 | 2 | 44 | 128 | 4 | 176 | 7·35 | $33\frac{1}{4}$ |
| 16 S. | 26 | $43\frac{3}{16}$ | 37 | $10\frac{1}{2} \times 14$ | $5\frac{3}{4} \times 15$ | $30\frac{5}{8}$ | 46 | 72 | 2 | 45 | 144 | 4 | 193 | 7·79 | $31\frac{1}{2}$ |
| 15 C. | 23 | $37\frac{3}{16}$ | 40 | $10\frac{1}{2} \times 14$ | $6 \times 11$ | $27\frac{1}{2}$ | 36 | 72 | 2 | 40 | 114 | 4 | 157 | 5·9 | $31\frac{3}{8}$ |
| 18 C. | $24\frac{1}{2}$ | $43\frac{3}{16}$ | 37 | $10\frac{1}{2} \times 14$ | $5\frac{3}{4} \times 15$ | $29\frac{1}{2}$ | 41 | 72 | 2 | 44 | 128 | 4 | 176 | 7·35 | $33\frac{1}{4}$ |
| 20 C. | 26 | $43\frac{3}{16}$ | 37 | $10\frac{1}{2} \times 14$ | $5\frac{3}{4} \times 15$ | $30\frac{5}{8}$ | 46 | 72 | 2 | 45 | 144 | 4 | 193 | 7·79 | $31\frac{1}{2}$ |
| 30 C. | $29\frac{1}{4}$ | $45\frac{5}{16}$ | 46 | $10\frac{1}{4} \times 14$ | $6 \times 21$ | $34\frac{1}{2}$ | 54 | 72 | 2 | 59·6 | 169·6 | 5·09 | 234·3 | 9·2 | $31\frac{1}{2}$ |

With two inches of water in the gauge-glass the 15 h.-p. contains 163 gallons; 18 h.-p. = 178 gallons; 20 h.-p. = 200 gallons; 30 h.-p. = 280 gallons.

FIG. 247. COMPOUND TRACTION ENGINE. PORT HURON CO.

FIG. 248. COMPOUND TRACTION ENGINE. THE RUSSELL CO.

forward ; the engine frame is on the ordinary lines. The distribution of cast-iron is such that all strains by the piston bring the line of tension within the greatest resistance for weight of metal used. The tables (pp. 405-6) give some useful information.

### THE RUSSELL COMPANY

A few years ago many of the American makers were pushing compound traction engines, but there is a falling off in this line. The Russell Company say : " We have been building the compound farm engine for the past nine years. We sell three compound engines to one single-cylinder engine. The Russell compound traction engine effects a saving of one-third in fuel and water. Increased power without additional weight is obtained." Fig. 248 shows the Russell compound traction engine ; the cylinders are of the tandem type—one piston-rod, one crosshead, one crank are used. A balanced slide-valve is arranged in the compound engine. The working pressure is 160 lbs. per square inch ; the hydraulic test pressure is 225 lbs. per square inch.

It will be seen from Fig. 248 the usual Corliss frame with a disc prevails. A long-stroke pump is worked from the crosshead. The two cylinders are placed a little apart, giving room enough to pack the piston-rod glands. The cab is a better protection to the engine-driver than that afforded by the ordinary roof canopy. A clutch is used in connection with the flywheel. The makers say : " A clutch which requires the stopping of the engine to engage or disengage it, is utterly useless. A clutch which must be driven apart by a hammer is worse than useless. A good clutch is an indispensable feature of an American traction engine. It makes an engine strong to help itself where otherwise it would be

# Traction Engines

TABLE XXI.

## THE RUSSELL COMPANY TANDEM COMPOUND NON-CONDENSING TRACTION ENGINES

| NOTE.—All Dimensions are in Inches (except as noted). | STANDARD. BURNS COAL OR WOOD. | | | UNIVERSAL. BURNS COAL, WOOD, OR STRAW. | | |
|---|---|---|---|---|---|---|
| Diameter of high-pressure cylinder | 5½ | 6 | 6½ | 6 | 6½ | 7¼ |
| ,, low-pressure ,, | 8 | 9 | 10 | 9 | 10 | 11 |
| Stroke of piston | 8 | 10 | 10 | 10 | 10 | 12 |
| Rated horse-power—traction | 12 | 16 | 20 | 16 | 20 | 25 |
| Revolutions per minute at rated horse-power | 250 | 225 | 225 | 225 | 225 | 200 |
| Indicated horse-power—engine running empty | 2 | 3·5 | 4 | 3·5 | 4 | 4 |
| ,, ,, ,, on road. | 7 | 12 | 15 | 12 | 15 | 18 |
| ,, ,, ,, pulling empty waggon (3,115 lbs.) | 8 | 13 | 16 | 13 | 16 | 19 |
| ,, ,, ,, load of 1 ton on wheels | 9 | 14 | 17 | 14 | 17 | 20 |
| ,, ,, ,, ,, 9 tons ,, | 15 | 18 | 21 | 18 | 21 | 23 |
| Maximum brake load in horse-power | 30 | 40 | 49 | 40 | 49 | 64 |
| Maximum load (in tons) engine will haul on wheels | 26 | 42 | 51 | 42 | 51 | 81 |
| Consumption of water in gallons per h.-p. per hour from 5 hours' test | 2·64 | 2·64 | 2·64 | 2·64 | 2·64 | 2·64 |
| ,, ,, coal in pounds per h.-p. per hour from 5 hours' test | 3·8 | 3·8 | 3·8 | 3·2 | 3·2 | 3·2 |
| Number of revolutions of engine to 1 of rear wheel | 19·4 | 18·50 | 18·50 | 18·65 | 18·65 | 20·0 |
| Speed on road in miles per hour | 2·2 | 2·50 | 2·50 | 2·35 | 2·35 | 2·0 |
| Diameter of steam-pipe | 1½ | 2½ | 2½ | 2 | 2½ | 2½ |
| ,, ,, exhaust | 2 | 2½ | 2½ | 2½ | 2½ | 3½ |
| ,, ,, shaft | 2⅝ | 3 | 3 | 3 | 3 | 3½ |
| Length of shaft | 48 | 58 | 58 | 58 | 62 | 66 |
| ,, ,, main bearing | 5⅝ | 5½ | 5½ | 5½ | 5½ | 6 |
| Diameter of balance wheel | 32 | 36 | 36 | 36 | 36 | 42 |
| Face of balance wheel | 8 | 10 | 10 | 10 | 10 | 14 |
| Weight of balance wheel | 280 | 470 | 470 | 470 | 470 | 920 |
| Diameter of rear road wheel | 58 | 58 | 58 | 66 | 66 | 66 |
| Face of rear road wheel | 12 | 16 | 20 | 20 | 20 | 24 |
| Diameter of front road wheel | 42 | 42 | 42 | 42 | 42 | 42 |
| Face of front road wheel | 6 | 8 | 8 | 10 | 10 | 10 |
| Diameter of circle in which engine will turn | 273 | 360 | 346 | 346 | 346 | 480 |

TABLE XXI.—*continuea*

| NOTE.—All Dimensions are in Inches except as noted). | Standard. Burns Coal or Wood. | | | | Universal. Burns Coal, Wood, or Straw. | | |
|---|---|---|---|---|---|---|---|
| Width of tread—centre to centre of wheels | 55¾ | 66¾ | 71¼ | 84½ | 77½ | 81 | 84½ |
| Length over all | 170 | 190 | 195 | 222 | 193 | 213 | 222 |
| Width over all | 70 | 84 | 87¼ | 106½ | 97½ | 104 | 106½ |
| Height over all | 100 | 105 | 114 | 116 | 112 | 115 | 116 |
| Diameter of shell of boiler | 22 | 26 | 28½ | 32 | 28½ | 32 | 32 |
| Length of tubes in boiler | 63 | 72 | 72 | 90 | 72 | 72 | 90 |
| Diameter of tubes in boiler | 1¾ | 2 | 2 | 2 | 2½ | 3 | 3 |
| Number of tubes in boiler | 28 | 33 | 38 | 50 | 30 | 28 | 28 |
| Diameter of cross-shaft | 2⅜ | 2¾ | 3¼ | 3½ | 3¼ | 3¼ | 3½ |
| Height of fire-box | 38 | 36½ | 39 | 44⅜ | 26⅝* | 28½ | 28½ |
| Length ,, | 29¾ | 29¾ | 32¾ | 48¾ | 42⅞* | 49 | 49 |
| Width ,, | 19 | 22 | 24 | 25¾ | 23½* | 27 | 27 |
| Number of square feet of heating surface | 100 | 136 | 156 | 251·3 | 162 | 190·18 | 223 |
| Area of grate surface—in square feet | 3·92 | 4·54 | 5·43 | 8·72 | 7 | 9·2 | 9·2 |
| Diameter of stack | 8¼ | 11 | 11 | 13 | 11 | 13 | 13 |
| Height of stack | 32 | 34 | 34 | 34 | 34 | 34 | 34 |
| Depth of smoke-box | 28 | 35 | 35 | 37 | 35 | 37 | 37 |
| Area of tubes—transverse internal | 53·5 | 84·3 | 197·1 | 127·8 | 122·7 | 170 | 170 |
| Weight of engine complete without water | 9,100 | 13,000 | 16,520 | 20,450 | 16,540 | 17,980 | 22,230 |
| ,, boiler without water | 2,430 | 3,132 | 3,575 | 4,522 | 3,900 | 4,260 | 4,562 |
| No. gallons of water in boiler when gauge-glass shows 2 inches | 70 | 125 | 166 | 300 | 180 | 300 | 320 |
| Shipping weight (in 2 boxes for ocean shipment) gross pounds | 11,375 | 13,950 | 19,920 | 24,090 | 20,350 | 21,880 | 26,180 |
| ,, ,, ,, tare ,, | 2,275 | 3,350 | 3,400 | 3,640 | 3,810 | 3,900 | 3,950 |
| ,, ,, ,, net ,, | 9,100 | 10,600 | 16,520 | 20,450 | 16,540 | 17,980 | 22,230 |
| Cubical contents in feet | 490 | 570 | 615 | 750 | 785 | 800 | 900 |
| Capacity of water-tanks—in gallons | 70 | 70 | 70 | 70 | 70 | 70 | 70 |

* This does not include Combustion Chamber.

# Traction Engines

## TABLE XXII.

### THE RUSSELL COMPANY'S TABULATED RESULTS OF FARM ENGINE ECONOMY TESTS

| | TEST No. 50. | TEST No. 51. | TEST No. 52. |
|---|---|---|---|
| DATE | *May 26th, 1896.* | *June 9th, 1896.* | *June 13th, 1896.* |
| Kind of boiler | Univ. Jacketed. | Loco. not Jacketed. | Univ. not Jacketed. |
| Size and number of boiler | 28½"×6' 8663 | 28½"×6' 8645 | 28½"×6' 8663 |
| Kind of engine | Tand. Com. Trac. | Tand. Com. Trac. | Tand. Com. Trac. |
| Size and number of engine | 6½"×10"×10" 8627 | 6½"×10"×10" 8599 | 6½"×10"×10" 8627 |
| Time of test | 12.30 to 5.30 p.m. | 1 p.m. to 6 p.m. | 6.30 to 11.30 a.m. |
| Speed in revolutions per minute | 225 | 225 | 225 |
| Average steam pressure above atmosphere in boiler | 148. lb. | 145. lb. | 145. lb. |
| ,, ,, ,, at throttle | 143. lb. | 139. lb. | 137. lb. |
| ,, ,, ,, in receiver | 41. lb. | 39. lb. | 44. lb. |
| Brake load in high pressure—net* | 29.1 | 29.2 | 26.6 lb. |
| Average indicated high pressure—high-pressure cylinder | 19.93 | 19.72 | 17.1 lb. |
| ,, ,, ,, —low-pressure ,, | 12.76 | 12.98 | 13. |
| ,, ,, ,, —both ,, | 32.6 | 32.7 | 30.16 |
| Fuel—kind of coal | West Va. Run of Mine. | West Va. Run of Mine. | West Va. Run of Mine. |
| ,, total amount burned | 467. lb. | 586.2 lb. | 425. lb. |
| ,, amount of ashes and clinkers | 100. lb. | 95. lb. | 64. lb. |
| ,, total amount of combustible | 367. lb. | 491.2 lb. | 361. lb. |
| ,, amount of moisture in coal | 70. lb. | 87.9 lb. | 64.75 lb. |
| ,, total amount of combustible pure and dry | 297. lb. | 403.3 lb. | 296.25 lb. |
| Water—total weighed to boiler | 3358. lb. | 3458. lb. | 3293. lb. |
| ,, amount consumed per high pressure per hour | 20.9 lb. | 21.15 lb. | 21.83 lb. |
| ,, ,, evaporated per lb. of combustible | 9.1 lb. | 7 lb. | 9.1 lb. |
| ,, ,, ,, ,, pure and dry | 11.3 lb. | 8.58 lb. | 11.16 lb. |
| ,, equivalent evaporated from and at 212° Fahr. | 12.72 lb. | 9.34 lb. | 12. lb. |
| Temperature—feed-water in tank | 80° F. | 80° F. | 75° F. |
| ,, ,, water entering boiler | 180° F. | 174° F. | 178° F. |
| ,, ,, test room | 74° F. | 75° F. | 67° F. |

\* This is not the maximum brake load that these engines are capable of developing, but simply the average load recorded in this particular test.

TABLE XXII.—*continued*

## THE RUSSELL COMPANY'S TABULATED RESULTS OF FARM ENGINE ECONOMY TESTS

| DATE ........ | TEST No. 53.<br>*June 18th, 1896.* | TEST No. 54.<br>*June 26th, 1896.* | TEST No. 55.<br>*September 14th, 1896.* |
|---|---|---|---|
| Kind of boiler | Univ. Jacketed. | Loco. Jacketed. | Loco. not Jacketed. |
| Size and number of boiler | 28½" × 6', 8663 | 28½" × 6', 8645 | 28½" × 6³ 7877 |
| Kind of engine | Tand. Com. Trac. | Tand. Com. Trac. | Simple Trac. |
| Size and number of engine | 6¼" × 10 × 10" 8627 | 6½" × 10" × 10" 8599 | 7¾" × 10" 8216 |
| Time of test | 6.30 to 11.30 a.m. | 12.30 to 5.30 p.m. | 1 to 6 p.m. |
| Speed in revolutions per minute | 225 | 225 | 225 |
| Average steam pressure above atmosphere in boiler | 145. lb. | 145. lb. | 112. lb. |
| ,, ,, ,, at throttle | 139. lb. | 140. lb. | 100. lb. |
| ,, ,, ,, in receiver | 37. lb. | 37. lb. | ...... |
| Brake load in high pressure—net* | 24.7 | 28.3 | 25.3 |
| Average indicated high pressure—high-pressure cylinder | 17.5 | 19.65 | 28.19 |
| ,, ,, —low-pressure ,, | 10.7 | 12.22 | ...... |
| ,, ,, —both ,, | 28.2 | 31.87 | ...... |
| Fuel—kind of coal | Best Mass. Lump. | Rest Mass. Lump. | West Va. Run of Mine. |
| ,, total amount burned | 390. lb. | 506. lb. | 723. lb. |
| ,, amount of ashes and clinkers | 44. lb. | 71. lb. | 86. lb. |
| ,, total amount of combustible | 346. lb. | 435. lb. | 637. lb. |
| ,, amount of moisture in coal | 58.5 lb. | 75.9 lb. | 108.45 lb. |
| ,, total amount of combustible pure and dry | 287.5 lb. | 359.1 lb. | 528.55 lb. |
| Water—total weighed to boiler | 3200. lb. | 3230. lb. | 3983. lb. |
| ,, amount consumed per high pressure per hour | 22.62 lb. | 20.2 lb. | 28.22 lb. |
| ,, evaporated per lb. of combustible | 9.2 lb. | 7.4 lb. | 6.23 lb. |
| ,, ,, ,, pure and dry | 11.48 lb. | 9. lb. | 7.5 lb. |
| ,, equivalent evaporated from and at 212° Fahr. | 12.48 lb. | 9.74 lb. | 8.3 lb. |
| Temperature—feed-water in tank | 75° F. | 83° F. | 84° F. |
| ,, water entering boiler | 177° F. | 179° F. | 148° F. |
| ,, test room | 70° F. | 82° F. | 82° F. |

* This is not the maximum brake load that these engines are capable of developing, but simply the average load recorded in this particular test.

413

weak. Where starting is particularly difficult, the engine may be given high motion, then be instantly thrown into gear, the momentum gained giving power at starting largely in excess of the ordinary power of the engine. This contact, though so effective, is yet gradual, so that a breakage of gearing has never occurred." Tables of dimensions of the compound traction engines are inserted on pages 410–13, and results of trials carried out on the traction engines.

A. W. STEVENS COMPANY

It is said "the demand for practical machinery is increasing, and that the fad for something experimental and out of the ordinary way is fast wearing itself out." Fig 249 shows a 25 horse-power simple traction engine ; the diameter of the cylinder is $9\frac{1}{4}$ in., and the stroke 12 in., the indicated horse-power is 50. An English traction engine of this size has developed just under 70 horse-power on the brake, running at 160 revolutions per minute, the steam pressure being 140 lbs. per square inch. If the engine above had run at 210 revolutions, instead of 160, a much higher power would have been developed by the English type. The makers describe this engine " as beautiful in construction, a giant in strength, designed for heavy work of all kinds on the road or belt." A Corliss pattern frame is used, an overneck crank-pin, and a balanced disc. The hind axle is placed across the boiler front beneath the fire-hole, and a foot-brake is provided ; the brake drum is keyed to the countershaft. A brake is not often provided on the American traction engine. The steam is taken from the top of the dome, the pipe passing through the hottest part of the boiler, thereby superheating the working steam before it enters the cylinder. A Pickering governor is employed ; it is

# American Traction Engines

placed horizontally so as to reduce vibration on the road. In England the governors are never used when the engine is travelling on the road ; it is only used when the engine is driving machinery from the flywheel. Coil springs are placed in the steering chains. A cast-steel connecting-rod is used ; it is three times the length of the stroke. The compensating gear is placed on the countershaft, the power is transmitted from the counter-

FIG. 249.   TRACTION ENGINE.   A. W. STEVENS CO.

shaft to the rims placed near the periphery of the driving-wheels. A single excentric reversing-gear is used ; a friction-clutch is employed, for which the makers claim many advantages. The style of driving-wheels and the shape of the cross-strips can be seen from the illustration.

There follows a table of dimensions of eight American coal-burning traction engines of practically the same rated horse-power, and the dimensions of one English

# Traction Engines

traction engine are also added of similar proportions. The actual horse-power must be taken as approximate only, as we have not sufficient particulars given by the makers to enable us to calculate exactly what each engine would develop by the friction-brake on the flywheel.

A small table showing the water and coal consumption of four single-cylinder traction engines is also given.

| Name of Maker.... | Advance. | Huber. | Foden. | Several English Makers. |
|---|---|---|---|---|
| Water per B.H P. per hour | 34·5 | 32·04 | 25·63 | 27·0 |
| Coal „ „ | 5·0 | 5·32 | 2·53 | 3·3 |

The first two columns are taken from the makers' catalogues ; the second column shows the results of trials at the World's Fair. The third column represents the figures obtained during some exhaustive trials at the Newcastle show of the Royal Agricultural Society of England.

The fourth column shows the results repeatedly obtained when thrashing under favourable conditions with the best English traction engines, having steam-jacketed cylinders, carefully proportioned and lagged boilers producing dry steam, fitted with a feed-water heater, and the link-motion notched up for producing an early cut-off.

TABLE XXIII.—TABLE OF DIMENSIONS OF AMERICAN TRACTION ENGINES

| Name of Maker ........ | Advance. | Pitts. | Jumbo. | Gaar Scott. | Port Huron. | Minnea-polis. | Stevens. | English Maker. | Case. |
|---|---|---|---|---|---|---|---|---|---|
| Rated horse-power . . | 16 | 15 | 16 | 16 | 16 | 16 | 16 | 7 | 16 |
| Actual horse-power . . | 30 | — | — | 33 | 31 | 33 | 32 | 35 | — |
| Diameter of cylinder, in. . | 8½ | 8½ | 8⅜ | 8¼ | 8 | 8 | 8⅛ | 8½ | 8¼ |
| Length of stroke, in. . | 10 | 10 | 12 | 11 | 10 | 11 | 10½ | 12 | 10 |
| Working pressure, lbs. . | 100 | — | — | 110 | 120 | 120 | 120 | 140 | — |
| Hydraulic test press . | — | — | — | — | 225 | 185 | — | 240 | — |
| Diameter of boiler, in. . | 29½ | 30 | 30 | 32 | 30⅝ | 40 | 28 | 32 | 29 |
| Width of fire-box, in. . | 24 | 25 | 25 | — | 26 | — | 26 | 24 | 24 |
| Length of fire-box, in. . | 42 | 40 | 40 | — | 44 | — | 39 | 33 | 40 |
| Number of tubes . . | 24 | 41 | 32 | — | 46 | 26 | 48 | 34 | 41 |
| Diameter of tubes, in. . | 2½ | 2 | 2½ | — | 2 | 2½ | 2 | 2¼ | 2 |
| Length of tubes, in. . | 93 | 72 | 78 | — | 72 | 88 | 72 | 72 | 96 |
| Flywheel sizes, in. . . | 40 × 10½ | 40 × 8½ | — | — | 40 × 10¼ | 42 × 8 | 40 × 9½ | 54 × 6½ | 36 × 9 |
| Driving-wheels, in. . | 66 × 18 | 66 × 16 | — | 62 × 14 | 66 × 16 | 56 × 16 | 60 × 17 | 69 × 16 | 66 × 16 |
| Revolutions per minute . | 225 | 240 | — | 221 | 220 | 225 | 220 | 160 | 250 |
| Speed on road, slow . | — | — | 2½ | — | 2½ | — | — | 3 | — |
| Speed on road, fast . | — | — | 4 | — | — | — | 4½ | 5 | — |

FIG. 250.   TOLEDO LONG-DISTANCE TOURING CAR

# INDEX

# Index

# Index

# Index

# Index

# Index

# Index

427

# Index